THE
WASHERWOMAN'S
Dream

THE WASHERWOMAN'S DREAM
This second edition published in 2007
First published in Australia in 2002 by
Simon & Schuster (Australia) Pty Limited
Suite 2, Lower Ground Floor
14–16 Suakin Street
Pymble NSW 2073

A CBS Company
Sydney New York London Toronto

Visit our website at www.simonsaysaustralia.com

Cataloguing-in-Publication data:

Lindsay, Hilarie, 1922- .
   The washerwoman's dream : the extraordinary life of
   Winifred Steger 1882-1981.
   Bibliography.
   ISBN 9780731813162.
   ISBN 0 7318 1316 2.
   1. Steger, Winifred, 1882-1981. 2. English - Australia -
   Biography. 3. Cameleers - Australia - Biography. I. Title.
305.821094

Cover design by Christabella Designs
Internal design by Kirby Jones
Typeset in 11 on 15pt Adobe Garamond by Kirby Jones
Printed in Australia by Griffin Press

10 9 8 7 6 5 4 3 2 1

THE
WASHERWOMAN'S
Dream

THE EXTRAORDINARY LIFE OF WINIFRED STEGER
1882–1981

HILARIE LINDSAY

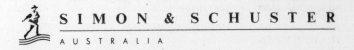

SIMON & SCHUSTER
AUSTRALIA

Winifred the Washerwoman [Mrs Winifred Stegar], a sketch by Pat Harvey.

To Philip Lindsay,
for his unfailing support

ACKNOWLEDGMENTS

I wish to thank all those who helped me with material for this book, especially Nancy Flannery (née Robinson), who preserved the Winifred Steger manuscripts; Stella Guthrie, who taped interviews with Winifred Steger from the late 1970s until just before Winifred's death in 1981, and, like Nancy, allowed me full access to this material.

Thanks also to the Steger family, Elizabeth Guy, Lynnie Plate, Jose Petrick, John Dallwitz, Horrie Simpson, Rae Sexton, Helen Baker, the late Margaret Potts, Dr Cedric Gregory, Sister Rose Barnes, John Rawsthorn, R.M. Williams, R.K. Bailey, Rene Pezy, Roy Luke, Shirley MacPherson, the late Ian Wood, Susanne Gervay, Moya Simons, Vashti Farrer and Natalie Scott from the Hughenden Gargoyles, Dr Patricia Gaut and those who listened, Professor Elizabeth Webby, my supervisor at Sydney University while I worked on my doctoral thesis; my editor, Julia Styles, my agent, Selwa Anthony, and the many others who answered my letters, sent me photographs and other material and generally shared my enthusiasm for Winifred Steger.

I am grateful for the assistance of the staff from the following institutions in Australia: the Mitchell Library, State Library of New South Wales; La Trobe Library, State Library of Victoria; the John Oxley Library, State Library of Queensland; the Mortlock Library, State Library of South Australia; the Toowoomba Library; the Australian Archives, South Australia; the South Australian Archives; the Australian Genealogical Society; the National Library; the Queensland State Archives; the Toowoomba Family History Society; the Dalby Family History Society; the Roma and District Family History Society; Fisher Library, University of Sydney; the Morven Historical Museum; the Mt Horrocks Historical Society; the Chinchilla Historical Society; the Alice Springs Library; the Public Library of Port Augusta; the archives of the Presbyterian Church, Queensland; the archives of the Alice Springs Hospital; the Country Women's Association, South Australia; the South Australian Theosophical Society; Oodnadatta Hospital and Health Services; the Islamic Society of South Australia; the *Sydney Morning Herald*; 'Australia All Over' (ABC Radio); and the Department of Environment and Natural Resources (South Australia), State Heritage Branch.

I also acknowledge the assistance of the following institutions in Great Britain: the Genealogical Society; the Minet Library, Lambeth; the Public Records Office, Kew; the Public Records Office, Chancery Lane; St Catherine's House; the Greater London Records Office; and the British Library.

AUTHOR'S NOTE

On 1 November 1929 the *Register* (South Australia) published 'A Page from Winifred's Indian Diary'. It is probable that Winifred Steger kept a diary at other times but, if so, I did not have access to it. There were no diaries among the Steger papers in the Mortlock Library.

The spelling of Arabic words in English is approximate. There is no one correct spelling universally accepted by all official sources. I have tried to use the spelling most familiar to English speaking readers.

Foreign language words not listed in the Macquarie Dictionary Third Edition have been printed in italics and definitions are provided in the Glossary at the back of the book.

... *suddenly from deep within my head*
the images appear
like moving pictures on a screen.

Strange places never been;
strange faces never seen.
Others I never thought to see again:
father and mother, sister and brother.
And stretching forth my hand
I feel their living presence in the room.

Until I wake.

The same sharp pain returns,
the sense of loss
that makes the hot tears burn.

I sleep again.

Once more in dreams my restless spirit
journeys deep into the country of the mind,
as if in constant search some truth I'll find,
some secret door that unlocked will reveal
which of the two lives that I live is real.

The Country of the Mind,
Hilarie Lindsay

*One of the hardest punishments is to be thrown
into the world with aspirations and dreams that cannot be
fulfilled for want of education ...*

*I received only a few weeks' schooling. Ignorant and alone
I lived in a world of make-believe.*

Winifred Steger

CONTENTS

INTRODUCTION

I first met Winifred Steger when she was coming to the end of her long journey, a journey that was to span almost a century. In 1973 I had seen her interviewed on *This Day Tonight* (ABC TV), when the paperback version of her book about her trip to Mecca, *Always Bells: Life with Ali*, was published. She was asked what she would say to younger writers; 'Grow mentally,' she replied. Her story captured my imagination and, as president of the Society of Women Writers (SWW), I wrote to congratulate her and to invite her to become a special member of the Society. Winifred accepted the invitation and we began to correspond.

At the time I had developed a special interest in Australian women writers because so many complained of difficulty in being published, or even writing. In 1971 I had written a letter to the newspapers in Australia, as well as the New York and London *Times*, inviting women writers who had experienced difficulty in getting published to write to me. In the first month I received four hundred letters and they continued to pour in, until I was overwhelmed by what I had started. The letters, some written by relatives, confirmed what I had suspected. Women spoke of outright opposition from husbands and male relatives, to the extent of being forbidden to write under their married name. Others spoke of lack of education, isolation, domestic work that consumed all their time and energy, and the problem of finding money for postage to send their work out. There was a feeling of deep frustration.

Out of all the women writers I encountered in my research it was Winifred Steger who impressed me the most. It was her indomitable spirit, her refusal to bow to old age, and the fact that she was still writing and could express herself so lucidly, that captured my imagination. I had no idea of the full story of her life, but one of her letters gave me a tantalising glimpse.

Dear Lady,
Today you wrote with your spirit and I felt it and somehow when I came to the signature 'affectionately' my eyes dimmed. It was a touch from some Never Never Land. This emotional life grows strange fancies. I am a relic, I suppose, of the old Victorian days. It would have been easier had I some Silver Trumpeter. I am, briefly, just an aged woman of ninety-four [born in 1882, Winifred was in fact ninety-one] *who since I could first write my letters have had a simple compulsion to write.*

Maybe I was a writer in a past life and maybe shall be a better one in the next one. At least I hope to have the sophisticated education that editors desire now. I feel dimly that I have a message but don't know what it is … and there you have the odd, complicated character that I know myself to be.

My first real effort at writing was when I was fifteen. Shaw Fitchett of London brought out his new magazine called Life. *A traveller on Cobb & Co … lost it on a lonely bush road. I found it. Reading it was marvellous. Something within me said, You too can write, so get to it. With pencil and paper I sat down and wrote 'The Adventures of a Bee and a Blue Bag'. Oh, yes, frightfully crude. A couple of months later came a cheque for one pound and my story in the next issue, entitled 'From a Rough Diamond'. And urging me to write again. Wildly excited I wrote another and this time added a title and it was printed.*

I was an unloved and neglected child left to battle alone. My first experience with real people [was] when at ten years I was put with outsiders to work at sixpence a week, later rising to a full half-a-crown. My only joy was in writing on paper scraps from the ends of books, or the back of envelopes.

Years, marriage, children, troubles and hardships, need I go on? Till finally I went disguised as a Turkish woman to the forbidden lands of Mecca. I loved my Moslem and insisted on going also and he so loved me that he consented. It's all so long ago.

Returning to Australia, I had met Annie Besant in India, so was asked to speak in [the] Adelaide Theosophical Hall. Which I did two Sundays running. The reporter came [the] second Sunday and after our return to cameleer life I was asked to write for the Register.

Then Ali died and the fight was mine. I took out a hawker's license and toured the far north cattle properties. Then a history of punctured tyres, broken parts, shortage of water etc etc … I left the north after running various Government messes during the War. I bought a little place near Clare and again more writing. From serials I started novels. Three I gave free to Clare newspapers, 80,000 word jobs. Took three years to finish publishing them.

May I add that the criticisms of Always Bells *were magnificent. Of my journey to Mecca the book tells. I feel as if I could put another cushion on the chair and write another dozen novels straight off … I'm not dead yet and have fourteen unwanted novels in the box. Give me another hundred years and I might have them accepted, as it is the God of Fire will have a glorious glowing feast. Anyway why worry. I believe in reincarnation and when I come back I mean to paint this old firmament in black shades of printer's ink.*

As our correspondence continued I discovered that Winifred had another identity as Winifred the Washerwoman, a pseudonym she continued to use long after she had ceased to be a washerwoman, to thumb her nose at the world. If the world despised the washerwoman engaged in honest toil, did it also despise Winifred the Washerwoman, the writer behind the warm and witty articles that engaged readers for many years in the *Register* and *Chronicle* in South Australia and the *Sun* in Victoria?

In 1976 I travelled to Adelaide to launch a branch of the Society of Women Writers (SWW) and invited Winifred to attend the meeting. I recall a sprightly woman in a blue dress, wearing a white wig. She was surprised to discover that I was much younger than she had imagined. 'I was thinking we could have collaborated,' she said. It was our only meeting.

Later, I tried to find a publisher for her novels, without success. When she threatened to burn them I contacted the staff at the National Library who offered to buy them. But that was not to be. Winifred had only one ambition — to see them in print.

Eventually Winifred's letters ceased and I had no idea of what happened to her, though she stayed in my mind. By this time my life had moved on. Then in 1992 I began a Master of Philosophy degree at Sydney University. Initially I intended to use the material I had collected on women writers as the basis for my thesis. However, Winifred soon began to take over and I realised my thesis was, in fact, a biography of her extraordinary life. My one difficulty was that I had nothing but her letters and a few tear sheets she had sent me of her three serials which had been published in the Clare's *Northern Argus*.

In 1993 I wrote to Helen Baker, a member of the SWW in Adelaide, to see if she knew what had happened to Winifred. She referred me to Stella Guthrie who had interviewed Winifred for Rural ABC Radio, recording interviews with the old writer until just before her death in 1981.

Like many who met Winifred, Stella had fallen in love with her and she offered to lend me the tapes on the proviso that I speak to Winifred's daughter, Pansy, first. From Pansy I confirmed that the trip to Mecca had really happened and that as a small child she had accompanied her mother. But, apart from a few anecdotes, she could tell me very little. 'Mother was a very private person. She did not talk about her past,' she said. This was something I was to hear repeated many times by other relatives.

In addition to lending me the tapes, Stella referred me to Nancy Robinson of Nadjuri Press. From Nancy I discovered that Winifred's manuscripts had not been burned on her death. Winifred had given them to Nancy in the hope of publication and they were kept in the Mortlock Library, South Australia, for safe keeping. Nancy gave me permission to research them. They were in ten cartons and I began work immediately.

As soon as I transcribed the Guthrie tapes I discovered the first of Winifred's lies. The story told in *Always Bells*, about the author being found under a rosebush in China and raised first by Buddhist priests and then by nuns, was a falsehood. She had, in fact, been born in Lambeth, England, and she and her father had migrated to Queensland.

I was to discover the reason for this deception when I read the correspondence between Winifred and Beatrice Davis of publishers Angus & Robertson. While Winifred was living on a poultry farm in Alice Springs after World War II she rewrote the story of her trip to Mecca, which had been published as a serial in the South Australian *Register*, and entered it in a novel writing competition run by the Adelaide *Advertiser*, under the title *With Ibn Saud to Mecca*. Though it did not win, one of the judges mentioned it to Beatrice Davis who wrote to Winifred asking to see a copy of the manuscript. At the same time the *Advertiser* offered to publish it as a serial. Eager to publish it as a book Winifred accepted the offer from Angus & Robertson. It was published as an autobiography. Once the lie about her childhood and marriage to Ali, whom she claimed she had met in China before migrating to Australia, was published, Winifred was stuck with it. It was the story she told to those who met her after the publication of the book, a story she repeated in interviews with the media.

Hoping to find some relatives of the Steger family I advertised in the *Sydney Morning Herald*, but without success. My first breakthrough came when I found some early copies of the *Register* at the Mitchell Library. These contained the serial she had written on Mecca under the title of 'Arabian Days: the Wanderings of Winifred the Washerwoman', with the by-line Bebe Hadjana Karum Bux. I wrote to Winifred's daughter to find out if Karum Bux was her father and received a reply from her daughter asking me not to write to her mother again, as she had told me all she knew.

I knew from the Guthrie tapes that Winifred had written a series called 'Star Dust and Soap Bubbles' for the *Register* and that she had also used the pseudonym Sapphire Bill. I travelled to Adelaide and spent days looking through the microfiche until I found first 'Star Dust and Soap Bubbles' and then 'The Tales of Sapphire Bill', both running as weekly serials. I also researched in the State Library of Victoria and found that the 'Star Dust and Soap Bubbles' stories had been syndicated. I was unsuccessful in finding them in the *Courier-Mail* where Winifred claimed also to have published, but I have no doubt that they are there somewhere. Without dates it is almost impossible to locate them.

My second breakthrough came when a friend found out that Winifred's maiden name was Oaten and I was able to get her birth certificate.

From this I learned that her father was Wilfred Oaten, son of a schoolmaster from Bath. Her mother was Louisa Dennis, whose address was given as 97 Tradescant Street, Lambeth. I went to England and found the house, one of a row of terraces which is still standing. I looked for a nearby school where Winifred may have had her early education and found Wyvil Road School on the other side of South Lambeth Road, about a five-minute walk from Tradescant Street. I was unable to verify that Winifred had been a pupil there as there are no records of this school in the archives of the Public Records Office in London. I could find no evidence of Winifred having attended school in Australia, though the Jondaryan School records seem to have disappeared. I believe Winifred's claim that the only schooling she had was in England is true.

From the Guthrie tapes I discovered that after migrating to Australia Winifred had lived on the Darling Downs, Queensland, with her father. I wrote a letter to the Dalby Historical Society and received a letter back telling me about her marriage to Charles Steger and the birth of two sons. It was some time before I discovered that there had been two later children from the marriage.

I found no mention of Wilfred Oaten and his daughter in the immigration records in the Greater London Records Office or in the Queensland State Library, though there I found details of the arrival of Wilfred's brother, William, and his wife, Lydia, in 1882. I did, however, find details of two land orders Wilfred Oaten received.

Winifred claimed, rightly, that she did not know what had happened to her father. I searched for a death certificate and found that he died intestate. In a corner of an official document someone had written in ink that a telegram sent to his daughter at Morven was returned. Now I knew where Winifred had gone after she left her husband, Charles. I wrote to the Morven Historical Society and found an old man, Stafford Burey, who remembered Winifred living with Ali Ackba Nuby, an Indian hawker who had a shop at Mungallala, and that they had had a little boy. An added bonus was a copy of a photograph Stafford had taken of Ali standing with a group of men on the steps of the Tryconnel Hotel, Mungallala. I followed this up with a search for a birth certificate and found out that Winifred had given birth to three children, Yusef, Rhamat and Pansy.

Through Winifred's papers, her unpublished novels and the newspaper serials, I was able to add to the biographical material I had gathered and build up a picture of the author's life, and of her thoughts and ideas which were reflected in the characters in her novels. Most had a heroine who had had a child out of wedlock without having to marry the father and who eventually found happiness, and acceptance of her child, with another man. The novels reflected the mores of the day, when an unmarried mother was an outcast and her children described as illegitimate. The injustice such women suffered, at a time when there was no supporting mother's benefit, no widow's pension, was a recurring theme and was a reflection of Winifred's own unhappiness, when she was forced into a loveless and early marriage, and of her struggle to survive as a washerwoman when she was left with three children to support.

At about this time I received a letter from Jose Petrick, who had written a book on street names in Alice Springs. The street where Winifred had had her poultry farm had been named after her. In her letter Jose mentioned that Horrie Simpson, a former Oodnadatta resident who used to deliver meat to ghantown (the name given to settlements where camel men lived), had told her of a note he had made in his diary of a wedding between Karum Bux and Winifred Steger on 26 June 1925. This confirmed that it was with Karum Bux and not Ali that Winifred had gone to Mecca, and it coincided with the dates of the story of the trip published later in the *Register*.

I could find no record of the articles in *Life* published by Shaw Fitchett, but I have no reason to doubt Winifred's word.

One question that intrigued me was what had happened to the family she left behind on the Darling Downs. I wrote to every person named Steger in the Australian telephone directory and received a letter from Winifred's great-grandaughter, Belinda, who told me of meeting Winifred when she returned to Queensland after Charles Steger died. Later, I met other members of the family in Queensland, and they confirmed what I had believed to be true about Winifred's disastrous relationship with her husband, Charles.

In 1997 I submitted my thesis and was awarded my doctorate. But Winifred had invaded my life. She would not let me rest. I knew I had to tell the story of this remarkable pioneer woman to a wider audience. She had travelled through the trackless wastes of the Australian desert with her husband and children and a family of Aborigines, a journey very few white women of her period had made. When Ali Ackba Nuby died in India she had supported herself and her children by taking in washing. She had made the trip to

Mecca with Karum Bux, and was rewarded by being made the Secretary to the Khalifat in Australia, a great honour. This was followed up with an invitation to become governess to the King and Queen of Afghanistan at a time of great political instability. Winifred wrote about the experience in a sequel to *Always Bells,* which she called *There Was a King.* It was too far-fetched to be believable and it was never published. Even I doubted that it was true, until I found a record of an interview published in the *Register* when she was on her way to India in 1928 to take up the appointment, and her later published dispatches from India about the situation in Afghanistan, in which she was referred to by the *Register* as a 'special correspondent'.

My thesis was an academic text, well documented, with quotations, references and footnotes, none of which had a place in the story I wanted to write. Instead I took the liberty of turning footnotes into people I conjured up out of my imagination. Mrs Watkins was the first to appear, as the kindly barrow woman who was representative of her times and who befriended the lonely child. Winifred had said that an old gentlemen befriended her on the trip to Australia, and so Mr Smithers was born. Mrs Dobson of Dalby may or may not run a general store, and so it went through the story. People I gave birth to in my imagination lived and breathed alongside the real people in Winifred's life. And walking beside me was Winifred, who had possessed me. I sensed her at my shoulder. She invaded my dreams while I slept, so that our thoughts blended and I felt as if her spirit had entered mine.

Now she is safely in the pages of this book, together with those I have raised from the dead, and those whom I have caused to walk this earth even though they only existed in my mind. I set myself a hard task and it is finished. I should be glad, but I have lived with Winifred for so long that without her my life is strangely empty. Yet I know the time has come to go our separate ways, to set her spirit free. *Salaam alaikum*, dear old friend.

Hilarie Lindsay

PART ONE

I

GROWING UP IN LAMBETH

ONE OF WINIFRED'S EARLIEST MEMORIES was of standing by the front gate watching the men come home from work as she waited for her father. Her mother was lying down. 'Stop bothering me. I've got a headache,' she had said when Winifred had asked if she would take her for a walk. 'Go and talk to Mrs Watkins.' But the neighbour was out with her fruit barrow. The child had gone to the front of the house and, dragging a stool to the door, had unlatched it and let herself into the street.

It was still warm, even though it was almost dusk. She stood watching a tram rumble along South Lambeth Road, the harness jingling, the driver sitting in the front flicking his whip at the horses. Nearby a man lurched past and she thought, 'He must be a tipsy man.' She'd heard her mother talking to Mrs Watkins about men who got tipsy. It was a strange word that sounded like 'gypsy'. She knew what they were. Sometimes they camped on the common and grazed their horses. 'They steal little children and they never see their mothers again,' Mrs Watkins had told her. Winifred had made up her mind there and then never ever to go near the common in case the gypsies got her and she never saw her mother again.

But the tipsy man wasn't on the common. Winifred thought he looked funny staggering from side to side. He grabbed hold of a lamppost for a moment, then staggered out of sight. Winifred went to the corner and saw him go into the lane behind the shop where her father bought his tobacco, and where her mother bought bags of flour, tapioca, sago and sugar. When her mother had no money the man in the shop put it on the slate. Sometimes he would beckon Winifred over to the counter and give her a paper spill of boiled lollies. She liked the black and white ones best. Mrs Watkins called them humbugs and said they were better than the human sort. She couldn't imagine a human shaped like a humbug. And you couldn't eat a human humbug unless you were a cannibal. She knew about the cannibal islands from a story her father read her. She liked her father's stories. They were all about adventure and sailing off to places far away. 'How would you like that, eh? Sail on a big ship far across the sea.' She thought she'd like it very much.

But her mother always said, 'Don't talk nonsense. You'll not get me on a ship.'

'We'll see. We'll see,' her father would say.

Winifred watched the tipsy man unbutton his fly and then a stream of urine came spurting out, splashing on the paling fence. He looked up and saw her standing there and began to laugh. 'Spying on me, are you, young'un? Come and have a good look.' He lurched towards her, holding something pink in his hand, something that moved. He put out one hand to grab her and she screamed and ran back to the corner shop and down the street. She hammered on the front door with her small fists but it had shut behind her. She wasn't tall enough to reach the door handle. No one came to open the door and she sat down on the doorstep feeling cold. The warmth had gone out of the day.

She was still sitting there when her father came round the corner carrying his bag. 'You're a strange one, sitting here by yourself.'

'I couldn't get the door open.'

'Did she lock you out again?' He opened the door and Winifred followed him down the dark hall and up the stairs to their room where her mother was lying down. Her father bent over the bed and shook her roughly. 'You lazy slut. Too lazy to look after your own child. I bring in the bread, the least you can do is look after her.'

Her mother sat up and, picking up her hairbrush from the dressing table, began to brush her long, fair hair. 'You know I never wanted her. I told you that when she was born. You wanted to keep her. You look after her.'

Her father raised his fist as if to strike her but restrained himself. 'God knows why I stay,' he said as he struck a match and lit the paraffin lamp. It shed a circle of pale light onto the small round table where he emptied some coins out of a leather purse. He handed them to Winifred. 'Run to the corner shop and get a bundle of saveloys and a loaf of bread. Take the basket.'

Winifred pressed herself against the door, shaking violently. 'There's a tipsy man … a tipsy man … I saw his willie,' and she burst into tears and flung herself to the floor.

Long after she had left England, Winifred would think back to her early life in London and the house where she had lived with her parents in two rooms on the top floor, though her room was more of a box room that overlooked the back lane and the tap in the yard and the length of rope which the women fought over as a clothes line. The privy, where they emptied their slop pails in the morning, stood in one corner.

The roof was slate and often in the night Winifred would hear something scrabbling across it. 'Them's water rats,' a boy once told her when she was down by the river. 'When I'm wif a *tosher* we chase 'em up the sewer and knock 'em on the head. It's capital sport … we git a farthing a dozen from the sanitary.' She shuddered and turned away when he held up a string of rats by the tails. He was one of the mudlarks who earned their living by diving in the river, looking for coins and bits of rag and bone that they sold to the man who came around with a horse and cart.

Winifred knew from a book her father had read to her that the River Thames separated their part of London from the other, where Parliament met and where Queen Victoria lived in her palace. She'd seen the palace's back entrance once when she'd walked with her father to Victoria Station. There were guards in uniform standing in the street. 'That's where the tradesmen go in and out,' her father had said.

'The butcher, the baker, the candlestick maker,' she had recited as she skipped along beside him. She liked to imagine the Queen sitting on her throne choosing the best cabbages and feeling the tomatoes to make sure they were not bruised, perhaps even biting into an apple. She wondered if the grocer gave her children spills of boiled lollies.

The thought of rats scrabbling on the roof frightened her. She would bury her face under the blankets in case one came scuttling down the chimney and under the crack beneath the door. It might find its way into her bed and bite her. She knew that rats had bubonic plague and made you sick until you died.

A sick man lived on the floor beneath them. She could hear him coughing when she passed his door. It was coal dust, her father said. He'd been a coal-whipper. It was something to do with unloading coal from boats that came down the river. Sometimes her father sent her in with a cup of milk. She would hesitate at the door, almost afraid to go in because of the smell of sweat, and piss in a bottle under his bed. He had a tin mug and sometimes it was full of blood. He'd gaze at her, his unshaven face almost transparent, so that she could see the bones poking through, and two bright spots of colour on each cheek like blood plums. He would beckon her to come closer, curling up one long thin finger with a blackened nail, trying to focus with his filmy blue eyes. She would sidle up to the bed and put the cup on the chair beside him before he could touch her. Then she would turn and be out the door like a flash, running helter-skelter into her own room. He was dying, her father said so: 'And the sooner the better. Otherwise it's the workhouse.'

Winifred often heard about the workhouse from Mrs Watkins when they walked past the forbidding building on their way to the markets. 'It's a cruel place,' she said, 'where poor folks are taken when they have no job. They lock them up, like in a prison, and send their children away. As if they were horphans. And they get whipped and made to clean the lavatories. I know. And they never git to taste a dish of hot peas or a plate of jellied eels but live on gruel and slops that is only fit for pigs. When my Watkins took to the drink and I had no money coming in, I thought about the workhouse and my Aggie being taken away and I went to the markets and bought some apples with my last shilling. It was the best thing I ever done. It don't matter whether my Watkins is working or taken with the drink, we get by. And it's honest work. Niver be afraid of honest work.' She leaned close to Winifred, the wart on the end of her nose wobbling while the child listened wide-eyed and shivered as she glanced at the high brick wall of the Lambeth Workhouse, imagining she could hear the children crying for their mothers and starving to death on gruel.

'You can't blame the men for being taken in drink,' Mrs Watkins said once as they walked past the Royal Albert Beer Engine. Men were spilling out onto the road and as the doors swung open and shut, smoke wafted out to the street, Winifred hopped nimbly to one side as a dollop of nicotine-laden spit landed at her feet. 'Times is hard. There's too many folks in London. I hear tell that there are more than three million souls in London all struggling to make a living. Some

8

of 'em be bad but most are just ordinary folks like your dad who come from the country. There ain't no work out there and they be hoping to find somethink to do in London, other than thievin'. We be honest folks.'

Mrs Watkins looked after Winifred — Lord knows, the child's mother certainly took no interest in her. As she trotted along beside Mrs Watkins, Winifred absorbed the sights and sounds of South Lambeth: the monstrous gasometer which dominated the skyline near Vauxhall Cross; the stench of rotting bones waiting to be boiled down at the soap works; the black smoke belching from the tall chimneys of the brewery; and the steam laundry where Aggie Watkins worked. Sometimes she was around when Aggie came home from work, her feet and ankles swollen and her hands red raw from being in the water all day. Winifred would watch as the young woman soaked her feet in a basin of hot water with a teaspoon of salt in it and rubbed sugar and dripping into her hands, drawing on a pair of white cotton gloves which she did not take off till the next morning when she went to work. She was walking out with a young man who had a job on the railways and they planned to get married 'by and by'.

The times Winifred liked best were when her father was in a good mood and told her stories about his childhood in Bath: the pure air; the swans and ducks on the river; the fish he caught when he had an afternoon off school; the song of the blackbird at dusk in their cottage garden. There were hollyhocks and marigolds, pansies and violets, lavender and roses. She would listen to the names rolling off her father's tongue and recite the words to herself as she lay in bed at night. He talked about the Assembly Rooms where rich people came to drink wine and play cards and dance and the baths where they took the waters for their health. Then there was the school where his father taught and where Wilfred and his brother William Ivanhoe had learned Latin, Greek, mathematics and English history. When she asked him about his sisters he said, 'My mother taught them their letters at home. They had to help in the house. There were boys who lived in, with beds to make, linen to sort, flowers to pick and put in vases and milk to be separated and made into butter. They were too busy to go to school. In any case, there were no girls in my father's school.'

When she asked if he would take her to visit Bath he would shake his head and say, 'There's nothing left of that life now. There's no going back. That part is finished. And even if it wasn't there's no money for fares.'

Other times he would be morose and angry, quarrelling with her mother. She would creep out the door and sit on the steps in the dark, listening to Mrs Watkins yelling at Mr Watkins and wondering if he would hit her and give her a black eye as he sometimes did when he was in the drink. She was glad her father didn't drink. But she wished he and her mother didn't fight all the time. It frightened her, wondering if one day he would clear out and she and her mother would end up in the workhouse. She would have liked to have asked him to take her with him if he left, but she didn't want to make him angry. Sometimes when he was angry he would hit her with a stick for no reason that she could see. Then he would yell at her, 'I'm sick of you gawking at me. Get out of my sight,' and she would run up the narrow stairs to her room and cry herself to sleep. Later she would wake to find him bending over her bed, stroking her forehead, or tucking the coarse grey woollen blanket around her, and hear him whisper, 'On Sunday we'll stroll across the bridge to the path and feed the ducks. Perhaps your mother will come with us. We'll have a little treat.' She would drift back to sleep again, not sure whether she had imagined it or not. It was a long while before Winifred realised that the blows were directed at her mother, but that he loved Louisa too much to hit her because he was afraid of losing her.

Sometimes when Winifred woke in the night and the wind was blowing from the right direction she would hear the train whistle at Victoria. It was a friendly sound — and exciting, because it meant travel. She liked to imagine the people sitting in the carriages in their fancy clothes, the men in top hats with a carnation in their buttonhole, and the women wearing diamond tiaras and feather boas. She thought that the train would be different from the train that took the working men down to the dockyard and the match girls to the Bryant and May's factory. Her father walked to work. He was a house painter and had a regular job, not like Mrs Watkins's husband who unloaded ships. He had to line up every morning with thousands of men, all hoping for a day's work. Sometimes when he got work he forgot to come home until morning, and spent his two and sixpence in the Wheatsheaf round the corner. Then there would be shouts and screams downstairs and Mrs Watkins would end up with a swollen face. Once the police came and she was taken to hospital.

But on a summer's morning when the sun shone into her room, Winifred could forget the screaming and shouting, the rats and the dying man. There would be sparrows pecking in the yard among the weeds and wildflowers that somehow had survived from the garden of the man who had been there before. She knew his name. It was Tradescant. She liked the way it sounded, though it was a long time before she could say it properly. She knew about John Tradescant from her father. He had been gardener to King Charles I and had grown the first pineapple in London.

She wondered what a pineapple tasted like and if it was anything like the apples Mrs Watkins sold in her barrow. Sometimes Mrs Watkins let her take an apple that had a brown speck in it. 'Just bite off the bad bit, dearie. It won't hurt you.' Winifred would choose one and polish it on her apron before biting into it, feeling the tartness on her tongue and the juice running down her chin.

Mrs Watkins often took Winifred with her when she went to the Cut to buy her apples. She was always careful to buy the cheapest apples, then she would spit on them, polish them on her apron and arrange them in a pyramid in her barrow. 'People will always pay a halfpenny extra for a nice shiny apple,' she would say as she trundled her barrow down the street. 'Fresh apples, only a penny,' she'd call out. 'An apple a day keeps the doctor away.' Winifred wasn't sure how an apple could keep the doctor away. When she asked, Mrs Watkins patted her on the shoulder and said, 'Poor folks can't afford the doctor but they can afford a penny apple.'

The Cut was an exciting place, with hundreds of people shouting their wares and people pushing barrows or driving horse and carts. 'You has to keep your wits about you here,' Mrs Watkins told her. 'This place is full of thieves and pickpockets who'll do you in for a dumpling.' She kept her money in the pocket of her apron and fastened it with a huge safety pin. Once she threw an apple at a policeman when he told her to move on. But he let her go — she couldn't have paid the fine. She had six children. Five of them had died. Now there was only Aggie.

Lambeth Walk was another of the child's favourite places. Sometimes she went with her father and mother on a Sunday if the weather was fine. In winter they would eat a penny pie for lunch or a dish of pea soup for a halfpenny, or maybe a hot potato with butter and salt. What she liked best was the ginger beer fountain, like a little piano on wheels. It had two pumps with brass handles that glinted in the sun. She loved the taste of the ginger beer with its bubbles that tickled her nose. Other times her father would buy her a glass of milk from the milkman on Clapham Common, while her parents sipped hot elderberry wine. She enjoyed being with her parents once they stopped bickering. But when they were in the middle of one of their quarrels she would creep outside the door and wait in the dark hall until the shouting had stopped.

Winifred was neither happy nor unhappy. She knew no other life. She accepted the fact that babies died and that men beat their wives when they were drunk. She never questioned the public houses on every corner where men drank their meagre earnings after a hard day humping cargo on the wharves or toiling on the railway tracks. If their families suffered it was taken for granted. And yet she knew that there were rich people who lived in fine houses with gardens — her father pointed them out to her on their Sunday afternoon walks. She had seen children in the park with their nannies, the girls with ringlets tied with ribbon wearing velvet dresses with lace collars and long socks and leather boots, bowling hoops along the paths; the boys in sailor suits, sailing toy boats in the Serpentine. Winifred viewed them with curiosity, as if they were a different species, knowing that they played no part in her life.

2

SCHOOL DAYS

WINIFRED HAD NO OLDER SIBLINGS or even friends of her own age to tell her what to expect when she started school. She had watched the children coming and going from school each day as she stood by her front gate. Mostly they ran past, yelling and laughing, though occasionally someone would yell at her, 'What are you staring at, fish-face?' or call her a guttersnipe if they saw her walking down the street helping Mrs Watkins push the barrow. Mrs Watkins would say, 'Take no notice of them, dearie. Names niver hurt nobody.'

The children Winifred met and talked with were mostly working for their living at the Cut, or scavenging by the Thames. They were too busy to go to school. She'd heard her father's stories about the schoolroom at Bath where he got a good whipping if he didn't learn his lessons. 'Sometimes I couldn't sit down for a week,' he used to tell her. 'Still, it did me no harm.' And she wondered if school would be like that for her. She didn't think she'd like to be whipped if she made a mistake.

Mrs Watkins was no help. Her education consisted of a few weeks tuition at a Sunday school 'We learned about God and the Bible. I niver thought it much help when your belly's empty. But sometimes they gave us a slice of bread and scrape, and a bag of boiled lollies at Christmas. My poor old Ma, God rest her soul, had sixteen children … she was fair worn out. She died when I was ten. I was the eldest living. It fell to me to take care o' the others.

'My Da took to the drink somethink awful after Ma died. He worked in the mines. They used to dish out the wages at the hotel on a Saturday. Many the times we went hungry because he'd spent all his money. I'd stand outside the hotel with the young'uns, shivering in the cold with only a few rags on my back, trying to git him to come home. But it made no difference. Sometimes a neighbour sent us in a bit of cold mutton, or a loaf of bread. Sometimes we ate grass … But no matter. That's in the past.

'I look at it like this. Schooling don't make you no better than anyone else. I don't sell any less apples because I can't write proper … I know how to mind me money … it comes natural to most folks. That's the most important thing. You can't learn that from books. Our Aggie's not much different. She were only ten when she went to work in the steam laundry. Book learnin' ain't much help when you're washin' shirts all day.'

When Winifred told her father what Mrs Watkins had said, he explained, 'Everyone has to go to school. You wouldn't understand, but the Government passed an act that once you turn five ... It'll be all right. You'll be able to read books.'

Because her birthday was in November, Winifred started school at the beginning of 1888. Her education was to last for a further two to three years until she left for Australia.

Wyvil Road School was only a few hundred yards from Tradescant Street on the other side of South Lambeth Road. The imposing two-storeyed building was built of the dark brick typical of the time. The boys entered through the main gates in South Lambeth Road; the infants and girls, who were educated separately, entered from a side street.

It was here that Winifred learned to read and write. She was one of a large class of children who were crowded into long desks which sloped in rows down to the front of the room where the teacher sat at her table.

Winifred's first day at school was one of bewilderment and terror once her father had left her in the care of the headmaster, who handed her over to one of the senior girls.

'Molly Smith, look after Winifred Oaten. She's new. Take her to the infants' room and tell Miss Jones I sent her.'

'Yes, sir,' Molly Smith curtsied.

Winifred stared at the big girl. She was wearing a navy woollen skirt, a white blouse under a red cardigan, and long black woollen stockings with lace-up boots. Winifred looked towards the front gate; she wanted to go home, but her father was out of sight. Tears prickled her eyelids and her bottom lip trembled.

The big girl gave her a little push. 'Cry-baby. Come on, the bell will be going soon. I want to finish my game of hopscotch.' She grabbed Winifred by the hand and hurried her along, pausing to ask, 'What does your old man do?'

'He paints things.'

'My father's an engine driver.' The older girl tossed her head. 'And I'm an ink monitor.'

Winifred didn't have the faintest idea what an ink monitor was and she had a stitch in her side from hurrying. Molly Smith came to a halt beside some steps leading up to a porch. 'Up there. That's where the babies go.'

The child stood there, bewildered. The older girl sighed, 'Just my bleedin' luck. Come on,' and she dragged Winifred up the stairs and to the door of a large classroom, where a woman was bending over stoking a coal fire. The woman turned when she heard Molly knock.

'It's a new girl, miss. Sir told me to bring her here.'

The woman advanced to meet them, her long black skirt swishing as she walked. Underneath, Winifred caught a glimpse of black-polished high-buttoned boots. She was wearing a white shirt-waist with a high collar and long leg-o'-mutton sleeves. When she spoke, her voice was soft and melodious and her face softened into a smile. 'Thank you, Molly. You can go now.'

Molly turned and hurried out the door and the teacher bent down towards Winifred. 'What's your name, child?'

'Jane Winifred Oaten.'

'And what do they call you at home?'

'Just Winifred.'

'Well, that's what I'll call you. It's a lovely name.' She took out a large book and wrote in it. 'There, you're on the roll now.' Winifred stared at the writing in the book. She had never seen her name written down before. It was something to tell her father. She thought that perhaps she might like school after all.

Miss Jones led Winifred into the hall where there was a row of pegs. 'Put your school bag there and your bonnet. Now come with me.' She took her by the hand and walked her outside. Winifred watched as a boy pulled a rope, making a bell clang. 'That's the school bell. You must always try and get here before the bell goes.' She led Winifred to where a group of small children was standing in two lines and put her at the end of the front line, saying, 'Today's Monday. We have school assembly. You must stand very still and be quiet,' and she walked down to the other end of the line.

Just then Winifred felt a violent push from behind and she almost fell over, and then someone tugged at her apron and she staggered backwards. She turned around and a freckle-faced boy with ginger hair poked out his tongue. She faced the front again. A man with a stick was walking towards them. He stopped in front of Winifred. She could feel her heart thumping in her chest like a frightened bird. Her throat felt constricted. 'What's your name?' he asked. She stared at him in panic. He was tall and thin and wore a black suit. His cold blue eyes seemed to bore into her and she hung her head, terrified. He poked her in the chest with his stick. 'What's your name?' She was unable to speak. She wanted her father. She wanted to be back home again, eating bread and sugar in Mrs Watkins's kitchen. School was horrible and she began to cry.

Then she heard Miss Jones's voice. 'This is Winifred Oaten. She's only new today.' Winifred threw herself towards

19

Miss Jones and buried her face in her skirt. The woman pulled away. 'Come now, Winifred, you mustn't go on like this. You want to learn to read, don't you?' She held out a white handkerchief. 'Blow your nose and stop crying.'

Winifred did as she was told. She felt better now and looked around the playground. A boy was playing the bugle and two other boys were hoisting the Union Jack up a flagpole until it fluttered in the breeze. She watched as the children stood to attention and chorused, 'I honour my God, I serve my Queen, I salute my flag.' Then the man with the stick called out, 'Quick march,' and the children turned and began to march, groups breaking off to go into their classrooms. Her group was last. They straggled along in two lines, sixty small children, with Winifred leading the way, holding the teacher's hand.

She was still confused after lunch when she heard the bell and followed her class back into their school room. She was also hungry. She had eaten her two slices of bread and dripping when the bell went for the first break and had had nothing left at lunchtime. While the older children sat in groups, she sat alone, feeling miserable and wishing it was time to go home. She knew that now she had started school she had to go every day. The idea frightened her; the squeaking of the slate pencil on the slate made her blood run cold and she had trouble shaping the pot-hooks that Miss Jones drew on the blackboard. She sat there after lunch feeling queasy, her stomach empty, even though she'd had a big drink of water from the tap when she went to the lavatory. Now the water she'd drunk made her want to go to the lavatory again. She fidgeted, twisting and turning until Miss Jones said, 'What's the matter, Winifred? You have to learn to sit still.'

'I want to pee,' Winifred said.

'You should have gone at lunchtime.'

'I did.'

'Well, go then and hurry up.'

The child opened the classroom door and went into the corridor. She could hear the sound of singing coming from the room on the end, and the hum of voices as children recited the twice-timestable in another room. She had no idea how to find the lavatory and stood there confused until a door opened and a girl came out. 'I'm looking for the lavatory,' Winifred said.

'Down the end of the corridor.' The girl grinned. 'I got sent out for talking. And I have to stay back after school and write lines.'

Winifred had no idea what lines were, and without saying thank you trotted to the end of the corridor and into the brick annexe with its row of metal troughs, brass taps and porcelain WCs. She was too short to reach the toilet chain but found that by standing on the seat she could manage. She felt very proud of herself.

The girl was still standing in the corridor when Winifred returned. 'You'd better go back or you'll cop it,' she said. Winifred scurried along back into her classroom. Miss Jones was reading a story about hobgoblins and Winifred was sorry she'd left the room. She decided that tomorrow she would save something for her lunch and forget about big drinks of water so she wouldn't miss hearing the story.

Later, as she crossed South Lambeth Road, she saw Mrs Watkins hurrying along the other side. She was panting by the time she caught up with the child. 'I told your da I'd watch out for you in case you got lorst. I told him you were a bright one and knew your way home. Your ma's gone out. Come and sit with me and tell me all about it. I'll make a cuppa tea and you can toast a bit o' bread once I get the fire lit.'

One morning Winifred woke imagining she could hear the school bell ringing. With a sense of terror she leapt out of bed and hurried to the cupboard, taking out a slice of bread and spreading it with dripping. She ate it hurriedly, washing it down with a glass of water from the jug on the dresser. Then she dipped her flannel in the jug and rubbed it over her face and eyes, pulled her white flannelette nightgown over her head and hung it on a peg behind the door. She always wore her drawers and bodice to bed.

In a kind of frenzied desperation she pulled on her long black worsted stockings, noticing there was a hole in the toe, then she sat on the floor to pull on her lace-up boots. Her brown and white checked dress was lying in a pile on the floor. It had a stain on the front from where she'd spilt the raspberry vinegar her father had brought home the night before. Winifred had been afraid to show her mother, knowing it would make her angry.

After she had put on her dress she found a clean white pinafore in a drawer and pulled this over her head. She looked at herself in the mirror on her mother's dressing table, relieved to find that the pinafore hid the stain, and picked up her hairbrush. She flicked it through her hair, wishing that she had a blue ribbon like some of the other girls. Instead, she fastened her hair back with a tortoiseshell clasp her father had bought her for her birthday.

Winifred glanced quickly at the bed where her mother lay

sleeping, the bedclothes pulled over her in a crumpled heap. She knew that if she woke her mother she would find her an errand to run or make her stay home to keep her company because she had one of her headaches. Winifred grabbed her sunbonnet from behind the door, picked up her school bag and an apple and ran downstairs to where Mrs Watkins was standing at the front gate, talking to Mrs Warby from next door. Winifred called, 'Good morning, Mrs Watkins, Mrs Warby,' as she dashed past. She felt her cheeks burn when she heard Mrs Warby whisper, 'Look at that poor child … pinafore strings undone, hair unbrushed. It's a disgrace. That mother of hers. She ought to be ashamed.'

The child paused briefly to gaze at a bucket of daffodils in the doorway of the corner shop. She wished she had some money to buy one. She'd already spent the halfpenny her father had given her on treacle-taffy. Still thinking about the daffodils, she dashed across South Lambeth Road without looking and almost ran into the path of a hackney cab. She heard the horse whinny and the voice of the driver calling out, 'Watch your bleedin' neck or you'll git your bleedin' head knocked horf.' But Winifred didn't pause to look back, intent on getting to school.

There was no one else running along the road and no sound of children playing in the schoolyard. She knew it must be late as she hurried into the cloakroom and hung up her sunbonnet. In the classroom her new teacher, Mr Cornwall, was calling the roll. She imagined she heard footsteps behind her in the hall, terrified that it might be the headmaster. Once he had made her stay back after school and read out her name on Monday at assembly;

she'd had to join the 'late squad' and march around the schoolyard as punishment.

Winifred opened the door and tried to sidle into the desk but it was no use. 'Ah, the late Winifred Oaten,' Mr Cornwall said. 'Have you an excuse?' Winifred flushed and hung her head. Everything was horrible. She put her head down on the desk and began to cry.

The teacher turned away. 'Today I'm going to read to you from a new book by Robert Louis Stevenson. I want you to listen carefully because I'm going to ask you some questions later.' He opened the book and began to read: 'Squire Trelawney, Dr Livesey, and the rest of these gentlemen having asked me to write down the rest of these particulars about Treasure Island …' He continued reading, glancing up from time to time to make sure the children were paying attention. Some of them were fidgeting at the back, others had a vacant look on their faces, but Winifred Oaten was sitting there, elbows on the desk, her chin in her hands, grey–green eyes shining with excitement, a look of rapture on her face.

That afternoon when the bell went for the end of lessons Mr Cornwall said, 'Winifred Oaten, I want you to stay behind.' He saw a look of panic cross her face. 'It's all right,' he said. 'You like hearing stories, don't you?' She nodded. He held out his copy of *Treasure Island*. 'This belongs to the school but you can borrow it. Take it home and bring it back when you've finished.'

Winifred was still holding the precious book in her hand as she ran across South Lambeth Road and into Tradescant Street. The daffodils had gone from outside the shop but she didn't care. The front door of her house was open and she heard Mrs Watkins call out, 'Is that you, Winnie? Your ma's out. Come and have a bite to eat and a cuppa tea.' But Winifred pretended she didn't hear. She flew up the steps, dropped her sunbonnet and school bag on the floor and, propping herself up on her bed, began to read

She showed the book to her father when he came home from work, being careful not to let her mother see it. She didn't approve of the child reading and 'filling her head with nonsense', while Mrs Watkins said, 'It'll fair ruin your eyes. Looking at books all the time ain't natural. My Watkins says that if God had meant us ter read we would've been born with spectacles. Someone he knowed of went blind.'

Fortunately for the child her father encouraged her, taking her to the newly opened public library. 'Fancy Lambeth being the first to have a library, even before London proper,' he said when they stood before shelves laden with books, some bound in cardboard, other in red leather, introducing her to Charles Kingsley's *The Water Babies*, Tennyson and his 'Daffodils'. This love of literature established a bond with his daughter that Louisa resented and never understood.

Winifred began to read avidly, waking in the morning at first light with a book under her pillow and at night reading till the candle guttered. Her new-found knowledge reflected itself in her school work for which she won a prize. She was filled with trepidation when the headmaster sent for her to come to his office, and she knocked timidly at his door, hesitating before opening it when he called, 'Come in.' She entered, looking nervously around, half expecting him to take out his cane. Instead he smiled at her. 'My dear, you have done very well this year. Your compositions are excellent, you have a very lively imagination and your behaviour is good. You have the makings of a pupil teacher in a couple of years, and after that, it wouldn't surprise me to see you becoming a fully fledged teacher.'

Still in a highly nervous state, his words didn't sink in till later. When he told her to select a book from an array spread out on his desk, she grabbed the first thing that came to hand: A *History of the Hawaiian Islands*, which was not the sort of book that appealed to her at all. But later when she showed it to her father he said, 'Well done,' and gave her threepence.

All her mother said was, 'You spoil that child.'

3

THE POVERTY TRAP

BY THE TIME WINIFRED HAD TURNED eight there was a major upheaval in the labour market. London was swept with industrial strife. First the match girls at Bryant and May's went on strike, then the dockworkers. It had far-reaching effects.

Winifred listened as her father read something from the paper about a woman called Annie Besant who had her own newspaper. She said that the match girls had to live on a pittance while the shareholders were getting thirty-eight per cent dividend.

Winifred wasn't sure what a dividend was but she knew about the match girls. Some of them lived in South Lambeth. She'd watched them running to work like scared rabbits. If they were late they got fined half a day's pay. And Mrs Watkins knew a woman who had a sick husband. She made matchboxes at home and only got twopence farthing for making a gross of matchboxes. Winifred worked it out once in her head and tried to imagine one hundred and forty-four matchboxes piled up. It didn't seem like much money when you had to keep four children and a sick husband. 'She has to burn the midnight oil,' Mrs Watkins said. 'Up half the night making matchboxes and tending to her poor old man who's ailing.' He'd had an accident at the wharves — a bale of wool had fallen on him and he'd broken his back. 'If he dies she'll have to go on the parish, for sure.'

Now, with the strike, Winifred wondered how the match girls got money for food, and how the poor woman who made matchboxes at home was managing when there were no matches to put in the boxes. Her father told her that the girls in the factory only earned eight or nine shillings a week. 'By the time they pay their rent they can barely afford to put food in their mouths. And it's nasty work too. I wouldn't like to see one of mine working in the match factory. The girls get phossy jaw. It's from the stuff they put on top of the match to make it burn. It's called phosphorus.'

When Winifred asked what phossy jaw was, he told her it was something that ate away at the jawbone 'until your face is gone and you die'. Just thinking about it made Winifred feel sick.

'And now the girls at the match factory have formed a trade union and the Trades Council is asking people to give money to the strike fund. If the folks don't give, the girls'll have no money for food. I put my shilling in.'

Winifred was pleased when her father told her that the strike had ended. 'They've got a clean room to eat their lunch, away from the phosphorus fumes, and they're not going to get fined any more.'

A year later the dockworkers went on strike. The work was hard and yet every day thousands of men gravitated to the dockyards seeking a few hours' casual work. Regular work was hard to come by. The gasworks laid off men in the summer because there was not so much demand and many other trades were seasonal. But people still had to eat and pay rent.

It was a bitter and drawn-out affair which lasted for five weeks. The churches and charity organisations such as the Salvation Army were hard pressed to feed the strikers and their families. School attendance dropped and there was an air of uncertainty. People stopped spending money.

Mrs Watkins knew all about it. 'My Watkins says that the foreman has his favourites. Sometimes the men fight each other and sometimes git killed, just fighting to git to the front, climbing on other men's backs like wild beasts, jist tryin' to git noticed. You know, dearie, the bosses ain't Christian. They ride round in carriages, own posh houses in Mayfair and live off the fat of the land. Money don't mean nothing to them. They pay half a crown for a cigar. Yet men like my Watkins slave away humpin' bales and only git half a crown for a day's work. If the strike goes on we'll be out in the street afore we know it. If it weren't for our Aggie, and the meal tickets they're handing out … I hate to think.'

As the strike dragged on, Wilfred Oaten became concerned. 'If this keeps on, there'll be no work for anyone. People are afraid to spend money having their houses painted. And they've stopped building new ones. If I can't get work, I don't know how we'll manage. I'm eating into my savings. Once they go, we'll be stuck here forever.'

The arguments between Wilfred and Louisa became more frequent, with Winifred's mother shouting and her father storming out of the house. Once Winifred woke in the night to the sound of raised voices coming from her parents' room. She crept down the stairs and heard her mother say, 'Go then, see if I care … I can look after myself. I did it once and I can do it again. And when you go, take your brat with you.' Standing by the door in her flannelette nightgown the child began to tremble, terrified that her father would rush out of the house and not come back, leaving her behind.

Then she heard her father's voice, very low and clear. It was the voice he used when he was angry. 'It was a bad day when we met and I fell for your blandishments. You and your pretty face, your extravagant ways. Don't you realise that if we stay here any longer I'll be ruined? Then what will we do?' He added in a softer tone, 'Louisa, don't let's fight. All I want is a better life away from here. If I can get some land, we can start a little farm. I'll be my own boss. You know I love you. There's never been anyone else but you.'

Winifred listened for a few moments but all was quiet and she crept back to her own bed. But the arguments continued. This time there was no refuge with Mrs Watkins, no warm arms to creep into, no cup of hot, milky tea and a bite of bread and sugar.

Mrs Watkins was looking haggard and ill and once Winifred found her crying. 'It's me nerves,' she said. 'I've had to pawn me barrow. It'll be me few sticks of furniture next and then we'll have nothing.' Winifred looked around

Mrs Watkins's room. There was a rickety table with one leg missing. It was propped up with a piece of wood. Three battered wooden chairs and a stool stood round the table. On the mantelpiece over the fireplace was a candle in an empty gin bottle, the treacle tin where Mrs Watkins kept her money, a spirit stove for cooking, a bottle of methylated spirits and a picture of Queen Victoria which Mrs Watkins had cut out of a magazine and pasted onto a sheet of cardboard. There was also a china teapot with a broken spout, four tin mugs and plates and some cheap knives and forks on a tin tray beside a blue willow-patterned tea caddy she had found in the street.

The child wondered if there was anything worth carting to the pawnshop, though she liked the blue and white tea caddy with the story painted on it. She thought about her mother's room, which was full of pretty things. There was an oak dressing table with a winged mirror so that you could see the back of your head, a silver-backed hairbrush and a bowl of face powder. Her mother's haircombs were in a little silver tray with some hairpins, and her dresses were in a tin trunk in the corner. The table was of polished wood and there were four chairs covered in brown leather. On the mantelpiece was a picture of Queen Victoria in a carved wooden frame. A set of china tea cups and saucers and a matching teapot with pink roses on it was on a little dresser where the lamp stood. The old white cups with chips around the rims, which they used every day, were kept inside the dresser with the bottle of paraffin oil for the lamp and her mother's treacle tin in which she kept her money. The floor was bare but her father had stained it black and in the winter, with the firelight dancing around the room, it was warm and cosy. Winifred wondered if her parents would have to take their things to the pawnshop if her father had no work and there was nothing to eat in the house.

'Yesterday they ran outa meal tickets.' Mrs Watkins gazed into Winifred's face with tears in her eyes. 'Twenty-five thousand souls all after the same thing and then there weren't none left for the likes of us. Poor Aggie, saving up to git married, and who wants shirts washed when they don't know where their next penny's coming from? It's a cruel business. There was a great march yesterday. I told my Watkins to stay away. I didn't want him fightin' with the police and going to gaol.'

Later, Winifred heard about the march from her father. 'I was going to take you but I was afraid there might be trouble. In the end there wasn't any fighting, only thousands of men carrying banners and flags. And the Salvation Army was there with a water cart to give them a drink … too many to feed. I had a slice of bread and dripping in my pocket. I gave it to a woman with a baby … She hadn't eaten for two days. Her man was one of the marchers. Watching them made me proud to be an Englishman.'

But it was the action of the Australian dockworkers that impressed Wilfred most. When the strike was finished he discovered that out of the £46 500 pounds donated to the strike fund, £30 000 had come from Queensland, where the dockers were earning one shilling and threepence an hour. The English dockers had fought for the right to earn sixpence an hour and eightpence overtime. This was the catalyst responsible for Wilfred Oaten leaving England.

But he kept his plans to himself, knowing that he would have to persuade Louisa, confident that once everything was organised she would have no choice but to accompany him. Away from the overcrowded house, the drunks who fell out of hotels after closing, the polluted air from factories and the coal dust that seeped into lungs and turned the washing on the line a dismal grey, she would change. He still loved her. His one desire was to make her happy.

One Sunday afternoon Wilfred took his wife and daughter to Hyde Park to hear one of the speakers who were travelling around the country urging people with trades to migrate to Australia. The Government was offering a hundred and seventy-six acres of land to any man with a wife and family. Later, Wilfred spoke to the man in private while Louisa and Winifred stood to one side. A cold wind blew through the park, and Louisa shivered in her blue muslin dress. She sent Winifred to tell her father to hurry up, but he only told his daughter to be quiet and went on talking. He was in a good mood when he rejoined them and took them to a tearoom where he ordered a pot of tea for himself and Louisa, a glass of milk for Winifred and a plate of little iced cakes like nothing the child had ever tasted before.

'Things are much better in Australia than here,' he said as they sat watching the afternoon crowds drifting down Oxford Street. You heard what the man said, 'It's a land of opportunity … a land where the sun shines and where every man is equal.'

Winifred only half listened, intent on nibbling every crumb of her cake and licking the delicious pink icing, picking the sugared cherry off the top and leaving it till last.

Though Louisa drank her tea and ate a cake, she seemed distant and out of sorts. Instead of sharing her husband's enthusiasm she said, 'I feel cold. I want to go home.' They caught the train to Vauxhall Station where the Salvation Army was singing hymns outside the hotel on the opposite corner. Wilfred gave his daughter sixpence to put in their collection box and in return a uniformed woman holding a tambourine gave her a tiny card decorated with painted violets and the words *God is love* printed on it. She watched from the other side of the road as her father tried to take Louisa's arm, but her mother broke away and hurried ahead. Wilfred let her go and waited for his daughter to cross over, then took her by the hand. 'You'd like to go to Australia, wouldn't you?' She said yes, without thinking, knowing it was what he wanted to hear.

It was a month before the letter came, telling him that he had been granted a land order in Queensland for ten pounds. He would receive a second one for twenty pounds if he stayed in Australia for two years. He was overjoyed, dancing around their room waving the letter, kissing Louisa, hugging Winifred, before running down to show Mrs Watkins. 'It's a new beginning. They tell me there's plenty of work and the wages are good. It'll be a wonderful life … a country where there's room to move and where the air is pure and fresh. It's like a dream come true.'

'You're one of the lucky ones.' Mrs Watkins lifted the black-iron kettle off the fire, pouring the boiling water into the teapot, and reached up to the shelf for an extra tin mug. 'They don't want the likes of us. What with my Watkins gittin' taken with the drink and not havin' a trade. But then

I ain't got the stomick for the sea. Wild horses wouldn't git me on a boat. I'll miss little Winnie, though. You mind you take care of her now. She's been like a daughter to me. I buried two of 'em and three little boys.' She wiped her eyes with her apron. 'Still, that's life and there's nothing we can do about it.'

She poured the tea and stirred a generous spoonful of sugar into each mug, before lifting one of the mugs high in the air. 'I ain't got nothing stronger in the house.' Her lips parted in a smile and the wart on the end of her nose wobbled. 'Here's to luck,' she said, and patted him on the cheek.

Wilfred drew on his savings to buy some tools: an axe, nails, a hammer and a shovel, things he had been told were cheaper in England than in Australia. And he gave Louisa some money. 'Get yourself something serviceable for the journey and get Winifred some strong boots and a dress, something that won't wear out in a hurry.'

Her mother took her to the Cut where she bought a length of grey flannel for a winter dress and a length of brown head-cloth for summer. Winifred was disappointed, gazing longingly at the muslin patterned with tiny pink roses, imagining herself in a pretty dress with a wide pink ribbon sash, pink ribbons in her hair and a pair of pink kid slippers. She knew it was no use asking her mother. She would only sneer and say, 'Look at yourself in the mirror … you're a joke. You take after your father's side of the family.'

The boots her mother bought for her were two sizes too large. 'You'll grow into them,' Louisa said when the child protested that she couldn't keep them on properly and that they felt heavy. For herself Louisa chose a length of violet velvet, a pair of black patent-leather boots with grey gussets which buttoned up the side, and a small felt hat with a veil to match her dress.

Louisa took the goods to a woman with a sewing machine who lived in a basement room in South Lambeth Road with her crippled son. She showed the woman the design she wanted copied from the fashion pages in the *Girl's Own* magazine which Louisa bought every week for a penny.

When her mother went for her final fitting Winifred thought the dress was the most beautiful thing she had ever seen. It had a high collar and was nipped in at the waist, the skirt falling in soft folds to just above the ground. Gazing at her mother as she stood there in her velvet dress, she swelled with longing and pride. She wanted to tell her mother how much she loved her, to reach out and hug her, but she knew that if she did her mother would push her away, saying, 'Leave me alone, child. You'll crush my dress.'

Winifred was excited, wondering how her father would react to her mother's new dress, but to her disappointment, when they got home Louisa folded it in tissue paper and placed it in a box under the bed. She hung Winifred's plain grey flannel and brown head-cloth dresses behind the door. Winifred had tried them on, looking in her mother's mirror. The brown head-cloth, with long straight sleeves, hung limply from her shoulders and she felt it made her look drab and ugly and the grey flannel prickled her skin. She knew it was no use complaining. She would have to wait until she was grown up before she could hope to have nice things like her mother.

Her father didn't ask to see her mother's new dress or even about how Louisa had spent the money. He was intent on his preparations for leaving England. There was so much to organise and only a short time to do it. Once he had made up his mind he could see no reason to delay. He secured a berth on one of the Black Ball Line ships which was willing to accept land orders in exchange for passage to Australia.

Within a few weeks everything was ready, their few possessions packed, including Wilfred's paintbrushes, which he knew he would need to get him started in his new land. He put their furniture into store, planning to send for it once he was settled.

The night before they were due to leave he tucked Winifred into bed and kissed her, 'No more rats on the roof, no more stink from the soap works. Soon we'll be in a place where the sun shines all day and where stars spangle the night sky like diamonds.'

4
SAYING GOODBYE
TO ENGLAND

THE CHILD HAD MIXED FEELINGS about the trip. On the one hand she wanted to please her father; on the other she shared Mrs Watkins's fears about the perils of sea travel. She was also disappointed that she had to leave school, where she was doing so well. There had been the chance of becoming a teacher, but now that was gone. But she welcomed an escape from her parents' quarrels, sharing her father's feelings that once they were in Australia her mother would be happier and become a different person.

On the day of departure, after a tearful farewell with Mrs Watkins the day before, Winifred stood on the wharf watching passengers going aboard — families laden with assorted bundles; women holding fretful children, clutching babies in shawls; men struggling up the gangplank, anxious to get settled before the ship left the channel and started rolling in the open sea.

Women carrying baskets of apples and oranges added to the din with their calls of 'Juicy oranges, rosy apples'. The lavender sellers joined in: 'Who'll buy my lavender? Lavender a penny a bunch.' Others with armfuls of hand-knitted woollen shawls importuned travellers at the foot of the gangplank, urging them to 'Feel the quality, m'lady, real Shetland wool. There won't be nothing like it where you're going.' And the muffin man was there with a tray of muffins on his head, ringing a bell and calling, 'Fresh muffins! Fresh muffins!'

Winifred watched as two nuns in black habits and wimples struggled with a cabin trunk and a small hand organ until an elderly man in a tweed suit came to their aid. Winifred thought he would burst the buttons on his waistcoat as he lugged the organ under one arm and pushed his portmanteau with his foot, making slow progress up the gangplank, his face red with exertion and his chest heaving, until at the top she saw a man lean forward, take the organ and place it on the deck. He helped the old man on board and then went to the assistance of the two women.

Winifred stared at the nuns with curiosity. One was fresh-faced and young; the other had a face like a withered apple, with splotches of colour on each cheek. Winifred wondered why they were moving to Australia. She couldn't imagine spending weeks on board with these 'papists', as her father called anyone who was a Roman Catholic. 'We're British,' he would say, 'we have our own Queen. They take their orders from Rome.' It was something the child wondered about but did not understand.

The nuns and the old man disappeared from sight and the child turned her attention back to the wharf, watching as someone threw an apple core into the water. She turned when she heard her father's voice. 'Come along now, Winifred. Don't stand there gawping.'

Obediently, she picked up her bundle of clothes tied in a grey blanket. She was wearing her flannel dress and on her head a grey woollen cap from which her brown curly hair escaped. Her legs were encased in thick black stockings and her feet seemed to swim in her stout black leather boots. It was serviceable garb, the garb of a working man's child. Her mother had made no attempt to make her look pretty and she clutched no doll or toy as many of the other children did. Though she was not an engaging child, there was something about her that made her stand out — her wide grey–green eyes, perhaps, which shone with intelligence, a look that belied her age.

Her father, holding a battered suitcase on one shoulder and a large bundle tied in a calico sheet in the other, hustled her up the gangplank. His paintbrushes and tools were in a tin box which he pushed with his foot. He glanced back and called to his wife, who was standing uncertainly on the wharf. 'Come along, Louisa. I want to get settled, otherwise we'll only get what no one else wants. It's a long way to Australia.'

The young woman looked up at the sound of his voice, then looked away again. Her fair hair was caught loosely in a knot at the nape of her neck and she wore the purple velvet dress with the matching felt hat. In her hand she held a bunch of daffodils.

Winifred looked down at her mother, standing apart, pensive, withdrawn. For the first time the child saw her as a person in her own right and not just her mother. She was so different from the other passengers in their serviceable greys and browns, the girls wearing pinafores to protect their dresses, the boys in knee-length navy serge trousers or brown tweeds with stout grey flannel shirts without a collar. Standing there in her finery, swaying slightly as the crowd jostled past, Louisa seemed like some rare exotic creature, a creature who did not belong in this setting. And then she looked up, her face drawn and pale, her eyes hidden behind her veil.

Wilfred called to her again. This time his voice was impatient. 'Don't hang about. Come aboard, Louisa. It's time to say goodbye to England. We'll be sailing soon.'

Louisa moved forward, dragging her carpet bag behind her. Wilfred pushed his way down to meet her. He picked up her bag and, taking his wife by the arm, propelled her up the gangplank until they were side by side on the deck. For a few seconds they swayed together, the slightly built young man and the beautiful young woman, while Winifred stood watching them. It was as if she did not exist, they were so intent on each other.

She saw her mother lean forward to say something to her father, but she could not catch the words. Winifred was surprised at his reaction. He staggered and clutched at the rail for support. Then her mother moved towards her and kissed her on the cheek. The child was conscious of the daffodils in her mother's arms as the petals brushed against her face. They felt cool and gave off a fresh, clean scent which she was to remember all her life with a feeling of pain. Her last memory of her mother was of seeing her running down the gangplank, her high-buttoned boots clattering and the carpetbag bumping along behind her, a trail of daffodils in its wake, as she pushed her way through the passengers coming aboard. As Winifred watched, she disappeared into the crowd.

Winifred turned to her father, feeling bewildered. He had his face hidden in his hands, his shoulders were shaking. She walked towards him as the funnel let out a huge shuddering blast. The 'all aboard' had gone a long while before and she had watched friends and relatives making their way down the gangplank, then stopping to gather on the wharf, calling, 'Don't forget to write!' and 'God bless you!' while they wiped tears from their eyes.

She wondered what it would be like to have relatives to come and see you off. She knew her father had sisters who lived in Taunton. But it was a long way from London, and she'd never met them. She'd seen a daguerreotype of her grandparents, but they were strangers too. There was a brother with his wife in Australia, but her father had no idea where they were or even if they were still alive. So for the moment there were just the two of them … all alone in the world … no mother … no Mrs Watkins with her bread and sugar, or an apple with a spot of brown that she couldn't sell. Winifred thought that perhaps it made them special, just the two of them, like people in a book.

Winifred looked up as the funnel gave another loud triumphant blast and snorted out a cloud of black smoke. She heard the command, 'Weight anchor', and knew that the great adventure was about to begin. Suddenly she was seized with a feeling of apprehension. She walked across to her father and took him by the hand. 'They're pulling up the anchor.'

Her father turned his head and, dropping her hand, gripped her by both shoulders. 'If anyone asks, your mother is dead.' He shook her violently and she struggled to break free. 'Your mother is dead — dead — do you understand? Dead, I say. You must never mention her name again.'

Winifred could feel her teeth chattering; a cold wind had sprung up and she was very afraid. She thought of the long voyage ahead and the stories she had read of shipwrecks, of storms and sea serpents and one-legged pirates who came aboard and made the passengers walk the plank. Then she thought of Mrs Watkins and the day she told her that the gypsies might take her and she'd never see her mother again. It was something too awful to think about and she began to cry.

Her father released her. 'You're cold, child. Let's go below and find a spot to spread our blankets. I've got some muffins and a bottle of raspberry cordial in my bag.'

5

ALL AT SEA

THE SHIP ON WHICH THE OATENS SAILED was crowded, the sleeping quarters for the steerage passengers were uncomfortable and cramped. Out of England they ran into bad weather and many of the passengers became seasick, including Wilfred. Accustomed to a father who had always been strong and able to care for her, Winifred became alarmed, especially as his sickness seemed to drag on long after the high seas had abated and the other passengers were eating and moving around on the lower deck enjoying the sunshine and the balmy weather.

She wondered what would happen to her if he died. She would have no one. The thought preyed on her mind but she had no one to tell her fears to. Then one day while she was sitting alone, Sister Angela, the older of the two nuns she had watched coming aboard, sat beside her and took her by the hand. 'You are always on your own, little one. Have you no one travelling with you?'

Winifred gazed into a pair of grey eyes, a soft upturned mouth and a wizened old face that wore a gentle smile.

'Only my father and he's sick.'

'What's the matter with him?'

'He's been seasick and he's still not right. I'm worried that he might die,' and she burst into tears.

She felt Sister Angela's arms about her and heard her say, 'We will pray to Our Lady to make him better. But first dry your eyes,' and she held a handkerchief to Winifred's nose and said, 'Blow.' The child did as she was told and wiped her eyes, looking with surprise at the old nun in her severe black habit and wondering why she reminded her of Mrs Watkins when they were nothing alike.

'You'd better take me to your father.' Sister Angela gathered her long black habit into her hands so that it swept clear of the deck and clambered down the steep steps to where Wilfred was lying on his grey blanket, his eyes sunken, his unshaven face gaunt and pale. Sister Angela bent over him. 'Peace be with you,' she said, then turned to the child. 'Fetch me a basin of water and a towel.'

When Winifred returned, Sister Angela dipped the towel in the water and washed her father's face and hands and then undid his flannel shirt and sponged his chest. 'Don't worry, child,' she said to Winifred, who was standing watching, worrying in case her father got angry with her for talking to papists. But she was even more afraid that he might die.

As if reading her mind, Sister Angela said, 'Don't worry. I nursed with Florence Nightingale in the Crimea. I know

45

about these things. Your father is weak. How long since he's eaten?'

'I don't know,' Winifred replied.

'Go and find Sister Beatrice. Ask her to bring some gruel.'

Under the ministrations of the two nuns Wilfred Oaten recovered enough to walk on deck, and the sea air gradually revived him, bringing the colour back into his cheeks. He didn't seem to mind when Winifred sat with the two women while they read the Office or told her about God and his angels and the mother of Jesus. On Sundays when the nuns brought out their hand organ and conducted a service, playing while the steerage passengers sang hymns, Wilfred joined in. It was as if he knew how hard it was going to be to raise his young daughter without a woman by his side.

Though the sea air revived Wilfred physically, it was a long while before he stopped grieving for his wife. He kept his own counsel and Winifred never confided in the nuns, who took it for granted that the child's mother was dead.

Winifred made one other friend on the ship. It was the old gentleman she had seen helping the nuns carry their gear on board. She was busy with her book and pencil one day, writing a story about mermaids in a magic cave beneath the ocean, when she saw a shadow beside her and looked up. 'Well, young lady, I'm glad to see you at your lessons.'

'I'm writing a story.'

'May I see it?' the man asked. She handed it to him and watched his face while he read it. She had seen him walking on the top deck and talking to the sailors but she did not know his name. Now he said, 'My name is Smithers ... and

I think you're a very clever little girl.' He patted her on the head and pulled a tin out of his pocket. 'Have a peppermint.'

Winifred took one and found it so hot that her mouth tingled. She pushed it to one side with her tongue, and as soon as he resumed his walk, dropped it overboard, wondering if it would make the water taste like peppermint.

After that they often had a conversation and he showed her his telescope, once letting her look through it at a whale spouting in the distance. He told her about the equator, that it was an imaginary line running around the earth, and she laughed, imagining a real lion running in circles all the time. 'It's always hot near the equator because of the angle of the sun. Days and nights are the same length. It gets dark very early.'

Gradually, as the ship approached the equator, the passengers changed into cooler clothing and spent more time on deck, often sleeping there to get a breath of fresh air. Winifred changed into her brown head-cloth but the tight sleeves made it hot and uncomfortable, until Mr Smithers suggested to Sister Beatrice that they cut them off. 'We can always stitch them on again,' Sister Beatrice said and she unpicked the seams so that the child felt cooler.

There was often lightning on the horizon and sudden showers of rain that swept over the salt-encrusted deck, washing it clean and sending the passengers scurrying for cover. Once the rain had passed, the air would be lighter, but then the harsh tropical sun would bake the decks again so that the waves of heat rose from the timbers, together with the stench of rotting seaweed and dried salt.

Sometimes on hot nights, surrounded by other people tossing and turning restlessly, Winifred would lie awake looking at the stars that seemed very close, and once she saw a shower of shooting stars. Mr Smithers had told her about the dog star and one night he showed it to her through his telescope. 'It's real name is Sirius and sailors can use it to plot the course of their ships.' The sight of it was a comfort to the child who imagined that it was shining for her alone. Other times as she lay awake Winifred would listen to the boards of the ship creaking, the water rushing underneath as the vessel steamed through the dark, the call of a night bird and the sighs and groans of other passengers. Sometimes she would hear her father call her mother's name, but she never knew whether he was awake or asleep.

Outwardly her father appeared to have made a full recovery from his illness. His face had tanned and he looked healthy, but he was still in the grip of a deep depression and kept to himself. If it had not been for the attention of Mr Smithers, Winifred would have been very lonely. She did not join in with the other passengers as they played shove-halfpenny on deck or dangled a fishing line from the stern to give them some fresh fish and a change from the monotony of hard biscuits with salt beef. The apples and oranges that people had brought on board had been eaten. During the afternoon the women sewed or did embroidery and sat in little groups gossiping while the young children played around their feet.

It was Mr Smithers who talked to Winifred of things she had never thought about before. 'See that bank of cloud. It looks like a flock of sheep ... they're called cumulus, a big round mass of clouds, one on top of the other. They look as if you could walk on them but they're only water. Water the

48

sun draws up and then drops again as rain.' And on windy days he would point out the long white clouds racing across the sky. 'God's picture gallery … see that alligator chasing a bear.' Often by the time she found it the wind was already drawing it into a different shape. 'There's always something to see in the sky,' he would say as he offered her a peppermint, which she no longer spat in the water because she had become accustomed to the peppery taste.

Once he pointed to the horizon. 'See how it looks as if it's curving away? Once men thought the earth was flat and if you sailed too close you fell off the edge and got eaten by monsters.' He laughed such a merry laugh, which set his watch chain rattling and his round stomach wobbling behind his waistcoat, that she couldn't help laughing too. 'Now we know that if you keep sailing in the same direction you'll come back to where you started.'

Other times he was serious when he talked about how an Italian man called Galileo had discovered that the world went round the sun by looking through a telescope at the way the stars moved. 'The Church didn't want to know. People believed that the sun went round the world, that the world was the most important thing and the sun was just there to give it light. They threatened to burn Galileo at the stake. So he said he'd made a mistake, even though he knew what he'd said was true. Poor Galileo. He found out that man is no more important than a drop of water in the ocean.'

Winifred didn't get much chance to talk to Sister Angela and Sister Beatrice. They were kept busy caring for the sick. Once Sister Angela delivered a baby while Sister Beatrice held the candle and the rest of the passengers stayed on deck.

Sister Beatrice brought the baby up to show them while the mother rested below. Winifred looked at the red-faced little scrap of humanity and had a sudden longing to take it in her arms. She wondered why her mother had never had another child. She would have liked a little sister, but then she thought of the little dead baby she had seen lying on the bed like a wax doll and Mrs Watkins crying because she had no money and had to go to the parish and bury it in a pauper's grave. When she asked her father about it he said, 'Sometimes it's for the best. Mr Watkins is out of work and there's no money for milk.'

Looking at the tiny baby in Sister Beatrice's arms Winifred was glad that it had survived. She thought that perhaps with Sister Angela and Sister Beatrice praying for it, the baby would stay alive until they reached Australia. And by then, she thought, it would be big enough not to need their prayers.

They were so long at sea that after a while Winifred felt she had known no other life. She revelled in the high seas, the waves that dashed against the portholes and smashed over the lower deck in rough weather. She was absorbing new sights and sounds with each successive day as she travelled further and further away from England and her old life.

Life at sea fell into a regular pattern. When the child wasn't writing in her book or talking to Mr Smithers, she went for walks with her father, watching the sailors swabbing the decks and polishing the brass railings. Sometimes she saw flying fish, or a palm tree on a distant island, or schools of porpoises diving around the ship. When the cook emptied food scraps over the stern there would be flocks of seagulls screeching above the water and often a great albatross following for miles.

Sometimes on dark nights the waves would be tipped with mysterious blue lights that danced along the water, the stars hidden by dark cloud until the moon rose out of the ocean in an orange glow. As it rose higher the sea would turn silver. To the child these nights were magic, nights when she could imagine mermaids rising out of the water, singing around the ship as it ploughed its way through the deep southern waters.

For the first time in her life Winifred felt free. The sea air suited her, her cheeks coloured and her face filled out. But most of all the attention of old Mr Smithers had given her a sense of self-worth she had never had before. She was sorry when the ship docked at Cape Town because Mr Smithers was leaving to visit his son. He had changed into a light suit of cream tussore silk, which he told her he had bought in India. 'Wild silk,' he said. 'From silkworms in the wild ... not as fine as Chinese silk but it washes well and is very cool in summer.'

When he said goodbye he took her by the hand, then bent and kissed her on the cheek. 'There may not be a school where you're going. You can learn just as much from books. And if there's no books, read the book of life.' With that he bowed to her and shook her father's hand.

Winifred stayed where she was, watching him as he walked down the gangplank. He turned at the bottom and waved and she waved back, a lump in her throat because she knew she would never see him again. Then he was gone.

Later she went ashore with her father. The sight of so many black people frightened her and she clung to his arm as they strolled through the market buying bananas, fresh dates and a coconut to take back to the ship. For the first time she tasted sugarcane juice, watching as an old man squashed long sticks of cane through a mangle, the green juice trickling into a jug. The sweet syrup tingled on her tongue as she drank from a tin mug.

Back on board she watched as the coal-lumpers shovelled coal and long lines of coloured men bowed under huge baskets of fresh victuals, which they stowed in the hold while the overseer yelled at them in a language she did not understand.

There was a happier spirit among the passengers after the boat sailed. Perhaps it was because they had had the chance to walk on dry land and buy some fresh food. And also because they had weathered the worst part of the voyage. Wilfred seemed more like his old self, as if he had put his grief behind him and was determined to make a success of his life without Louisa. However, a blight was cast over the steerage passengers when a woman died of fever a few days out of Cape Town.

The next day everyone assembled on deck while the captain read from the Book of Common Prayer. The body, sewn into a piece of canvas, had been placed on a wooden trestle. Beside it was a bunch of red lilies someone had brought on board from Cape Town.

When they began to sing 'Abide with Me' Winifred became conscious that her father was crying. She wondered why. Winifred didn't think he'd ever spoken to the dead woman. She'd seen the woman's son before. Now he was standing by his mother's body wearing a black armband. He was about her own age. She didn't like boys, they were bullies and she'd always kept away from them at school. But she felt sorry for this boy, who began to sob as they lowered his mother's body over the side, while the captain said, 'Lord, we commend her body to the deep.'

As the body splashed into the water someone threw the lilies after it. The flowers floated but the body went straight down into the deep. Winifred wondered about the deep. She liked to imagine that underneath the sea was a wonderful cave, lined with mother of pearl, where the King and Queen of the Sea lived, surrounded by mermaids. Now she wasn't so sure. She thought about the bodies of drowned sailors and the body of the boy's mother. There had been seals around the ship as they left Cape Town, and a great flock of pelicans. All sorts of creatures lived in the sea. She wondered if the body would lie there in its canvas shroud forever, or whether it would be eaten by fish.

The boy was still standing forlornly leaning over the rail when everyone else had left. Winifred watched him for a while. Mr Smithers had told her that the boy's stepfather was in New South Wales. The boy and his mother had been on their way to start a new life.

Winifred went up to the boy and touched him on the shoulder. When he turned around she could see his face all red and swollen from crying. 'My mother's dead too,' she said, and the thought made her feel sad until she realised it wasn't true.

The boy looked at her. 'When did it happen?'

'Oh, a long time ago, when I was eight.'

'What's it like not having a mother?'

'It's all right.'

'What did she die of?'

'Oh, she was drowned.' In her mind's eye Winifred could see her mother's body in its violet dress being sucked into a whirlpool, drawn deeper and deeper into the water until only her head was visible. Then it, too, disappeared. A few daffodils floated, until one by one they vanished and the surface of the water was smooth again, as if nothing had disturbed it. The picture was so real that she almost convinced herself. For the first time she realised how easy it was to tell lies.

6

WILD CATTLE COUNTRY

IF WILFRED OATEN HARBOURED DOUBTS about the future when he saw the land he had been allocated in Queensland, he made light of them in a letter he wrote to his sister in Taunton, England, soon after his arrival in Australia. His land was at Boonarga, on the summit of the Darling Downs.

1st Day of March 1891
My dear Clare
We have arrived safely at our destination for which we thank God. The voyage was tolerable though steerage was very crowded & we were heartily sick of salt beef & biscuits by the time we got to Brisbane. There is no school here for Winifred,

more's the pity. There were two nuns on board who took an interest in the child but they are going further north. They were kind to me when I was ill.

I have to tell you that Louisa did not make the trip, for which I was sorry. But it's in the past now & there is just Winifred and myself. You wouldn't recognise us, we are the colour of walnuts & Winifred is growing so quickly that the clothes we brought from England are almost too small. It is the custom here to make clothes out of sugar and flourbags. I expect we will come to that soon, though I am no needlewoman.

I have a piece of land. The Government Land Agent met us in his buggy & drove us here. I must say that at first I was not happy with what he offered. There is a plant growing here called prickly pear. They tell us it has yellow flowers & I believe you can eat the fruit. But so far we have not seen any. It is like a forest, so thick that it strangles everything else except a few belah and ironbarks & some brigalow scrub. But the agent assures me that it is easy to remove. You chop it & burn it.

I must tell you that the agent was surprised to find that I only had a small daughter to help. He told me that I needed a few strong lads — there's no hope of that now. I have put out an enquiry for brother William. If I can get him to come and manage the farm then I can go out to work and earn some money. We need a lot of things. We couldn't take much on board, only bare essentials. We are sleeping rough on the hard ground with blankets. The mosquitoes drive us mad. I think it's our English skin. Here they burn cow-dung. They say it helps. As soon as I get a patch cleared I'll build a hut.

There are great distances between neighbours. A Scotsman, McNab, called on us. He brought over a batch of scones which we ate for supper. I think he got word of us from the local store. He's got ten children and drives a buggy. So far I have no means of transport except shank's pony. The land agent dropped us off at a general store run by a widow, Mrs Dobson. I got a few supplies. We had a five- mile walk back to our land. It was very trying in the heat & and not much shade, except under the prickly pear. We were afraid to sit down for fear of snakes. I bought a billy can & she filled it with water from her well. I was hoping for a natural spring or a well on our land. As it is Winifred has to walk down a track to the creek to fetch back what she can carry. I read Tennyson to her at night by the light of a candle. She likes to make up stories. She's very like what you were at her age.

I often think of us sitting round the table at home, with a loaf of Mother's bread on the table & a pot of damson jam & a pat of butter. It was a good life & on Sunday in our pew in the old stone church listening to Father reading the lesson. He had a beautiful voice. I like to think he would be proud of me. This is a far cry from Bath. Just the same, a man can get ahead if he works. There is a sense of freedom & wide open spaces & everyone is equal.

I yearn for news of home, so write to me care of Dobson's at Dalby. It'll find its way to me. I'll send this letter with Winifred when she goes to McNab's tomorrow to get some fresh meat. He'll drop it off when he goes into town.

Give my best to everyone at home and let me know if you have news of William,

Your loving brother, Wilfred

It was a strangely isolated life for a child born in the midst of a big city, her ears attuned to the buzz of the street, the raised voices of neighbours quarrelling, the cries of hawkers, the rattle of horse trams and the occasional wail of a train whistle carried on the wind.

Now, their closest neighbours, the McNabs, were miles down the road, shorter if you knew your way across the bush track that led past the creek.

The child had hung back shyly when Mr McNab had poked his head into the clearing her father had cut in the prickly pear, to where they were lying in their blankets in a state of lethargy, still tired after the effort of getting to their land. Her father had risen and taken the outstretched hand of this tall, raw-boned man who stood like a giant beside him. McNab wore moleskin leggings and a leather waistcoat over a grey flannel undershirt. On his head was a battered broad-brimmed hat, and in his hand a stick almost as thick as his forearm. 'Ye always need a stout stick when ye go into the bush,' he said as he laid it at his feet.

The two men squatted by the side of the road while the child listened to the sound of their voices from the shelter of the clearing, until her father called, 'Winifred, fetch Mr McNab a mug of water.'

She was conscious of the man's eyes on her when she handed him a tin mug with a splash of water in the bottom. 'The billy can's empty,' she said.

'Ye best go down to the creek. Ye can do yer washing there … hae a bath. Collect yer drinking water.' He turned to her father, 'Do ye nay have any sons?'

'No, only my daughter here.'

'Well then, mon, I pity ye. This country needs strong men. Me, I got ten bonny lads. O'course blind Billy canna do much since he got stung in the eyes by bees. 'Twas his own fault, pokin' the hive with a stick. Still, he can milk the cows … long as someone sets the pail right.' He drained the tin mug in one gulp and put it on the ground.

Wilfred was silent, listening to the Scotsman's voice as he droned on. He did not need to be reminded of the difficulty facing him without anyone to help clear the land and build a hut.

'We be humpin' and clearin' the pear day in and day out. The accursed spikes git in yer hair, in yer clothes, in yer blankets. Burnin's no good. It just comes up again. I knowed folks who walked off their land, left everything they owned. Even their plates and cups, tea still in the pot.' He leaned forward until the brim of his hat was almost touching Wilfred's face. 'The prickly pear started growing through the floor … if they'd stayed much longer it woulda strangled 'em in their beds.'

'Surely it's not as bad as that.' Wilfred stood, wondering where he could go to escape the sun. He could feel the heat boring into his back, and he took a handkerchief from his pocket and draped it around his bare neck. He thought McNab was exaggerating because he was a newcomer. As if he had read Wilfred's mind the Scotsman got to his feet and took Wilfred by the arm. 'I be telling ye the truth, mon. We lost some of our best land to it. Now we hae only one paddock under wheat and a few sheep in t'other … Aye, it was a bonny sight at first … tall grass up to yer shoulders. Ye could graze cattle … fields of wheat wavin' in the wind … I thought I'd found heaven when we got here. But not any more. Now it's the divil's work.'

He put his hand on Wilfred's shoulder. 'What will you do then? Ye canna stay here.'

Winifred saw her father stiffen. 'This is our land and this is where we stay.'

'Ooh, aye. You're game then. Send the wee lassie over with threepence. I'll gie ye a bit of meat. The lads are killin' a sheep.'

The sea voyage had acted as a barrier between the child's old life and the new. She had had time to come to terms with her mother's desertion and accept the fact that Louisa had gone from her life. Her father meant more to her, anyway. He had always been the one she had looked to for physical and moral support. But nothing had prepared her for her change in circumstances.

The prickly pear formed high prison walls, so that all inside the prison was in perpetual gloom. Outside the prison walls the sun hit the dusty road with an unrelenting glare that made Winifred shade her eyes. In the heat of the day the almost deafening drone of insects rose with a shrill crescendo from the thicket; it fell away with a sudden hush as she approached, only to burst forth again the minute she stood still.

As she listened to the raking call of the currawong, she longed for the familiar sound of blackbirds singing. Yet she was elated by glimpses of grey kangaroos and the sight of a koala crawling up the trunk of a gum with a baby on its back. She learned to keep her distance from the green stinging ants after she had brushed underneath a tree and been bitten, and she cast a wary eye at the large spiders that built their webs from branch to branch, until she plucked up courage to break their webs with a stick so that she could pass underneath.

Accustomed to the greyness of the English sky, the air smoke-laden from coal fires and the pea-souper fogs that hung in the air in winter like some deadly miasma, the clean air here was a surprise. The landscape was filled with strange trees — ironbark, yellow box, belah — so different from the English oaks, elms and larches.

When night came to the bush it was like a shutter being drawn, an immediate and utter blackness. It was years before she rid herself of the feeling of terror once the sun went down.

There was no sound of voices to break the silence, no street lamps to penetrate the gloom, only the blackness that surrounded them where they lay, with one sputtering candle to cast a feeble light.

And with the night came clouds of mosquitoes, like an evil presence to torment the child and her father. In the stillness Winifred could hear dingoes howling in the distance and sometimes a rustling in the bushes and she imagined a snake slithering onto her blanket.

'Them deaf adders now,' Mrs Dobson had told her when they had stopped at her store in Dalby for a bag of flour and some sugar, a tin of treacle, a box of candles, some matches and a billy can, 'once they bite you, you're as good as dead.'

It was the widow Dobson who told them to burn cow dung for the mosquitoes. She tried to sell them some citronella but Wilfred had said sharply, 'Leave it ... we'll manage.' Winifred knew that he was short of money. 'We must buy only the bare essentials until the farm starts to produce,' he had told her. His one luxury was a packet of tea and some tobacco twists for his pipe.

The shopkeeper had offered Winifred a boiled lolly from a jar and the girl thought with longing of the spills of lollies that the man in the corner shop had given her when she lived in Lambeth. She chose a black and white striped humbug and popped it in her mouth. She tried to make it last forever while her father leaned on the counter listening to the woman gossiping. Winifred was not interested in long-winded descriptions of how to make damper on an open fire, and she only half heard the warning to keep the food on a table with the legs in tins of water because of the ants. She had not been able to conceive such things. She'd had no notion that the life of high adventure her father had talked of might be a myth. But that was before they had arrived at the property; surrounded by the prickly pear, the heat, the flies, the unrelenting isolation, it didn't take long for Winifred to realise her father's dream had been a false one.

On the day after Mr McNab's visit Winifred's father sent her to collect the meat they had been promised and to ask Mr McNab to post the letter to his sister when next he went to town. Winifred went the long way by the road, walking in the middle, fearful of snakes and other creatures she did not yet know about. Once she almost stepped on a huge goanna basking in the sun on the hot road. It reared up at her and she saw two rows of sharp teeth, a long tongue and a throat the colour of blood. She stood still, sick with fear, until it ran up a gum tree.

She would have liked to turn around and go back to her father, but she knew she couldn't. Except for Mrs McNab's scones, they'd eaten nothing but damper and treacle washed down with black tea since they arrived. 'We can't live on that forever,' her father had said. 'We need meat or we'll starve.'

When she finally reached her destination she was greeted by the sight of a dozen or so chooks pecking around a two-roomed slab hut and a mean-looking tan dog which began to bark loudly, straining at its leash as if it would like to rip her limb from limb. She hung back, afraid to walk past, until Mrs McNab poked her head out of a lean-to attached to the side of the house. Wiping her hands on her apron she called, 'Come in. Come in. Ye must be the Oaten girl. Sit ye down, lassie.' She picked up a black and white cat that was lying on a bench by the fireplace and shooed it out into the yard. 'She's afeared of the dog. We got her to keep the rats outa the henhouse. But I think she's afeared o' them too. Some of 'em are almost as big as her'n. When she gits her kittens I'll gie you one — that's if yer Pa'll let ya. Sit ye down. Would ye like a drink o' tea? The kettle's on the boil.'

The child shook her head. 'I'd like a drink of water, please.' Then she remembered the letter and took it out of her pocket and put it on the table. 'My father said to ask if Mr McNab could post this when he goes to town next.'

'I'll gie it to my husband.' Mrs McNab put it on the mantelpiece and lifted a tin mug off a nail on the wall, filling it with water from an empty kerosene tin that had a length of wire through it to make a handle. 'This is good water,' she said as she offered Winifred the mug. 'When the creek floods ye never know what ye'll find.'

Winifred took the proffered mug and sipped the water. She was thirsty after the long hot walk, and hungry.

'I'm sorry I can't offer you a girdle cake or a slice of bread … the flourbag's empty. Until McNab gets back from the shop there won't be none. I only got some cold meat and potatoes, and that's for the boys when they come in from the paddock.'

Winifred looked around the kitchen. There was an open fireplace with a spit for roasting meat; two enormous black-iron pots and a black-bottomed frying pan hung on nails by the chimney, alongside a collection of tin mugs. The kettle was steaming away on the fire. 'I like to keep the kettle boiling. It's like another person in the house. Sometimes we have long conversations. Ye know what I miss most? It's the sound of a woman's voice. When's your Ma coming?'

'I don't have a mother,' Winifred said.

'Oh, you poor wee bairn. What did she die of?'

Winifred was about to say that her mother had drowned, until she remembered her father. If he found out she had told Mrs McNab that, he would beat her. She wasn't even supposed to mention her mother's name. Instead she said, 'I don't know.'

'My Ma died having a bairn. I was only ten and in service in a great house. I worked as a scullery maid. Never saw my ain folk once I started work there until the day the cook told me I was wanted at home. When I got there I found my Ma had died and the wee babe too. There were four bairns younger than me. I had to stay home to look after 'em.

'I don't know why the Lord made life so hard to women. You either die givin' birth, or the bairn does. If it lives, you end up beside yerself with work. McNab don't understand.

64

He says havin' babies comes natural and animals does it all the time. But the cow don't have to git out o' bed afore she feels like it after she's had her calf an' wash clothes an' scrub floors an' mend and make do until she's fair wore out. Then he expects me to feed the chickens, milk the cow when the lads is busy, and carry his tea down to the far paddock when it's boiling in the shade.' She wiped the sweat from her forehead with her apron. 'I niver could take the heat.'

Winifred wanted to ask her for another drink of water. The sun was blazing down on the tin roof and the kettle was still steaming on the stove. The room was stifling, but she didn't like to interrupt.

'Where I grew up there was always a breeze off the loch and snow on the mountains in winter. Aye, it was bonny. And there was always fresh-caught salmon on the laird's table. The cook'd scrape little bits off the underneath and gie me a wee taste on a slice of bread. Here I'm lucky to hae bread to put in my bairns' mouths. The elders of the kirk fixed up for me to marry McNab when me father was put off his land. My wee brothers and sister went to a foundling home. I cried the day they were took ... They clung to my skirt screaming. I never seen sight nor sound of 'em since.'

Her voice broke and Winifred watched as a tear ran down her cheek. The woman wiped it off with the back of her hand. 'The elders said McNab was a good man and would take care o' me. He was coming to Queensland where they were gieing away land. He needed a wife and my father gave his permission even though ... even though I was barely fifteen. But McNab dinna love me. Nay, he dinna love me, lassie. A body needs that.' She put her apron to her face and a sob escaped her. Then she gave Winifred a half-smile and blew her nose on her apron.

'Aye, it's been a struggle. Things weren't how I thought they'd be … McNab's a good man. I can't deny it, but sometimes a body needs more.'

Winifred fidgeted uneasily. She felt sorry for Mrs McNab but she was a grown-up. She knew they had troubles — she'd listened to Mrs Watkins often enough — but she had worries of her own. She wasn't sure of the time. It wasn't like England where there was a long twilight. If it was late she would have to find her way home in the dark, and there was still water to fetch from the creek. She wondered how much longer Mrs McNab would go on talking. She put the tin mug down and stood up. 'Can I have the meat please? I have to get home.' She took a scrap of cloth out of her apron pocket, undid the knot and put threepence on the table.

'It's hanging in the meat room. I'll get it.'

Winifred followed her across the yard to a small wooden shed roofed with iron where the bloodied fleece of a sheep was spread out to dry. She caught her breath at the rank smell and winced at the sight of a solid mass of flies clustered on the skin. Inside the shed she saw the carcase of a sheep wrapped in a hessian bag hanging from a hook. Mrs McNab banged the bag with a stick and an evil-looking cloud of black flies rose in the air. Then she opened the bag and lifted a sheep's head from the bottom. She put it in an empty flourbag that had been lying on the dirt floor and handed it to Winifred. Some of the flies settled on the bag, while the rest clustered back on the outside of the carcase once Mrs McNab had rewrapped it.

'Be sure to hang what's left o' the meat in the shade and rub plenty of salt into it so that it won't go bad. When you've ate it you can bring back the bag. Wash it in the creek first.'

She led Winifred out of the shed. 'You'd best gang along afore it gits dark. Come and visit again.' She put her arms around the girl and kissed her on the cheek. 'It's done my poor heart good to talk to you.'

Just before Winifred turned to leave, the woman darted back inside the shed and came out with a brown onion in her hand. 'I'll gie ye this, lassie. You can boil up what left o' the head and make a bit of broth.'

The heat had gone out of the day as Winifred started the long walk back along the road, carrying the bag of meat, the onion safely in her apron pocket. She shooed the flies that followed her with a piece of stick she picked up off the ground. The sheep's head felt heavy and she had a sickening vision of its eyes staring at her and the bloodied neck with bones showing through where it had been hacked off.

The long walk, and having to listen to Mrs McNab, plus her worry about finding her way home again had left her feeling inexpressibly tired. After only a short while she yearned to stop and sit by the road to rest, but she remembered the creature she had almost trodden on because it was the same colour as the dirt. She was terrified it might still be there.

Further along the road she heard a scuffling noise and saw the goanna, looking more like a dragon than ever, pattering towards her in a cloud of dust. She fancied it was chasing her and she began to run, wondering if it was her or the sheep's head it was after. She thought about throwing the meat away but knew that her father would be angry. Instead, clutching the bag to her chest, she began to run faster, her breath coming in laboured gasps, with a stitch in her side until she could hardly breathe. When she finally stopped and looked back, the creature had disappeared.

The night was closing in, and though she was glad of the cooler air she felt worried because she had no idea how much further she had to go. As the sun set she knew she had no hope of finding her way and tears began to run down her cheeks, though she still plodded on, slower now, afraid of the dark ahead and the dark behind.

Then she heard her father's voice calling out, 'Winifred, Winifred,' and saw a wavering light coming towards her. She ran forward and threw herself sobbing into his arms. Her father took the bag and, holding the candle in his other hand, led her to their clearing by the road.

'What kept you, child? You should have been home long ago.'

'It was Mrs McNab. She wouldn't stop talking. And I've had nothing to eat. And a thing like a dragon chased me.'

'I should never have let you go alone,' he said as he put his arm around her and held her. 'You're safe now. We'll have a good feed. I'll grill a chop once the fire has burned down.' He struck a match and the dry kindling the girl had gathered that morning sprang into life. Then he opened the flourbag and lifted out the bloodied head with its staring eyes, holding it at arm's length. 'I mighta known … a bloody Scotsman. Mean as a pikestaff.'

'Mrs McNab said to rub it with salt and hang it on a tree so that it doesn't go bad.' Winifred took the onion out of her pocket. 'And she gave me this to make some soup.'

'It'll do for tomorrow. I'll put it in the billy can and boil it up once we've had our tea.'

He mixed some flour and water in a basin. 'I'll make a damper. There's some treacle left in the tin.'

Later, as they were eating their meal, Winifred said, 'Mrs McNab asked me when my mother was coming.'

'Interfering busybody. We don't want the likes of her prying into our business. You keep away from her.'

If Wilfred's heart failed him when he considered what he had got himself into, he refused to admit it. He had sunk all his savings into the venture and there was no turning back. He was not the sort of man to return to England with his tail between his legs. No matter what happened, he would never admit defeat, not even to himself, and least of all to Louisa.

The first task he had set himself was to clear the ground for a shanty, slashing at the walls of prickly pear with an axe until he had an opening by the side of the road. He chopped a few brigalows and ironbarks for the outside walls and stripped bark to make a roof, putting a sheet of bark on four forked sticks to make a table.

He borrowed a maul from Mr McNab to make slabs for the sides of their shanty, which he did by splitting lengths of brigalow and banging them flat. But when the walls were in place there were great gaps between the boards. He had nothing to fill them with until he hit on the idea of using mud. It fell to Winifred to fetch the water from the creek to mix the mud and to fill the cracks. It proved useless. As it dried it fell out in great lumps, sometimes striking Winifred as she lay, wrapped in a grey blanket, sleeping beside her father on the dirt floor.

They eked out a miserable living, as Wilfred continued the task of clearing his land, helped by his young daughter who, like him, had never done hard manual work and whose hands were soft and tender when they first arrived. Now they were covered in blisters and festering sores where thorns from the pear had penetrated the skin.

There was no mention of Winifred going to school.

Even if Wilfred could spare her, the nearest school was too far to walk. Until they could afford a horse, they had no means of getting around except on foot.

One of the child's jobs was to pile the cut pear on the fire while her father slashed and hacked, slashed and hacked. But the pear was green and there was not enough wood to keep the fire going. More often than not the slashed green pear, which lay in great heaps on the ground, simply sent up more shoots.

Three times a day her father sent her on the two-mile walk to the creek. She had no bucket, even if she had the strength to carry it full of water. Instead she used a bottle and a billy can. Often she would find that when she returned her father would be so thirsty he'd empty the water in a few big gulps then send her off again, no matter how exhausted she felt.

As Winifred lay awake in the dark at the end of another long day, she would cry quietly to herself, wishing she was back in England trotting alongside Mrs Watkins with her barrow. Sometimes she would try to conjure up a picture of her mother in their room at Lambeth as they sat drinking tea and listening to her father tell stories about Australia. Now she wondered whether her mother had been right all the time, that they should have stayed in England, though she felt sure that things would have been better if her mother had come with them. She would have insisted on finding somewhere else to live, with a real bed and proper chairs, instead of the ones her father had made out of the ends of the saplings he had cut for the uprights of their shanty. The legs were of different lengths, so that they wobbled when you sat on them, and sometimes overbalanced so you found yourself on the ground with the chair on top of you.

Her father spent the days alternating between terrible rages in which he lashed out at his daughter until she ran sobbing to the creek, and bouts of crying after she had crept back towards evening to find him filled with remorse, a fire lit and a meagre meal on the table. He would hug her over and over, saying, 'I'm sorry. I'm sorry. I've ruined your life. We should never have come to this accursed land.'

The coming of Cobb and Co brought the world closer, but in the three years she had spent in isolation with her father, the prickly pear, like some voracious monster, had invaded almost every inch of their land — there wasn't even a small patch on which to grow a few potatoes or cabbages. They had only been able to stay on their land because their hut was beside the road and a group of itinerant workers was employed to keep the road free of pear.

It was a grim and futile existence, with Wilfred's savings diminishing and his health failing.

The child had no idea that her father was suffering as he was, that the harsh words he spoke which brought tears to her eyes, or the beatings that made her cry out in pain and outrage, were symptoms of Wilfred's deep distress at losing the woman he loved, and the knowledge that he had made a terrible mistake. The child began to feel that it was her fault and was certain that he did not love her, seeing her as a burden he did not want. The kind father she'd known in England, who took her to the Cut and brought her a halfpenny worth of treacle-taffy on Sundays and read her stories, had vanished for all time.

And yet there was a resilience in the young girl that kept her going, once she realised this was her life and she must make the best of it. The creek was her solace. Its banks were a place of refuge where she could escape from her father and daydream, lazily swishing around a piece of bush to keep away the persistent flies, listening to the creek talking and watching as the sun glinted off the wings of dragonflies as they skimmed the surface, while below the beetle-like water boatmen paddled furiously.

Some days the wind rippled across the surface of the water and rustled through the saplings that lined the banks, stirring dead leaves that littered the ground, while the girl drowsed in the sun. Sometimes a crow came to rest on a bough above her head, taking no more notice of her than if she was part of the landscape. These were the moments she felt at peace, knowing that the wild cattle were on the other side of the creek and couldn't touch her.

Once she had been frightened when a whole herd of these long-horned beasts came charging past her while she hid behind the trunk of a tree. She had seen cows before in the cow-keeper's yard near Clapham Common, but they were moon-eyed, docile creatures that chewed their cud while their keepers coaxed jets of rich creamy milk from their udders. Often she had been sent to fetch a jug of milk from the cow-keeper who walked along South Lambeth Road, balancing two wooden pails on a stout pole and calling, 'Fresh milk. Fresh from the cow.'

These red-eyed beasts were a different breed altogether. Their coats were tangled with briars and they were thin and wiry and tough, with a mean look in their eyes. Winifred imagined that if she got caught by one alone on the track it would toss her up in the air on its horns and she would land in the prickly pear and be pierced to death by the thorns. By the time her father missed her it would be too late.

When she had tried to tell her father she was afraid of them he had turned on her angrily, picking up a stick and beating her around the shoulders, while he screamed at her that she was useless. Later he had come into the hut where she was lying down, her face buried in her blanket, and smoothed her hair. When she opened her eyes she saw that he had been crying, his face streaked where the tears had cut a path through the black dust that covered his face. He pressed her close and said, as he always did, 'I should never have come to this accursed place.'

7
END OF CHILDHOOD

THE CHILD HAD NO ONE TO TURN to for help as she watched her father's condition deteriorate. She had been told to keep away from the McNabs. But when he sank into a morose silence and made no effort to get out of bed, refusing the tea and damper she offered, she became alarmed. She hailed one of the bullock drivers who was taking a load of timber to the mill. He stopped his team, put down his whip and, pushing his cabbage tree hat to the back of his head, followed her to where her father lay, his face flushed, his body racked with a hacking cough.

'Hae ye some water, lassie?' The man held the mug of water she gave him to her father's lips, cradling him in his arms. 'Come on, laddie, tae a wee sup, you're on fire. Tis a fever ye hae. We'd best get ye to the hospital.' He took the red cotton scarf from around his neck and, pouring a little water over it, wiped Wilfred's face.

'Get your clothes together, lassie. Ye canna stay here alone.'

She did as he asked and tied up her few belongings in her blanket, then made a bundle of her father's clothes, including his cut-throat razor, razor strop and his hairbrush, all the time wondering where they were going.

The man told her his name was Angus McDonald and, as if reading her thoughts, said, 'There'll be nay room at the cottage hospital for ye. But I know someone who has a wee bairn. She could do wi' an extra pair o' hands. She'll most likely gie ye a sixpenny bit for yer trouble.'

He looked around the small hut then picked up the billy can which was half full of water and handed it to Winifred, 'In case yer pa needs a drink.'

Wilfred did not protest when the bullock driver wrapped a blanket around him and carried him out to the bullock dray. With Winifred beside her father, the bundles and billy can resting at her feet, the driver cracked his long whip in the air and called out, 'Gang away, boys,' and with a jolt the team lurched forward and settled into a slow, measured tread.

The air was hot and humid, with a bank of black clouds away to the west. Angus pointed with his whip. 'Some poor body'll get a wettin' tonight. Many's the night I've spent by a flooded creek, rain peltin' down, frogs croakin', nothing for my tay but flour and water, and mozzies and sandflies eating me alive.'

He gave Winifred a quizzical look and drew on his pipe, a cloud of smoke rising in the air. 'It's a good life but it's hard. Plod along at five mile an hour, no one to talk to, nothin' to see but trees. Ye find yerself talkin' to the bullocks.' He looked sideways at Winifred and began to laugh. It was an infectious laugh and she found herself joining in.

Angus patted her on the hand. 'That's better. Ye look a bit peaky. Yer Pa'll be all right. But he needs to git off that land afore it kills him. The Government done wrong selling folks worthless land. I ganged away ... bought a team instead. O'course your Pa ain't strong enough to run a team. Ye need plenty of brawn, and plenty of patience. 'Tis a lonely life but it suits me ... since the Lord took Annie.'

He fell silent, drawing on his pipe and gazing away into the distance.

Winifred thought that perhaps Annie was his wife but she didn't like to ask. In any case she had worries of her own. She looked at her father who had his eyes closed. She put out her hand to make sure that he was still alive and felt the heat rising from his body. It frightened her, thinking he might die. And if he died, what would happen to her? Perhaps she could go and live with Uncle William and his wife, but she had no idea where they were.

Angus turned to her, blowing a great cloud of tobacco smoke over her head. 'Don't fash yeself, lassie. It'll be a change for ye ... like a holiday,' and he smiled at her and once again patted her on the hand. 'Has anyone told ye yer a bonnie wee lass?'

She tried to smile back but instead felt tears prickling her eyes and looked away. She felt weighed down with apprehension. She knew nothing about housework. She'd kept house for her father in a sort of a way, but a small hut with a dirt floor wasn't a real house. She knew how to sweep out their hut with a broom made of twigs after emptying the dregs of the tea on it to keep down the dust. And sometimes she picked wild flowers, or a handful of feathery pink grass, which she placed in a jam tin on the table. She rinsed the plates and mugs in the creek, as well as washing the clothes which she hung on bushes to dry while she dangled her feet in the water, wearing one of her father's old shirts which served as underwear and nightgown.

The knowledge that she was being sent to strangers frightened her more than anything. She had lived in isolation for so long that she did not know how to relate to other people. Any social graces she had acquired from her mother had disappeared. She was also mortified because the clothes she had arrived with three years ago hung in tatters which barely covered her body. The boots, which were once two sizes too big, were now too small. Her father had cut the toes out with a knife but the soles had separated from the uppers and flapped up and down when she walked, so that she had to be careful not to trip. Her hair still curled around her face but it was matted and unkempt and needed a good brushing. Her father either did not notice or did not care, knowing that no one ever saw her. He had discouraged visitors, wanting to be left alone.

If the doctor who examined Wilfred and admitted him to hospital raised his eyebrows when he saw the girl in a skimpy dress that barely reached beyond her thighs, he did not comment. He was used to the way the settlers' children looked. He knew how poor most of the farmers were, with their wives forever having children which he delivered, receiving in lieu of his fee half a sheep or pig when they killed a beast. There was no money to buy clothes. Instead they turned sugar bags into shirts and dresses and their children ran round bare-footed, their toes splayed and the soles of their feet developing the texture of leather.

It was he who drove Winifred in his buggy to the house where she was to stay, after a tearful farewell with her father whom she wondered if she would ever see again. The doctor took her to the door and, after a whispered conversation with a woman inside, said goodbye to Winifred and drove off.

Winifred found herself in a large room divided off with a piece of hessian. A woman was seated at a table with a baby at her breast and another young child clinging to her skirts, its thumb in its mouth. Winifred glanced around the room at the black fuel stove in one corner and the two long planks of wood supported by rough-cut timber legs which ran along each side of the table and served as seats. In one corner a cradle made from a butter box rested on a wooden stand. Winifred put down her bundle of clothes, wondering where she was going to sleep, but afraid to ask, and turned shyly towards her new employer.

'I'm Mrs John Smith. The doctor tells me your name is Winifred Oaten, that you're strong and healthy and I'm to give you sixpence a week. Here, take the baby,' and she handed the small, red-faced scrap to the girl who, never having held a newborn infant before, took her gingerly, afraid that she might drop her.

'Put her down,' the woman said, and pointed to the cradle.

Winifred did as she was told, gazing at the baby, who had her eyes open and was staring back at her. She put out her hand and the baby reached out and touched it.

'There's no time to play. The men will be in for their dinner, and I've got to give little Freddie some titty-bottle. The cow's gone dry and the goat ain't giving any milk.' She picked up the toddler and put him to her breast where he started to suck lustily, kicking his legs. 'You'd best hurry. There's two little ones asleep and they'll be wanting something to eat soon.'

The woman looked at Winifred, as if seeing her for the first time. 'How old are you, child?'

'Nearly twelve.'

'Have you no pinafore to cover your modesty?'

Winifred shook her head.

The woman reached out and handed Winifred a sugar bag apron which was hanging on a nail on the wall. 'Put this on. It ain't right for a big girl like you to be showing so much. My boys are grown men. If you excite their passions, then where will we be?'

Winifred pulled on the garment which covered her from head to foot and tied it at the back.

'That's much better. Now run along and fetch a bucket of water from the well and see that the goat has water.'

The girl stepped out into the yard, wondering how she would find the well, then she saw the goat lying in the shade of a tree. It had a rope round its neck which had become tangled around the tree trunk. She wondered if she was expected to disentangle it, but she was afraid of the creature and kept her distance. It had kicked over a cut-down kerosene tin which she thought must be for water. She picked it up and carried it to the well which was at the far end of the home paddock. The well had a wooden cover and she struggled to lift it, finally managing to push it far enough to one side to make an opening. There was a pail hanging above it which was attached to a windlass and she turned the handle, hearing the pail hitting the sides of the well until, a long way down, it splashed into the water. She filled it and began to wind it up again, feeling the pull on her muscles, until she had it to the top. She filled the goat's dish and carried it over to where the goat was lying, then returned and emptied the rest into her bucket. It was only half full and she wondered whether she should fill it but didn't want to waste any more time. The water was alive with wrigglers, not like the clear water she got from the creek. Without replacing the cover on the well, Winifred struggled back to the house. Mrs Smith was busy at the stove when Winifred carried the bucket inside and put it on the floor. 'It's got things in it.'

'They won't hurt,' the woman said. 'Fill the kettle and empty the rest into the tin dish by the door. The men'll want a wash. Did you put the cover back on the well?'

Winifred shook her head. 'It's too heavy.'

'Nonsense! You're a big strong girl. I hope you're not going to be useless.' She wiped her hands on her apron and grabbed the empty bucket. 'I'd best go and do it myself. The children had a pet wallaby last year, drowned itself in the well and we couldn't hardly drink the water for weeks.' She pointed to a black pot on the stove with a huge metal spoon in it. 'Stir the porridge and make sure it don't burn.'

Winifred put her hand around the spoon and the metal bit deep into her palm. It was red hot from the boiling porridge and she dropped the spoon back in the pot, tears in her eyes from the pain. She took a corner of her apron, and wrapped the cloth around the handle of the spoon and began to stir, splashing some of the contents of the pot on the stove.

'Not like that!' the woman came bustling into the kitchen.

'The spoon was too hot and it burnt me,' Winifred said.

'Nonsense,' said Mrs Smith, who put her hand on the spoon and began to stir. 'Go and fetch some wood. If there's no kindling you'll have to chop some. Use the axe. And watch out for snakes. They're bad this year.'

The girl did as she was bid, looking at her hand as soon as she got out the door. It was very painful and an ugly blister had formed in the centre of her palm. She was relieved to see that there was plenty of wood and picked up an armful, piling it in her apron, stopping to look at some green ants that were building a nest in an ironbark and a crow lazily circling the paddock. She turned and hurried back to the house. She could hear the sound of men's voices and knew that they were coming in for their midday dinner. She was hungry and hoped there would be enough for her as well.

There were four sons in the Smith family and Winifred learned later that they were the sons of the first wife, who had died of snakebite. They ranged in age from seventeen down to thirteen, and after sluicing water over their face and hands, they sat on either side of the table. Their stepmother handed them a plate of cold meat with a spoonful of pickles which she had taken from a small boxlike structure covered in netting. There was a loaf of bread on the table and the eldest of the boys cut it into thick slices which they ate hungrily.

'Make the tea, Winifred,' Mrs Smith said and handed her a large grey enamel teapot. 'Put in a handful of tea leaves and fill it with water. There should be enough for us to have a cup when the boys is done. Don't forget to rinse the pot afore you put the tea in, and make sure the water's boiling.'

Winifred lifted the tea caddy down from a shelf over the stove and then tried to lift the kettle, but was deterred by the steam pouring out of the spout, frightened that the metal handle might be hot. Her hand was still hurting from her burn.

'For heaven's sake, child, what's the matter with you? I've a good mind to send you straight back.' She pushed Winifred to one side and, lifting the steaming kettle, poured a little water into the teapot. This she empied into the tin wash dish and then, tossing in a handful of tea leaves, filled the teapot with water and put it on the table. She turned towards the girl. 'Do I have to tell you everything? Don't stand there like a bag of wheat. Fetch the tin mugs and the sugar.'

Winifred did as she was told, conscious of four pairs of eyes staring at her. She hung her head and went to the corner where the baby was sleeping with a piece of netting thrown over the cradle to keep the flies away. There was no sign of the other children, whom she imagined must be sleeping in another room.

'This is Winifred Oaten. She's come to help me for a couple of weeks until her dad gets better.' She turned to Winifred. 'These are the boys — Matthew, Mark, Luke and John. They run the farm while their father is away droving.'

Winifred looked at them. They were busy cleaning up the last of the loaf of bread, dunking it in the strong black tea. Luke looked up briefly, ran his eyes over her and then went on eating. When they had finished they pushed back the long wooden bench and, without speaking, picked up their broad-brimmed hats which they had hung by the door and went out into the heat of the afternoon sun.

The room seemed empty once they had gone. Mrs Smith lifted two tin bowls from a shelf and carried them to the stove where she spooned in a generous serving of hot porridge. 'Here.' She handed a bowl and a tin spoon to Winifred. 'You must be hungry. Pour yourself a cup of tea. I save the meat for the boys. They do all the hard work. There's no milk ... the cow's dry. If you hear her bellowing presently, it's because she needs a bull. I'm waiting for John to take her, but it's a good ten-mile walk and he's helping Luke repair the fence in the back paddock. Kangaroos got in and flattened the wheat. Their dad'll go mad when he finds out. He'll take a stockwhip to the boys if he can catch them. Yet it weren't no one's fault.'

The job was hard but it had its compensations. Mrs Smith taught Winifred how to bake bread, something she had never done before because her father still cooked on an open fire and his only attempt at bread-making was damper cooked on the coals. The girl enjoyed kneading the dough and watching it rise, then punching it down again, later savouring the taste of bread still warm from the oven. And once the boys brought in a pair of rabbits they had trapped and she learned how to skin and dress them and bake them stuffed with chopped onion and bread. It was a meal she remembered for a long while.

She slept on a calico sack filled with bracken fern which Mrs Smith spread on the kitchen floor by the baby's cradle. Mrs Smith and her three other children slept in a small room inside and the boys slept behind the hessian curtain.

Winifred could hear them talking and later grunting and snoring in their sleep.

One night she woke, conscious that someone was bending over her, then she felt a hand slide beneath her blanket and over her breasts. She held her breath, too frightened to call out and then a voice she recognised as Luke's whispered, 'There's nothing of you yet, more's the pity. You'll keep.' She held her breath until she heard him open the back door and then the sound of him making water. It reminded her of the cab horses she had seen in Lambeth, standing with water streaming out in great bursts. And she had a sudden vision of the man in the lane behind Tradescant Street who had frightened her when she was only a tiny girl. She shivered and pulled her blanket tightly around her. When she woke it was morning and the baby was crying. She got up and carried her into her mother.

It fell to Winifred to care for the infant, getting up when she cried in the night to change the wet rag for a dry one, and in the cool of the afternoon carrying her outside and sitting with her under the shade of a tree. The toddler and the two older children sat by her side, and she made up fairy stories to entertain them.

But there were a thousand and one other jobs for her to do as well, and she had no time to sit and daydream as had been her custom. There was washing to do — first carrying the water to an old kerosene tin in the yard, lighting a fire underneath and stirring the clothes with a pot stick. The boys' work clothes were heavy and after rinsing them in a tin bath she struggled to lift them onto a rope tied between two trees. Later there was the ironing to do with an old black iron which she heated on the fuel stove, spitting on it to test the heat as she had seen Mrs Smith do.

Though she was learning valuable lessons that would help her earn her living, she knew she was being imposed on for sixpence a week and she was always tired. Her nights were disturbed by the boys walking past her to relieve themselves in the yard and the baby crying because she had wet herself.

On her last visit to her father, when she had once again spent her sixpence on twist tobacco, she was overjoyed to hear him say, 'I'll come for you next week. The doctor says I can go home. There's good news. I've found William and his wife. They're coming to live with us. William will work the land and I can get work at Jondaryan Station and bring in some money. You'll have your Aunt Lydia for company.'

Three days later Angus McDonald gave them a lift home on the way to one of the stations further out where he was to pick up a load of wool and deliver some supplies. He dropped them at their front door and came in for a cup of tea. The place was in a shambles — bush rats had moved in and devoured their bag of flour and prickly pear was growing through the walls.

'I'll stay and gie ye a hand,' the bullock driver said. 'Another day or two … no matter.'

He had brought bread and cheese to eat on the way, and the canvas bag hanging on the side of the dray was full of fresh water. He divided the food into three portions, lit a fire and produced a bottle of rum. Long after Winifred had gone to bed she could hear the two men talking around the fire, which they kept burning all night to keep the rats at bay, and later there was the sound of Angus singing in a deep rich voice and then her father joined in with his light baritone. When she finally drifted off to sleep, she did so with a sense of peace, secure in the knowledge that her father had recovered and that things would be even better once her aunt and uncle arrived.

8

THE LOOKING GLASS

WILLIAM IVANHOE OATEN AND HIS WIFE Lydia arrived by Cobb and Co coach in April 1893 and there was a joyous reunion between the two brothers. For the first time since he had arrived in Australia Wilfred felt at ease. He had the support of his older brother whom he had always looked up to.

For some reason Winifred did not take to her Uncle William. He arrived wearing a three-piece navy serge suit and a bowler hat and he carried a leather valise. He was a slightly larger replica of her father, with the same grey eyes and brown hair, the same mannerism of pulling at his left ear when he was thinking; but he had a slight potbelly and a puffiness under his eyes, unlike her father with his taut, thin body and haggard face from hard work and fatigue. It could have been the sardonic look in her uncle's eyes as he stared at her with her long matted hair and suntanned face, wearing an outfit made from two sugar bags with holes cut out for the arms and head. Her bare legs were covered in festering sores from contact with the prickly pear, her dirty bare toes protruding from worn boots. Without greeting her he turned and handed his wife down from the coach.

Winifred stood transfixed at the sight of her Aunt Lydia. She had dark hair that formed a widow's peak and was streaked with grey. It reminded the girl of the wings of a bird. Her eyes were dark brown and she wore a dress of taffeta of the same colour. It had a fashionable bustle, a braid trim in the front with a matching mantle, and with it she wore a little brown velour hat trimmed with a pheasant's feather. On her hands were brown kid gloves and she carried a reticule made of the same material as her dress.

The woman hesitated when her eyes lit on the hut standing forlornly by the road, the prickly pear towering behind it, and Winifred saw a shadow pass over her face. But then she turned to the girl and smiled a dazzling smile. 'I'm your Aunt Lydia. I'm looking forward to getting to know you, *mon chérie*,' and she embraced her lightly, kissing her on both cheeks.

As she did so Winifred caught a faint whiff of lavender and had a sudden vision of her mother reaching out for the bottle of lavender water on her dressing table. A wave of nostalgia and sadness swept over her. She was jolted out of it by her aunt's voice: 'I'm parched … I hope there's a cup of tea.' She hurried back into the hut and, clutching the bottle and the billy can, made her way down to the creek.

Later Aunt Lydia unpacked her wooden chest containing her clothes and bed linen, a white woven tablecloth which she spread on the bark table at mealtimes, and some fringed Spanish shawls which she placed over the backs of the chairs. There was also a paraffin lamp with pink glass which threw a soft light around the crude room at night.

To separate Winifred's sleeping quarters from the room where they ate, Lydia hung a length of chintz patterned in pink roses, which had covered the front window of her home in Brisbane, where William had been the highly respected stationmaster at Bald Hills Railway Station. But the thing that captured Winifred's heart was a silver teapot which her Aunt Liddy placed in the centre of the table and into which the girl gazed, seeing herself reflected in its gleaming surface.

These simple measures transformed the hut and turned it into a home, a place where the girl felt a sense of security as she watched her aunt, soft white hands, with a gold wedding band on one finger and a sparkling amethyst on another, poised over the teapot as she poured the tea. In the place of tin mugs there were white china cups that did not burn your lips when you drank.

Then there were white cotton bedsheets. Winifred had not slept between sheets since she left England. It meant washing her feet in the tin dish before she got into bed so that the sheets did not get stained from the black soil, as well as carrying the sheets down to the creek to wash. Later she and her aunt would stand facing each other, holding the sheets by the corners, stretching them until they were straight and then folding them before putting them back into Lydia's wooden trunk that smelt of lavender.

Lydia taught the girl how to make a bed, smoothing the sheets, making sure the end with the wide hem was at the top, tucking in the corners, and folding the blanket at the bottom of the bed where it could be pulled up 'in case you feel cold'. By this time Winifred had acquired a real bed made of black iron and a mattress made from a calico bag stuffed with chaff. It had come by bullock dray with a terse message from the driver as he dropped it off: 'I'm on the way through to collect a load of wool. Yer dad asked me to deliver this.'

The next time the bullock dray came past it was carrying a camp oven. This meant that they could make bread and scones and girdle cakes, as well as roast meat and bake vegetables. Rabbits had multiplied in the district and a pair of rabbits could be had for threepence. With Wilfred earning a regular wage at Jondaryan Station, their life had become easier. The days of living on damper and treacle, with an occasional wallaby which a small Aboriginal boy would sell to them for threepence, were over.

Wilfred was enjoying his new life. In addition to the money he earned, he had the companionship of other men, and away from the sight of the prickly pear he could put it from his mind. He did not realise that his trust in his brother was misplaced and that William had not been honest with him. William and Lydia had sought him out, not through any family feeling, but because William had been disgraced and needed somewhere to go.

William had been dismissed from the Railways Department for being drunk on duty. It meant not only the loss of face, but also his salary of one hundred and thirty pounds a year and the stationmaster's house that went with the position. In a way it was a relief for Lydia, who had come to dread the sight of the police buggy pulling to a stop in front of their house while the local sergeant helped William to the front door.

When she opened it the sergeant would say, 'I've brought your husband home, Mrs Oaten,' and help her get him into bed. William was always full of remorse the next day, promising a tearful Lydia that he would stay away from hotels. For a while he kept his promise, but his need for alcohol was too great and eventually he started keeping a bottle of whisky in his desk. It was all right for a man to come home the worse for drink after a convivial evening with friends, but to be drunk on duty when he was in charge of a railway station was a different matter because it could interfere with the safety of the trains. Once his behaviour was noticed he was dismissed without a reference.

It was a terrible blow to Lydia, who lost her cherished home and her social position as the wife of a senior civil servant. She was accustomed to being 'at home' every Wednesday to the other wives who moved in the same circle. No one had called on her once they heard about her husband's downfall and Lydia packed up her home alone. She brought her treasures with her, together with their beds and bedding, and put the rest of their goods and chattels in store until they could find somewhere else to live.

She knew that there was no prospect of her husband getting another position in the Civil Service unless they travelled interstate where he was not known. But first she had to wean him off the drink. She thought this would be possible away from the city.

In England Lydia had been a poorly paid nursery governess to one of the old families. It was a step above the downstairs staff — she took her meals in the nursery and had regular contact with her employer when she made her evening visit to see her children. Like all their staff she travelled with the family when they made their annual trip to take the waters at Bath. It was here that she met her husband at a church social, long after she had given up all thought of marriage. When he followed her to Reading after the family returned home, she married him in the parish church of St Mary's, even though she did not love him. Her employer gave her a dowry of household linen and ten gold sovereigns. When William suggested migrating to Australia, she went with him gladly.

Living in a makeshift humpy with a husband whose one thought was of alcohol was difficult but she tried to make the best of it. It was the friendship with Winifred that sustained her. She was touched by the neglected appearance of the girl. She made an effort to get her hair into some sort of order, lending her her hairbrush and showing her how to braid her hair, then giving her two blue hair ribbons to tie at the ends. She cut down several of her old gowns to make Winifred dresses, laying out the garments on the bark-topped table and showing her niece how to sew, taking out scissors, needle, thread and a thimble from a cane workbasket with a top of orange cretonne and a drawstring cord. While her aunt was busy with the scissors, Winifred would take out the tortoiseshell box of buttons, arranging them in rows, separating the mother-of-pearl shirt buttons from the bone trouser buttons. One day she pored over the blue glass buttons with a white daisy in the centre. 'I got those when your uncle and I were in Venice,' Lydia said and gave Winifred one to keep. She had it for a long while until she lost it through a crack in the wall when she was playing with it in bed and it was consumed by the prickly pear.

It was the time the older woman and the young girl sat together sewing that forged a close bond. Starved of affection, Winifred loved to listen to her aunt's stories, particularly the one of how her grandmama was smuggled 'from the great chateau in the dead of night in a cart full of washing. There was no room for my great-grandmama and my great-grandpapa. They went to the guillotine because they'd worked in a noble house — beheaded, just like Queen Marie Antoinette.' Lydia's eyes would sparkle and flash and then grow sad.

'But what had they done?' Winifred would ask, her eyes shining with unshed tears.

'Nothing … it was the revolution.'

'But why?' No matter how often Winifred heard the story, she always asked the same questions.

'Well, times were hard and some people couldn't afford to buy bread. When the Queen heard, she said, "Let them eat cake." But you see, if they couldn't afford bread, how could they buy cake?'

'What sort of cake?' Winifred put down her needle and cotton, and with her elbows on the table, rested her chin in her hands.

'They're a sweet type of pastry that French people eat for breakfast. Flaky and light and made from yeast. You dip them in your morning coffee.'

'Have you ever tasted one?'

'Often. There was a French cook in the manor house where I worked.' Lydia picked up a shirt-waist she was making for Winifred and sewed on a pearl button.

'Tell me about the great house where your grandmother lived.'

'Some other time, *chéri*.'

Winifred never heard the end of the story because her aunt would always jump up, glance out the door and say, 'The sun's in the west. It's time to take your uncle some tea and a scone. He must be parched. The kettle's boiling. You make the tea and I'll get the bread in the oven and stew some prickly pears. The fruit is such a beautiful colour once it's cooked … like a topaz.'

The girl would put some tea leaves in the billy can, fill it with boiling water, then sweeten it with sugar and turn the lid upside down. Balancing a tin mug and a scone on top, she would carry this in her left hand and in her right hand a stick, in case a death adder should appear. By now, though, she had lost her fear, knowing that if she made enough noise anything on the path would slide into the dense thicket of pear, the only indication of its presence was the sound of rustling as she approached.

As weeks went by Winifred had more and more trouble finding her uncle. When he had first arrived she would know where he was by the sound of an axe. But lately it had been strangely quiet in the afternoon. One day she followed a long tunnel he had cut in the prickly pear. It reminded her of the tunnel Alice had fallen down, except that this one went sideways through the pear. And where Alice's tunnel had been black, this was all green, almost like being at the bottom of the sea.

Winifred came across her uncle in a little clearing. He was lying there with his eyes closed, an empty whisky bottle by his side. For a minute she thought he was asleep and then she realised that he was in a drunken stupor. She hesitated, wondering whether to try to rouse him, and then, putting the billy can on the ground, ran back to get her aunt.

It was a mistake, because her uncle never forgave her for exposing his weakness.

She lay awake that night listening to her aunt pleading and crying with her uncle as she tried to make him promise to give up the drink. The next morning William followed Winifred outside and hissed at her, 'You little sneak, you great fat ugly thing.' He was so close that she could feel his spittle on her face. She turned and ran in her nightshirt to the creek, without having anything to eat or drink. She stayed there for a long while, thinking back to her childhood and how her mother had told her she was ugly, almost convincing herself that it must be true.

Eventually she was able to compose herself as she watched the water bubbling over the round polished stones on the creek bed and the sky with its drift of clouds. She had a sudden memory of Mr Smithers, who had once said to her, 'Life can be hard but nothing can hurt you unless you let it.' He had treated her kindly and told her she was clever.

Later, she heard her aunt's light tread coming down the track. She had a plate in her hand with a slice of bread and jam on it, and a mug of tea. 'I have been worried about you, *chéri*. Did we upset you last night?' She sat beside Winifred and put her arm around her, holding her close. 'Your uncle cannot help himself. He got into bad company in Brisbane and lost his job. That's why we came here. Now we must watch him to make sure that he doesn't get hold of strong drink … otherwise there's no hope for him.'

Winifred tried to do as her aunt had asked, watching her uncle, following him surreptitiously when he went down the tunnel to the clearing he had made in the prickly pear to see if he had a bottle hidden anywhere. But if he caught her staring at him he would wait until he had her alone and then continue his verbal onslaught, never hitting her but putting her down with his tongue. 'Did anyone ever tell you how fat and ugly you are? No one will ever want you.'

Though she tried not to let it upset her, he had the power to wound her and she found herself spending more and more time by the creek, unable to confide in her aunt because she did not want to hurt her.

It was at this time that her father sent home an invitation to the Shearers' Feast at Jondaryan, a celebration to mark the end of shearing. 'Put a dress on that kid, and clean up her hair,' he wrote to her aunt. 'I'll call for you in a sulky.' With the note was a roll of black moulton cloth, a heavy black material normally used for making blazers, and some cards of pink baby ribbon. 'I'm sure you can whip up something. I was a bit late getting to the shop and this was all that was left.'

The invitation occupied Lydia and Winifred. Uncle William found himself left to his own devices, having decided not to go. A sly-grog shanty had opened up on the main road, within walking distance of the Oatens' land. It was a one-room bark hut without windows, and a door just wide enough for a man to squeeze through. When Winifred asked about it Aunt Lydia told her that wine shanties sprung up wherever shearers and itinerant workers gathered at the end of the season with their cheques. 'Many intend to return to their home, if they have one, others plan to buy a passage back to their country of birth. It's very sad. After a few drinks, *chéri*, they forget and spend all their money.'

One day Lydia and Winifred walked past the shanty and saw the men spilling out onto the road, drinking from tin pannikins and bottles. William was among them. When she saw him Lydia averted her eyes, knowing that he was spending their savings. Her one consolation was that as soon as the men returned to work, the shanty would close, to spring up again next year. But by that time she hoped to have her husband safely out of the way.

Though Winifred felt sorry for her aunt, she was pleased her uncle was occupied elsewhere, certain that he would have spoiled her enjoyment of the party and her excitement about having a new dress. If Lydia had misgivings about the way the long black dress looked on her niece, she put them to one side. To lighten the look of the thick black material she had decorated the dress with tiny pink ribbon bows.

Wilfred made no comment on his daughter's appearance when he called for her and her aunt in a horse and sulky which he had bought out of his earnings. Lydia had braided Winifred's hair and looped it on either side of her head, tying it in pink ribbon bows. Standing back to admire her handiwork she was disconcerted to see how the dress stood stiffly around the young girl like a tent, but she thought that perhaps away from the city the other young women would be dressed in a similar fashion.

As they waited to get into the sulky Lydia kissed Winifred on both cheeks. 'You'll be the belle of the ball. You look so beautiful with colour in your cheeks and your eyes sparkling.' Under her praise Winifred glowed and pressed close to her aunt as her father whipped up the horse for the run to Jondaryan.

The long driveway was a blaze of lights with pitch-covered poles that had been driven into the ground and set alight. On the verandah there were long tables set with all manner of dainties: iced cakes, scones, cold meats and pitchers of fruit juices. Winifred had never seen such a spread. The sound of an accordion and a violin floated out from a large room where people were dancing.

Wilfred secured the horse to a post and led the two women through the double doors. The music had just stopped and men and women were returning to their seats. Framed in the doorway in her black dress Winifred was conspicuous and she was conscious of people staring at her and then a wave of suppressed mirth.

Winifred gazed back at the women in light-coloured dresses that ended at their calves, with their necks bare and flowers at their waist and hair. She was suddenly conscious of how she looked in comparison. She moved closer to her aunt, who said, 'Come along, Winifred. The music will be starting soon. We'll have to find you a partner.' They found seats along the wall, while Wilfred went to join a group of men who were standing talking.

The music started and the master of ceremonies began to call for people to form a set for an eightsome reel. Winifred watched as young men approached young women, taking them by the hand and leading them to the centre of the hall. The music started and she sat beside her aunt, knowing that her dress was all wrong, certain that people were laughing at her as they danced past.

Later, when a woman came and sat next to her aunt and they began to talk, Winifred stood quietly and made her way out the door into the night. She passed the glowing poles that lined the driveway until she reached the road and began to walk home. It was here her father found her sometime later, her face streaked with tears, certain that what her uncle had said about her was true: she was a great ugly thing that no one would want.

Wilfred was home for a few days, angry when he saw that there had been no advance in the clearing of the prickly pear since William had arrived; if anything, the pest was worse. He took his older brother to task. 'I thought you'd be a help to me but all you've done is eat your head off at my expense. You ought to be ashamed of yourself.'

'Ah, no, little brother, the boot's on the other foot. It's you who ought to be ashamed of yourself. You live like a peasant, you who were brought up in a decent God-fearing home where you were taught manners, how to dress, how to live like a gentleman. Look at you now … and as for that daughter of yours, she'd frighten the crows. Lydia has tried to do what she can but that girl's a lost cause. My wife is different, she's a lady. It was an insult to bring her here.'

'Hush, dear,' and Lydia put her hand on her husband's arm, but he shook it off. 'Keep out of this. This is between my brother and me.' William stepped up to his younger brother and, pointing his finger at him, said, 'The best thing you can do is to pack your bags, go back to England. See if your wife'll have you back … that's if she hasn't found someone else by now.'

Before his brother could answer William began to walk briskly down the road, while Wilfred leapt into his sulky, whipped up his horse and galloped off in the opposite direction.

Lydia went into the hut where Winifred was sobbing on the bed. She held the girl in her arms, saying, 'Hush, child. It's nothing. Men often have their arguments but they blow over. Tomorrow they'll be laughing about it.'

Neither of the men returned for dinner, and the two women ate a solitary meal of cold mutton, and bread and treacle washed down with strong black tea. There was a feeling of sadness in the air. Even the sound of a cricket singing in the corner could not enliven the gloom. Lydia made an effort at conversation. 'A cricket singing on the hearth means good luck. In China the children keep crickets in little cages like some people keep canaries.'

Winifred did not respond. Her eyes were red-rimmed from crying. She gave her aunt a lacklustre look and went and lay down on her bed without saying goodnight.

Lydia washed the dishes and put the meat into the meat safe, then she stood the treacle tin back in its dish of water to protect it from ants. She took up her crochet hook and began to work on a lace tablecloth she was making to fit the bark table. When she heard her husband at the door she took the lamp and went to meet him.

'Pack your things, Lydia. I've booked two seats on tomorrow's coach. I've taken rooms in town and I've made an appointment to meet the land agent.'

Winifred heard the news at breakfast. Her father had returned sometime in the night but, exhausted, she had slept through the sound of the sulky pulling up. She could only stare at her aunt, wondering how she would survive without her gentle presence. As soon as breakfast was over she washed the dishes and then, instead of waiting to help her aunt pack, set off for the creek where she sat for a long while wondering what would become of her now.

The girl thought of her uncle's words — that she would frighten the crows — and knew it wasn't true. Often when she was quiet by the creek a crow would come and perch beside her on a tree, regarding her with its bright eyes as she talked to it. She watched some green ants running up and down the trunk of a sapling and felt the warmth of the sun on her face. The sky was blue and cloudless and a fresh breeze rustled through the reeds, where a few ducks were dabbling as they searched for food. Suddenly she felt at peace with herself. Her aunt was leaving but she would see her again. Even if Uncle William hated her, Aunt Lydia loved her and she loved her aunt. She turned and began to hurry, worried that her aunt may have already left before they had a chance to say goodbye.

She met her aunt halfway down the track. 'Dear heart,' Lydia said. 'I thought I might have to leave without saying goodbye.' She took Winifred by the hand. 'Don't fret, chéri. Once we're settled you can come and visit. We couldn't have stayed here forever and neither can you. You need to be with people in a proper house where you can learn to become a young lady.'

It was a tearful farewell for Winifred as she watched the coach disappear in a cloud of dust, taking her aunt and uncle with it. Gone were the pink shaded lamp, the Spanish shawls, the silver teapot and, worst of all, gentle Lydia who had taken the place of her mother.

Her father was not there to say goodbye and the girl stood by the side of the road disconsolately until she heard the sound of her father's sulky. She watched as he threw the reins over the hitching post.

Instead of greeting her he glowered at her. 'What are you staring at? Get inside and light the stove.'

She hurried into the hut, put half a loaf of bread and some prickly pear jelly on the table and boiled the black kettle, making the tea in the billy can. Then she put two mugs and plates on the bark table and waited for her father to come inside.

He ate in sullen silence, and when he had finished, said, 'You're old enough to start work. I've found you a job and I've bought another block of land. We'll be out of here by the end of the week.' Before she could ask him any questions he left the table and went outside, where he stood smoking his pipe.

9

THE SKIVVY

ON THE DAY THEY WERE TO LEAVE the prickly pear ranch, as her father called it, Winifred packed her clothes into a bundle and climbed into the sulky beside him. She began to cry as the horse drew away, looking back with longing at the little hut that had been their home for three years, thinking of her Aunt Lydia who had transformed it into a home with her pretty things, wondering if she would ever see her again.

She felt her father's eyes on her once or twice until he said, 'It's a two-day journey ahead of us and I don't want you snivelling all the way. I want you to make a good impression. Where you're going they're only taking you as a favour to me. You'll be helping in a shop among other things. They'll expect you to smile.'

Winifred turned towards her father and put her hand on his arm. 'Please ... Can't I stay with you? I don't want to go to a strange place to work.'

He turned to face the front and said firmly, 'No.' Then he whipped up the horse and, holding the reins tightly, began to draw on his pipe.

Winifred studied his face. His lips were turned down and he was frowning and she knew that she had no hope of making him change his mind. She thought about Uncle William's outburst when he had told her father to go back to England. Unbidden, the words rose to her tongue: 'I hate you ... I want to go home ... to England ... to my mother.'

Her father turned towards her and the expression on his face frightened her. He raised his whip and flicked it sideways. She gave a cry of pain as it wrapped around her shoulders, biting through her thin cotton dress. Then he pulled on the reins, brought the sulky to a halt and gathered her in his arms.

'Can't you understand? There is no going back. The past is over ... You have to grow up, learn to fend for yourself. Where I'm taking you you'll be taught how to keep house ... sleep between clean sheets. Then, in a few years' time, you can get a proper job at ten shillings a week until you find someone to marry you.'

He reached behind him and took a piece of damper out of a cloth. He poured a drink of water into a tin mug and handed it to her. 'We'll stop here for a few minutes, give the horse a spell.' He jumped from the sulky and led the horse to the side of the road where there was a small patch of grass. Winifred followed disconsolately after him.

It was late the next day when they arrived at Toowoomba, a rundown shop in front of a dwelling run by a Mrs Sybil. Winifred's heart sank when she was led inside by her father and introduced to a stout woman with dyed red hair who called her father 'ducky'. She smiled at the child through blackened front teeth but there was no corresponding smile in her eyes.

'You must call me Mother Sybil.' She put her arms around the girl and looked across at Wilfred. 'She'll be like a daughter to me … Don't worry about her. I'll take good care of her.'

Then she held the girl at arm's length, taking in the skimpy cotton dress, the thin frame, the small breasts. 'I was expecting someone more mature. How old is she?'

'Fourteen,' her father lied. 'She's small for her age.'

They sat together in the parlour with Mrs Sybil and drank tea and ate thinly sliced buttered bread while Wilfred talked about the block of land he was buying where he planned to run a few cattle and take a few outside painting jobs.

'You're a marvel,' the woman simpered. 'You'll be rich as houses before you know it, won't he, my love?' and she patted Winifred on the knee, her lips parted in a thin smile, 'and then he'll take you to England to meet the Queen. I can just see you in a white satin gown with long white feathers on your head … You'll marry some handsome man just like your dad. Now run along to the shop. There's a tray of home-made toffees. Help yourself.'

The girl was glad to escape. She made her way through the hall to the front of the shop where there were a few fans and shawls and on top of the counter a tray of sticky toffees wrapped in paper. She took one, removed it from the paper and began to suck, feeling soothed by the sweetness on her tongue. Then she went back into the hall and heard Mrs Sybil say, 'Will you take a drop then? I always have a little something at night. It keeps the damp out of my bones … There's always mist at the top of the range.'

As Winifred stood at the door of the parlour she saw Mrs Sybil lift a stone jar off the mantelpiece and pour some clear liquid into her father's tea cup and then into her own. Her father lifted his cup in the air, 'To your bright eyes,' he said as he drained it in one gulp. 'Now I must be off. I've a long trip ahead of me.'

Winifred was seized by a feeling of terror. She knew that at any moment her father would get to his feet and drive away, leaving her with this raddled hag with the atrocious red hair, who she knew had no intention of treating her like one of the family. As Wilfred rose to his feet she clung to his hand and followed him down the dark hall, through the shop with its shawls and fans and the tray of home-made toffees, to where he had hitched the sulky. She threw her arms around his knees and clung to him as he tried to get in the sulky, begging him to take her with him.

He pushed her roughly to one side and said between clenched teeth, 'Behave yourself! If you make a show of me I'll tan the hide off you.'

She released her hold and with tears streaming down her cheeks watched as he whipped up the horse and rattled down the street.

That night, as she lay between two blankets on a stretcher on a back verandah, where a length of hessian served as a blind and mosquitoes buzzed around her face, she wished with all her heart that she was back in their little hut on the Downs. Later she heard a sound that she was to hear often during the coming nights — the sound of men's voices and women's laughter. Winifred never knew what went on in the upstairs rooms because she was not allowed inside the house once she had gone to bed.

Each morning she was expected to rise early, wash herself at a tap in the yard, get dressed and light the fire. She'd boil the kettle to make a pot of tea and toast some bread, which she carried upstairs to where Mother Sybil would be waiting, her hair in curling papers, a crimson shawl around her shoulders. Winifred would put the tea tray on a table beside the bed and draw back the red silk curtains, pausing briefly to glance at the mist rising from the valley, listening for the whistle of the steam train as it laboured up the Toowoomba Ranges, until Mother Sybil would say, 'There's work to do. I don't pay you to stand around.'

The girl would stoop and pick up the chamber pot under the bed, then carry it downstairs to empty into the slop bucket at the door, before rinsing it under the tap in the yard and returning it to the upstairs room where she placed it in the commode. Sometimes there were chamber pots to empty in other rooms and beds to make. Once this was done Winifred returned to the kitchen and filled a jug with hot water, which she carried upstairs and poured into the washbasin decorated with red poppies to match the chamber pot.

Winifred was free for a few minutes after this while Mother Sybil dressed. She could indulge herself with toasted bread and jam and no one to see how much she ate. She would wash it down with a cup of tea with milk and three teaspoons of sugar, rising hurriedly to wash the dishes when she heard Mother Sybil's footsteps on the stairs and her voice calling, 'You're not still in the kitchen? There's the shop to be dusted … and I've a batch of toffees to make. I hope you haven't been helping yourself to the sugar.'

On Saturday the older woman took a bath. It fell to Winifred to carry the jugs of hot water out to the bathhouse in the backyard. Once she peeped through the cracks and was amazed at the sight of the woman's body overflowing the bathtub, her breasts swinging as she leaned forward to scrub her back. The girl found it hard to reconcile this almost mystical being, her body glistening white like some exotic sea creature, with the red-haired harridan in the tight corsets who scolded her and sometimes slapped her across the face if she burnt a saucepan or let the milk boil over when she was making a custard.

Thinking about it in bed, an image floated into her mind of a night in Lambeth when it had been too hot to sleep, and she had crept downstairs to see if her parents were still awake. She had opened the door a crack and seen her father bending over her mother, who was sitting naked in a tin tub of water while he washed her back. And then she saw him lean forward and kiss her on the shoulder. Her mother looked up at him and smiled and her father gathered her in a towel and carried her to bed.

The child tiptoed back upstairs. When she woke the next morning she could not be sure whether or not it was a dream. Now she wondered whether her father still loved her mother and if he was unhappy at losing her. He had told her there was no going back, that the past was dead. Perhaps her mother was dead too and that's what he meant. She had thought her mother might have written a letter but then she wouldn't know where to send it. Winifred wished now she'd stayed in England. Even if her mother had died, Mrs Watkins would have looked after her.

Winifred had a lone friend in the man who came once a week to empty the lavatory pan. She would listen for the sound of his cart rattling down the street until it was close enough to smell. The first time the man called he caught her inside the privy, reading from the scraps of cut-up newspaper that served as lavatory paper. He pulled open the trapdoor in the back, ready to slide out the pan and replace it with an empty one, but retreated to the corner of the yard where he squatted on the ground, chewing a grass stalk, until she emerged looking around to see where he was. He raised his cap, 'Mornin', miss. Nice day, ain't it? You must be the new skivvy.'

Winifred watched as he slid out the full pan and replaced it with an empty one. Then, with the heavy pan on his grey-flannel-clad shoulder, he grinned at her and ran down the passage, back into the street where she heard the rattle of the pans in the back of the cart as the horse moved slowly along the road.

Once he brought a boy with him. He was about her own age and the two exchanged glances. Winifred gave him a toffee from the shop, hoping that Mother Sybil wouldn't notice; but at the end of the week, when she normally received a few pence, the woman said, 'That's five toffees you've had this week, including the one you gave the sanitary carter's son. You'll get no money this week — you've eaten it all.'

The girl had been promised two shilling a week when her father had left her there. Later she was told it was too much. 'You're only worth a shilling a week but I'll be generous and make it one and threepence.'

When her father wrote that he would be in the area and would come to visit, Winifred waited nervously, hoping that if she could speak to him privately and tell him how she was being treated he would take her away. But on the morning of his visit Mother Sybil told Winifred to have a bath. The girl was embarrassed when the woman came into the bathhouse while she was sitting there naked and dropped a handful of bath salts into the water before scrubbing her back and washing her hair, rinsing it with a tin dipper of warm water.

Later Winifred stood shame-faced, while Mother Sybil rubbed her breasts and thighs with a white towel, patting the pubic hair that had begun to sprout and saying, 'You're coming along nicely. Once you get rid of the dirt you're a pretty little thing. We'll make something of you yet.'

She led Winifred upstairs, still wrapped in the towel, and handed her a clean chemise and pair of drawers. 'Here, put these on.' She took a red silk dress out of her wardrobe and held it up to the girl, but it was much too large. Eventually she found a printed muslin that someone had left behind. 'You can wear it when your dad gets here,' and she gave her a length of pink satin ribbon to tie round her waist. 'Now run along and tidy up the parlour, but don't get yourself covered in grime. You can leave the fireplace until your dad's gone. I don't want him to see you covered in ashes.'

Winifred's hopes of persuading her father to take her away were dashed when he kissed her, pleased to see her looking so pretty in the muslin dress printed with sprigs of pink roses. Then he glanced down at her feet and frowned. She was wearing a pair of down-at-heel slippers which had once belonged to Mother Sybil.

'She needs new shoes,' the woman said.

Wilfred stared at her, 'I thought … I thought our arrangement was that in return for my daughter's work you would clothe and feed her, and give her two shillings a week.'

Mrs Sybil smiled at him, her head on one side. 'You men are all the same. I'm only a poor widow woman with no man to help, and your daughter, she eats her head off. And what do I get in return? Very little. I've had to teach her everything.'

Winifred was silent, even though she knew this wasn't true. Perhaps if she could get her father alone she could tell him what it was really like … but not in front of Mother Sybil.

Her father drew a leather pouch out of his coat pocket and counted out five shillings. 'Buy my daughter a pair of boots.' He looked thoughtful and then added another five shillings. 'See that she has everything she needs.'

Mother Sybil's eyes glinted as she pocketed the money. Winifred knew instinctively that the only boots she would receive would be ones that someone else had discarded. The best she could hope for was that they wouldn't be too small.

The girl went into the kitchen to make the tea and butter the bread, which she placed on a tray and carried back into the parlour where Mother Sybil was laughing at something her father had said, her hand on his knee. The stone jar was on the table and her father was drinking from a glass.

Later, when her father rose to leave, Winifred followed him to the front gate, knowing that it was no use complaining, he would not believe her. As she watched his sulky disappear around the corner she steeled herself not to cry, knowing she would have to remain where she was until she was old enough to look after herself.

She woke one morning to a strangely quiet house. A thick mist swirled around the yard and she shivered, trying to burrow deeper into her bed, until she realised that she would be scolded if she didn't rise and make breakfast for her employer. She had had a disturbed night, with people shouting and the sound of running footsteps, and later she had heard a horse whinnying at the front gate and then the sound of galloping hooves, but she had taken no notice. The house was often noisy at night and where they were situated there was a steady stream of horse-drawn vehicles at all hours — carts from out of town taking milk, cheese and butter to the railway station, and travellers coming and going.

The water in the tap in the yard was icy as Winifred splashed it on her face and dressed hurriedly before going into the kitchen, looking forward to the warmth from the fuel stove once she had lit it. The first thing she noticed was that the black iron kettle and pots were gone. Then she noticed that the tea caddy was missing, and the bags of sugar, flour and oatmeal. She hurried upstairs to tell Mother Sybil, but her room was empty, except for a broken cardboard hatbox, a few sheets of crumpled tissue paper and an empty henna bottle lying on the floor. Mother Sybil had gone.

Her first emotion was one of joy. She was free at last. But then the thought came to her that she had nowhere else to go. Her father had moved. Where, she had no idea. And she had nothing, only the blankets on her bed, a pair of second-hand boots that Mother Sybil had given her, and the worn-out dresses she had brought with her when she first came She searched in the upstairs rooms for the sprigged muslin dress she had been given, but it had gone, along with everything else in the house.

Puzzled, the girl walked through to the shop. It, too, was empty except for a tray of toffees on the counter. She took one and began to suck it as she opened the front door and went outside.

It was here that the local police constable, Harold West, found Winifred when he went cycling past on his morning rounds. He stopped, leaning his bike against the front fence. 'Where did you spring from?'

'I work here, I'm the skivvy … But everyone's gone, and I'm hungry and I haven't been paid for weeks …'

'Did a moonlight flit, eh? Good riddance, I say. And who might you be?'

'Winifred Oaten.'

He wrote her name in his book. 'And how old might you be, Winifred Oaten?'

'I'm going on fourteen.'

'I see, thirteen … too young to be here on your own. You'd better come with me.'

'Am I being arrested? I haven't done anything.'

'Arrested? No, not you. You're only a young lass, you ain't done nothing wrong. You should be at school. We got to find where your folks is and get you back home.'

'I don't have any folks, only my father, and I haven't seen him for a long time … he's moved.'

'Don't worry your pretty little head about that. We'll find him. I'll help you get your things together, then I'll take you down to the missus. You're shivering. Do you not have a shawl? It's mighty nippy this morning.'

Later, wrapped in her blanket, her bundle of clothes balanced on the handlebars, Winifred perched behind Harold, clinging to his waist while he pedalled to the police station and took her to his quarters out the back where his wife was busy in the laundry.

'I've brought a visitor, Mrs West. I found this young person abandoned. She needs a hot bath and a good feed of fried bread with sausages, and a mug of hot tea wouldn't go astray either. After that I'll work out what to do with her.'

'I want to go home,' Winifred said.

'Easier said than done. We got to find your father first … And you can't stay here, unless you want to go in the lock-up. A right proper bunch of villains — horse thieves, a few drunks that got in a fight and woke up feeling sorry for themselves — couldn't even eat the nice hot oatmeal the missus cooked 'em — and there's a murderer too. I try and keep 'em in order until their case is heard. You wouldn't like it in there, I can tell you.' He winked at Winifred and burst out laughing, but she looked at him and frowned, a tight knot of pain in her stomach, too worried about what would become of her to share the joke.

He patted her on the shoulder, saying, 'Cheer up, there's nothing to worry about. I'll see you right.'

Later she tried on a dress the constable's wife gave her. 'My niece left it here when she was on a holiday. She grew out of it.' And to wear with it she was given a pair of black woollen stockings and a knitted shawl.

When Winifred looked in the mirror on Mrs West's dressing table she hardly recognised herself in the navy serge dress with white braid down the front, which reached to her calves. And with the black woollen stockings on, her feet felt warm for the first time in weeks.

The woman brushed the hair off Winifred's face and braided it into one thick pigtail which she tied with a red ribbon. 'You look like a real young lady,' she said. 'You must learn to take a pride in yourself,' and she bent and kissed her lightly on the cheek.

Late that afternoon Constable West took Winifred to meet the Jackson family. 'You'll like it there. Mr Jackson runs a small bakery at Drayton. It's on t'other side of the railway line There's three children in the family. You'll be helping Mr Jackson with the pie-cart and they'll give you two shillings and sixpence a week. What do you say?'

'I want to go home.'

'And you will, but until we find your father you need somewhere to stay.'

It was three weeks before the constable called to tell her that her father had taken up land near Evergreen and that he was rarely there, travelling long distances doing painting jobs on the outback stations. He had sent a message that he wanted Winifred to stay where she was and that he'd visit when he could.

Winifred was surprised at her reaction. She had waited so long for the news, half expecting that her father would not want her back and yet unwilling to acknowledge it to herself. But now, instead of feeling resentful, she felt relieved. She had come to enjoy the work, the company of the younger girls when they returned from school, and most of all the time she spent on the pie-cart with Mr Jackson.

It fell to Winifred to care for the pie-stand which sat in the back of an open dray drawn by a bay mare called Jezebel, though Mr Jackson referred to her as Jez, 'Because,' as he explained to Winifred the first time he took her out on the pie-cart, 'Mrs Jackson don't think Jezebel's a proper name for a horse.' He shook the reins lightly and Jezebel broke into a trot and then slowed down again.

'She was a real goer once, a racehorse. And then she got too old. I rescued her from the boiling-down works. You know about the boiling-down works?' Winifred shook her head. 'Well, when times is hard or beasts get too old to work, they send them to the boiling-down works to turn into tallow for soap … The stench is something awful. Once you've smelt it you'd never forget.'

The girl thought back to Lambeth and the blood and bone works by the Thames. She knew the smell but she had always thought they were just old bones that the rag-and-bones man collected, not live creatures like Jezebel.

'Calling her Jezebel was a joke — the old girl ain't got a kick left in her,' Mr Jackson said. He was silent for a few minutes, watching the road as the horse laboured up the big hill, clicking his tongue and calling, 'Steady as she goes, girl,' until they reached the top and the horse turned into Rutherford Street. Then he turned to Winifred. 'You've not read the Bible then?'

'No.'

'There's lots of good stories in the Bible. I suppose you've not been to church either? I'm a freethinker myself. Mrs Jackson follows the Methodists. She don't approve of me selling pies on Sunday, says it's the Lord's day of rest. But I say to her, if it's good enough for the preacher to work on Sunday and get paid, it's good enough for me.

'See that church over there,' he pointed with his whip, 'that's St Patrick's where the Catholics go, every Sunday first thing, on an empty stomach ... Now, after lots of prayers and a long-winded sermon, the priest goes home to roast mutton and a glass of port ... as for the rest — Jackson's pies hot from the oven and the smell wafting into the church to whet their appetite. I'd be a fool to miss out on all those thruppences.'

Winifred gazed at the church as the horse stopped. She'd never been to this side of town before. She could hear music and voices and thought that perhaps when the music stopped hundreds of people would come running out the doors to where they were waiting all holding up threepences ... a whole lot of people like she'd seen at the Cut, people pushing and shoving in case there weren't enough pies to go round.

She heard Mr Jackson say, 'How old are you?'

'I was eight when I left England and now I'm nearly fourteen.'

'I was away to sea when I was your age ... sailed round the world on a square-rigger. Many's the time I expected to be drowned. The ship'd go down to the bottom of a wave and then up again … Sometimes they'd tie me to the mast … The waves'd crash over the deck and take everything with it that weren't tied down, including the crew. First time I heard the cry "Man overboard!" I thought they'd fetch him back. Throw a rope or something. I soon learned there's no hope in Hades of fetching him back … Swim like a fish, but in the end the sea wins.'

There was something so engaging about Mr Jackson that Winifred couldn't help smiling. He was so different from her own father, with his bad moods, his long silences. Mr Jackson was always talking and laughing. For the first time Winifred realised what it meant to be part of a family. She had been accepted by the two young girls, who hung on the stories she told them once the candle had been blown out after Mrs Jackson had heard their prayers and kissed them goodnight.

The first time Mrs Jackson had come into the bedroom after their supper of bread and milk Winifred had stood watching as the children knelt by their beds and prayed aloud. 'God bless Father and Mother, God bless my sisters and brothers, God bless Grandfather and God bless me.'

'And God bless Winifred,' their mother prompted gently. Then she turned to Winifred. 'Do you not say your prayers?'

Winifred shook her head.

'Even though your father is far away you should pray to God to keep him safe.'

Later Winifred had knelt beside her bed, closing her eyes and putting her hands together while she tried to concentrate on God, praying silently that He would make her father love her and then adding a prayer for Jezebel, the old horse that she had come to love, as well as her Aunt Lydia. She thought about Uncle William but decided not to mention him in her prayers because he did not deserve it.

Her days fell into a routine. In the morning there was a bowl of hot oatmeal porridge which Mrs Jackson prepared, keeping some warm on the side of the stove for her husband when he woke. He spent most nights out on the pie-cart, moving from hotels to the railway station and back again, wherever there were people out and about.

After the children had left for school Winifred would go out into the yard, wearing a pinafore over one of her old dresses, and talk to Jezebel, filling her nosebag with chaff and her dish with water before taking the currycomb and brush to the horse's coat until it gleamed. Sometimes she would plait Jezebel's mane and tail like the horses on the hackney cabs in London, later holding out her palm with a teaspoon of sugar on it, feeling the rasp of the animal's tongue as it licked up the last grain. Next she scrubbed the inside of the pie oven and polished the brass corners until they shone, a picture in her mind of the ginger beer machine on Clapham Common like a shining little piano.

Once Mr Jackson was dressed and had eaten his porridge and sometimes a plate of streaky bacon, wiping out the dish with fried bread, then washing it all down with great draughts of milky tea, he would turn to Winifred and say, 'Ready for the baking?' Together they would go out to the bakehouse, where Mr Jackson had already lit the fire, to begin the real work of the day.

First he chopped the huge mound of beef into small pieces while Winifred peeled the onions, a job she hated because it made her eyes tingle until tears fell and she had to wipe her face with her apron. She never complained though; she was afraid that if she did they might send her away. While the meat and onions were simmering in a huge iron saucepan, to which Winifred had added a tablespoon of salt and two teaspoons of black pepper, Mr Jackson measured the flour into an enormous mixing bowl, sometimes upending the flourbag and sending up a cloud of white dust that turned his hair and eyebrows white.

Next began the task of adding great chunks of beef dripping; then, with his sleeves rolled to his elbows, he plunged his hands into the mixture, squeezing and turning it until he thought it was just right. He would make a well in the centre of the mixture while Winifred stood by with a dipper of cold water. When he said the word she began to pour it in slowly, until the mixture had formed into a large ball of dough which he would divide into three portions.

Mr Jackson would wipe his hands on his leather apron and then pour a dipper of flour onto the table. Placing one of the portions of dough onto the flour, he would pick up the rolling pin and begin to roll the pastry, stretching it thinner and thinner until it was almost transparent. 'It takes muscle,' he'd say. 'Folks don't want a big lump of pastry ... Light and flaky with plenty of meat and gravy ... Jackson's pies is special.'

When he had finished rolling out the pastry Winifred cut it into circles, which she placed in pie tins she had greased with dripping. Once this was done Mr Jackson would lift the partly cooked meat mixture off the stove to cool and then spoon it into the pie cases, while Winifred busied herself with cutting smaller circles for the tops which she later brushed over with cold water.

The pies would be left to stand while Mr Jackson tipped a large bowl of dried peas, which had been soaking since the night before, into a boiler filled with water from the tank, adding a tablespoon of sugar, a dash of vinegar, a big piece of butter and a handful of mint from the backyard. These would be left to simmer all afternoon, then at about four o'clock Mr Jackson would begin to cook the pies so that they would be hot when he began his nightly round.

Winifred would wipe the sweat from her forehead with her apron when the work was done, the bakehouse hot from the stove, the air full of the smell of baking pies. When she saw the pies laid out in rows in the kitchen ready to be loaded into the pie oven where a brazier full of hot coals kept them warm, she could hardly speak because she felt so happy. She would run outside and hug the old horse and say, 'I wish I could come with you.' But Mr Jackson had said, 'Staying up all night, going round hotels — it's no place for a young person, especially a girl.'

One morning after breakfast Mrs Jackson stopped Winifred as she was about to go out into the yard to clean the pie-cart. 'Mr Jackson won't be going on his rounds today.'

Winifred knew he'd come home last night because she'd already been outside to say good morning to Jezebel. 'Is he sick?'

'No, child. He's gone to collect his father.'

'Will he be baking today?'

Mrs Jackson shook her head. 'He'll be gone all day. You can help me clean out the boxroom. The old man will need somewhere on his own.'

Winifred picked up the broom. 'I'll go and sweep down the cobwebs.'

'Wait.' Mrs Jackson put her hand on the girl's arm. 'Things will change.'

The girl stared at her with a feeling of alarm, wondering if they were planning to send her away. She relaxed again when Mrs Jackson said, 'You won't have so much time to help with the pies. The old man ... well ... he's been shut away ... but my husband worries. He wants the children to know their grandfather ... He had an accident, his horse bolted and he got thrown on his head. His brains is a bit addled ... Mr Jackson feels that it ain't right to leave his father with mad folks ... Do you understand?'

Winifred wasn't sure what Mrs Jackson meant but thought that perhaps it would be nice for the children to have an older person around. She'd never known her grandparents.

When he arrived late that night with Mr Jackson the children were still awake, peering over the stairs to catch a glimpse. Their father saw them and called, 'Go to bed, children, your mother will be up shortly. Grandpa is tired.'

Winifred was still up and waited in the kitchen until Mrs Jackson had greeted her father-in-law. When she returned she seemed agitated. 'You go to bed, dear. Grandpa's not himself ... I'll take him a cup of tea once he's in bed. A good night's sleep will probably fix him.'

For the first few days Grandpa, as everyone called him, seemed content to sit by the kitchen stove where it was warm, leaving Winifred free to help with the baking. The children accepted the fact that he was ill and regarded him curiously when he muttered to himself, sometimes getting angry and throwing punches in the air at an imaginary assailant. Other times he sat in silence, threading his fingers through his beard, staring into the distance.

He took his meals with the family, but the minute his meal was put before him he would cram it into his mouth with both hands, before Mrs Jackson had a chance to sit down and say, 'Lord, we ask you to bless our food.' As soon as he had finished, he would give a furtive look around and return to his seat by the stove.

Once five-year-old Joshua said, 'Grandpa has got bad manners.' Winifred flinched when Mrs Jackson picked up the serving spoon and rapped him hard across the knuckles, and then sent him crying to his room. She had never seen Mrs Jackson angry before, certain that it was the old man who was the problem. The next day the children were quiet and hurried off to school, keeping well away from their grandfather.

After breakfast Mrs Jackson told Winifred to take the old man for a walk, saying, 'A change of scenery will do him good.'

Reluctantly the girl obeyed, leading him by the hand as they walked down the street. At the blacksmith's shop the old man broke free and startled one of the horses waiting to be shod, poking it with his walking stick. It reared up and lashed out, kicking a bucket of nails into the fire and narrowly missing the smithy, who leapt to one side, yelling out, 'Bejeasus! What the hell!' But the old man had already darted off, with Winifred in hot pursuit. She found him around the corner of the next street sitting in the gutter with a vacant look in his eye.

For the next two weeks he led her a merry dance, walking along the railway line, stopping to watch the fettlers at work, sometimes poking them with his stick and then running away until he had to stop because he was out of breath. He seemed to be aware that Winifred was following him and tried to give her the slip, darting into doorways, around corners, running around the sides of houses, sometimes emerging with a shirt on the end of his walking stick before he took off again. All Winifred could do was to leave the garment on the fence and run after him.

When they returned home at night she was almost too tired to eat, later lying awake wondering how much longer she could continue. The job she had loved with Jezebel and the pie-making had changed into a battle with an old man who seemed to have no sense of right or wrong … Sometimes she wondered if he knew who he was.

She was upstairs resting one afternoon after a particularly trying day with the old man. He had insisted on walking between the railway tracks, kicking the heads off the wildflowers that had sprung up between the lines, then he suddenly raised his stick as if to hit her. She jumped back and a group of fettlers who were boiling their billy rushed to her aid, taking the stick away and sitting the old man down beside the fire, sharing their bread and cheese with him and Winifred. By the time he had rested and had a cup of tea he had quietened down, but it was Winifred who carried the walking stick as they made their way back to the bakery.

She had tried to explain everything to Mrs Jackson, but she did not seem to understand. 'It's all right, he's harmless, he wouldn't hurt a fly. Just be careful.'

'But he knows I follow him. He hides all the time,' said Winifred as she burst into tears.

The next day Mrs Jackson kept the old man home and Winifred resumed her old duties, helping with the pie-making, grooming Jezebel and cleaning the pie-cart. Things were quiet until the children returned home from school and she heard Joshua screaming. Mr Jackson ran into the kitchen where he found his father holding the child over the fuel stove. 'It's cold … it's cold,' was all the old man could say when they took the child from him.

Winifred sensed the tension in the air as they ate their supper. Mr Jackson had gone out with the pie-cart. Instead of their usual chatter, the children were silent, watching their grandfather as he gulped down a plate of cold mutton with pickles. Instead of eating his pink blancmange he gathered it up in his hands and smeared it over his bald head.

Mrs Jackson picked up a damp cloth and wiped the old man down, sighing, 'Oh Grandpa, what are we going to do with you?'

When Mrs Jackson took the children up to bed, Winifred went with her rather than stay alone in the kitchen with the old man, waiting until Mrs Jackson went downstairs again so that she could help with the washing-up. While Winifred wiped the dishes Mrs Jackson put the old man to bed, pushing a chair against the door. 'In case he wanders in the night … we'll hear him. I'll have to get my husband to put a bolt on the outside of the door. I fear he's quite mad. I tried to take his walking stick but he got angry. I thought he was going to hit me. I'm afraid he might hurt one of the children.'

Winifred's nerves were on edge when she went to bed. Mr Jackson was still out and she lay awake straining her ears. Boards creaked, a possum ran across the roof, a breeze stirred the leaves on the gum tree beside the stable. She was still awake when the horse and cart returned. She heard the jingle of the harness as Mr Jackson unsaddled the horse and the sound of him shutting the stable door, then coming into the house and up the stairs into the room he shared with Mrs Jackson, closing the door softly behind him.

When the moon rose and a swathe of moonlight cut across the room, she was still awake, listening intently for noises from downstairs, afraid to go to sleep, imagining that at any moment she would hear the sound of the chair crashing to the floor. Next the handle on her door would turn and the old man would come in, brandishing his walking stick.

She knew there was no way she could spend another night in the house with the old man. Even if she survived the night she would still be expected to take him out the next day. The fettlers had saved her once. But what if there were no fettlers? He might kill her.

Outside, the yard was bathed in moonlight. She looked out at the gum tree, wondering if she could get from the windowsill onto the roof of the stable and then climb down the tree's branches without being hurt.

She rose stealthily, afraid to make a noise. Her clothes were on a chair beside the bed and she tied them into a bundle in her blanket. Then she opened the window and climbed onto the windowsill. Holding her bundle in one hand and her boots in the other, she jumped onto the roof of the stable, terrified that the noise might wake up the household. She listened for a few moments. Except for Jezebel stirring in her stable, all was quiet. Dropping her boots and bundle to the ground, she climbed down the gum tree.

The moon had gone under a cloud and it was dark in the yard. Winifred leaned against the stable door and whispered, 'Goodbye, Jezebel. I'll miss you. I used to like it here ... but not any more.'

She could hear the rumble of the sanitary cart in the distance and knew it must be close to morning. She took a dress out of her bundle and pulled it over her nightgown and put on her stockings and boots. Then quickly, before the clouds parted and the moon came out again, she went out the front gate and began to run as fast as she could until she had turned the corner and was out of sight of the house.

10

HOMECOMING

WILFRED WOKE ONE MORNING to hear his daughter's voice calling. At first he thought he must be dreaming, but then he rose and opened the door to find her crouched on the doorstep, crying hysterically. It was hours before he could piece together the story of her escape.

'It was still dark when I got to the station ... I waited and caught the milk train. I only had four shillings and twopence and that only took me to Oakey Creek ... and then ... and then I had to walk ... A man at the station told me it was eighteen miles. I had nothing to eat and only drinks of water from the creek. When I got tired I lay down by the side of the road. And this morning I saw the barn with the red cow painted on the side that you told me about and knew I was nearly home.'

Her father had mixed feelings about her return, but just

the same he bathed her feet, which were blistered from the long walk, made her a cup of tea and some toast with jam and put her to bed.

Later, as she lay there watching her father shave, she asked, 'Are you angry with me?' she asked.

He put down his razor and, wiping the lather off his face with a towel, came and stood beside her. 'No, not angry. It's inconvenient, that's all. I don't come home every night — my work takes me all over the place. You were lucky to find me here. Today I'm starting a new job near Jondaryan. You'll have to look to yourself. I'll be late home … Don't worry, I'll bring a tin of beans. We can eat that for supper.'

Then, in a rare gesture of affection, he put out his hand and stroked her hair. 'It'll be nice having someone here at night. Sometimes when I'm on my own I find myself talking to the mice in the chimney … I hear them chittering and chattering away and imagine that they're talking about me, wondering how soon I'll be asleep so that they can come into the kitchen and raid the flourbag. I warn them I've set traps, but it doesn't seem to make any difference.' He laughed and she found herself laughing with him.

He bent and kissed her on the forehead and tucked the blanket around her. 'Welcome home. I've missed you.'

She slept again for a few hours until the heat of the day woke her. It took a few minutes to realise where she was as she gazed around the tin walls of the hut with holes cut out for windows. Sheets of bark secured to the iron with a strip of rawhide served as shutters, which were propped open with a length of sapling. There was a constant stream of flies in and out of the openings.

Winifred rose and walked to the door. Looking out, she saw a small patch of corn with a flock of cockatoos like large white flowers perched on the top of the cornstalks which swayed under their weight.

They were stripping the ripening cobs of corn and she ran towards them in her nightgown, waving a stick she picked up from the woodheap and calling, 'Shoo! Shoo!' The birds flew off in a cloud, circling overhead and squawking before settling on a tall gum tree.

Winifred picked up the cobs which had fallen to the ground, heaped them into the front of her nightgown and carried them inside, wondering where to put them. If she put them on the table the mice would eat them. She remembered seeing the meat safe hanging from a tree by the door and she piled the corn into this and fastened the wire door.

The kettle was half full of water; she poured a little into a tin dish and washed herself, then dressed. She pulled on her boots which were scuffed, the soles worn thin from the long hard walk from Oakey Creek. She wondered briefly whether she should try to go barefoot and keep her boots for best, but the ground outside was stony and there was a nest of ants by the door, and she knew there could be snakes in the long grass that grew around the corn patch. If her boots wore out she would ask her father to buy her new ones.

She went outside again and chased off the cockatoos that had returned to the corn patch. She wasn't sure of the time but thought it must be the middle of the day because the sun was almost directly overhead. She lit the fire and hung the iron pot over it to boil up a few corncobs, which she ate for lunch. There was no bread and after she had washed her plate and cleaned up the scraps from her meal she looked around for the flourbag.

She found it standing in an empty wooden cask which had a piece of bark held down with a large stone as a lid. She jumped back when she saw a mousetrap alongside with a dead mouse in it. She picked up the trap and threw it out the window. The next time she went outside she saw that the body was alive with large ants, and by evening there was nothing left except the skeleton.

That afternoon Winifred busied herself making a loaf of bread, mixing sugar and yeast from a bottle over the stove, absorbed as she kneaded the dough, covering it with a cloth once it was in the breadtin, smiling when she saw how it had risen. She punched it down and watched it rise again before placing it in the camp oven with hot coals in the lid, imagining her father's face when he saw the fresh bread on the table.

While it cooked she washed two empty flourbags which she hung to dry on the roof of the hut and then unpicked them and sewed them together to make a cloth for the table. There were some empty cornsacks in the corner which she also unpicked, before spreading them over the dirt floor as she had seen Aunt Lydia do. She thought about the pink shaded lamp and the Spanish silk shawls that Aunt Lydia had used to decorate their other house, but Winifred had only her white woollen shawl, and she needed that to keep her warm. And the only lamp was a little kerosene one with a clear glass cover and a discoloured brass base. Later she walked along the side of the road gathering yellow daisies which she placed in an empty pickle bottle in the centre of the table.

She was so absorbed in her efforts to improve the look of the tin hut, as well as trying to keep the cockatoos out of the corn, that she forgot all about the bread until she smelt it burning. She hastened to take the lid off the camp oven to find the bread had caught on the bottom. She felt like crying but scraped it with a knife and, wrapping it in a cloth, put it on the table.

She lit the lamp as the light faded outside and sat by the table waiting for her father until she heard the sound of his horse. With the lamp in her hand she walked to the fence where she undid the sliprail to let the sulky through.

Later, as they sat eating their meal of hot beans on bread, she saw her father glance at the floor. 'Cornsacks are worth money,' he said. 'I need them to store the corn in so that I can send it to be milled.'

'There were cockatoos. I tried to shoo them away but they kept on coming back. I picked up the cobs and put them in the meat safe.'

Her father jumped to his feet and, grabbing the lantern, ran outside where he saw the bruised and broken crop of corn. Winifred followed him out into the night. The moon was rising over the Great Dividing Range and she stood there watching it until her father picked up a length of wood and went crashing through the corn patch, where she could hear squeaking noises.

'Hell and damnation. This country will be the death of me … I lost the potato crop to the floods, but I thought … I hoped … that with the ground moist and the warmth of the sun … Is it too much to ask for a bit of corn that we can send to the mill and pay off the money we owe the storekeeper and have enough left to bake a few loaves of bread? It's hopeless. If it's not the cockatoos, it's the wallabies or the rats and mice.'

'I picked up what corn I could and put it in the meat safe away from the mice,' Winifred told him again.

'Well tomorrow you'd better pick what's left. I'll bring home something to scrape the corn off the cobs. There won't be enough to send to the mill. You'll have to do it with a hand mill. It's slow but you haven't got anything else to do. You'd best get to bed now. You'll have your work cut out tomorrow picking up what's left after the rats and mice have finished.'

Winifred's days fell into a pattern. She tried to keep the house clean, shaking the cornsacks she had used as floor coverings outside, emptying the dregs of the billy can onto the dirt to keep down the dust. There was wood to collect for the fire and she became adept at using an axe to split it into kindling. And she learned how to separate the corn from the cob and then crush the grain to make a coarse meal.

In the afternoons when Cobb and Co came by she would hang over the front fence to wave to the passengers. She was there one day when a sheet of newsprint flew from the upper deck of the coach and she ran out into the road to pick it up. It was the front and back pages of a magazine called *Life*, published by Shaw Fitchett, and she leaned on the fence reading the homely little stories about life in Australia. While she was setting the bread to rise she thought about what she had read and decided she could write just as well.

She had no proper writing paper, only a sheet of brown paper, and she used a flat carpenter's pencil to write her story about an imaginary incident when she was stung by a bee and applied a touch of the blue-bag as a remedy. The next time Cobb and Co came along the road she stopped the coach and asked the driver to post her letter to the publishers.

Two months later she received a copy of the magazine with her story in it with the title of 'A Rough Diamond' and a cheque for one pound. Her father was astonished when she showed him her story and his eyes glinted at the sight of the cheque. 'This will pay off what we owe the storekeeper,' and he put it in the empty bottle where he kept a few loose coins.

At his words her heart gave a sickening lurch and she turned on him. 'I have nothing, no clothes that fit, no boots. I work hard all day cleaning this place.' She waved her arms around the squalid tin hut. 'When I was in Drayton I was well fed and lived in a proper house with sheets, and now … and now, when I get some money to buy myself a few things, you take it.' She burst into tears and ran out into the night.

There was a chill wind blowing from the south and she shivered as she stood by the front gate, wrapping her arms around herself to keep warm. The sky was very dark and the stars hung low. She had a sudden memory of the night before they left England, when her father had tucked her into bed and said, 'No more rats on the roof and at night the sky will sparkle with diamonds.' The stars did look like diamonds. He had been right about that. But as for the rats, they must have followed them from London. They had come in their hundreds once they put the corn out to dry, running through the opening in the wall, over their beds at night, leaving droppings on the table, trying to burrow their way through the wooden cask to get to the flourbag, until her father moved the corn onto the roof of the ramshackle lean-to where the horses were stabled. And there were rat-traps set everywhere so that she had to be careful not to tread on them. The mice weren't so bad and once she found a nest with five naked little pink babies curled up with their eyes closed. When she showed it to her father he had grabbed a lump of wood and clubbed them to death and then scattered the nest, kicking the bodies into a patch of grass, saying, 'The ants'll have a feast.'

'But they were only babies,' the girl said with tears in her eyes.

'In this world it's dog eat dog. Everything feeds off something else. It's them or us.'

Now as her eyes became accustomed to the light she could see the shapes of trees and the outline of the sulky. She was still angry with her father, though her mood had softened. But instead of going inside she climbed into the sulky and tried to settle herself to sleep. It was no use. Her mind kept going back to London. There was Mrs Watkins who never had anything for herself. All her earnings went on food for the family, and Aggie who wanted to get married but couldn't afford to. Her father had kept her mother and her in comfort with clothes to wear and food to eat. She had taken it all for granted and now, when she had earned some real money and could help her father, she wanted to spend it all on herself. She had chosen to come with him to Australia … She thought of the cold in England, how her breath came out like steam when she ran to school in winter and how her hands felt as if they would fall off because they were so cold. It was cold here in winter too, but it was different. The sun shone and in the middle of the day you could walk around in the open and feel it warming your bones.

Curled up on the hard seat of the sulky she felt chilled through. Inside was her bed with its warm blanket and pillow. She wondered if her father was still awake; the lamp had gone out a long time ago. She climbed down from the sulky, and the horses stirred. She heard an owl hooting from a gum tree beside the road and the sound of mice squeaking in the heap of corncobs drying on the roof of the stable. Then, picking her way carefully through the grass in case she trod on a snake, she made her way back to the hut, opened the door stealthily and crept into bed, where she snuggled into her blankets trying to get warm until she fell into a deep dreamless sleep.

Her father had already left when she woke. She no longer felt angry with him and had made up her mind to let him have the money to pay off the bills, certain that she could write more stories and get paid for them until they had all the money they needed.

When she heard her father returning in his sulky, she went and opened the gate as usual, feeling apprehensive in case he was angry with her. Instead he greeted her cheerfully and handed her a newspaper packet. 'Be careful with those ... a woman gave me some eggs. We'll fry them up for tea.' She shut the gate after him and took the eggs into the kitchen where she laid them carefully on the table. She got out the black iron frying pan and put some dripping in the bottom, waiting until her father had unharnessed the horses and had a wash before she put it on the fire.

Later, he said, 'The woman who gave me the eggs has got a sister who's a dressmaker. She's here on a holiday and wants to earn some money. She brought some piece goods with her. The postmistress said to bring you in on Saturday and she'll cash your cheque. Then you can get the things you need.'

The news of Winifred's success travelled along the grapevine, particularly when the editor of *Life* wrote, urging her to send in another story, which they subsequently published. She kept on writing, buying clothes and little luxuries with the money she earned.

By the time she was fifteen she had become known as 'that clever little Miss Oaten' and found herself being invited to afternoon tea in some of the more affluent households, often staying overnight because she had no way of travelling except on foot.

She was still shy in company but her new clothes had given her confidence, and when she was asked what she found to write about, her face lit up and her grey–green eyes shone. 'I'm very fond of crows. If you see them sitting on a branch … they're like people … They talk to one another, squabble, fight … They're so beautiful. Lots of people don't like them but I do.'

She was at the manager's homestead at Jondaryan where she had been invited by Mrs Williams, the manager's wife, to meet the mother of an itinerant minister. The woman was staying at Jondaryan while her son visited the stations further out to marry couples and baptise children.

The two women exchanged glances at Winifred's words and Mrs Williams said, 'Fancy that, crows now. They're such an ugly bird. My husband shoots them, vermin he calls them … make a terrible mess of the wheat.'

'But they're still God's creatures.' The minister's mother smiled at Winifred. 'Everything in this world was created by God.'

Winifred wanted to ask if that meant fleas, mice, rats and snakes, but she didn't like to argue with this staid woman in her black dress and bonnet. Fleas were beastly because they burrowed into your blankets and kept you awake at night. And she hated rats. And she didn't care for snakes. One morning she had watched a huge brown snake slide across her bed while her father whispered, 'Don't move or speak.' The snake kept going until it slithered through a hole in the wall.

She was going to tell them about the time she saw ten crows standing in a circle around a dead crow. The birds looked so solemn that she thought they must be holding a funeral, but then she looked at the minister's mother and decided she might not like it. She was intimidated by her, though she liked Mrs Williams and often spent the night at the station telling stories to the children, tucking them into bed and walking back home after breakfast. And when Mrs Williams had her last baby Winifred stayed for six weeks.

Now Mrs Williams turned to her. 'Winifred, be a dear, run into the kitchen and get another cup and saucer. Mr Williams said he'd be in for tea.'

The young woman did as she was asked and was on the way down the hall to the sitting room when she heard the older woman say, 'She's a clever little thing and nicely spoken. Who are her people?'

'Oh, she doesn't have people as such, only a father. He does a few painting jobs for my husband. When there's no work here he travels around doing odd jobs. He's got a small holding. They came from London. I try to have her over as often as I can.'

'Well, I hope she finds a good husband ... she's got a nice way with her and such a pretty face.'

Then they heard her coming and changed the subject.

Winifred enjoyed walking round Jondaryan, watching the shearers and the blacksmith working at his forge. There was the smell of fresh bread from the bakery, and they killed their own meat so that there was fresh meat every night and fresh eggs for breakfast. Sometimes she walked the children, who were not yet at school, down to the dairy to watch the cows being milked and to drink a tumbler of warm foamy milk. Other times she took them to a paddock where yellow daisies grew among the lucerne and showed them how to make daisy chains.

Everyone called her Miss Oaten and she felt very grown-up. One day she was invited to a party at Jondaryan. She wore her dimity dress and joined in the dancing, thinking back to that first dance when she had run away because everyone had laughed at her in her peculiar black dress. Now young men wanted to talk to her, and she was flattered when Charles, the young man who played the piano accordion for the dances, invited her onto the verandah to take supper with him.

'I haven't seen you at the dances before,' he said as he handed her a glass of lemon cordial and a slice of cream sponge on a plate.

'I've been working in Toowoomba,' she replied. 'Now I live with my father near Bowenville. I'm staying at the homestead.'

'I've been watching you. I like the way you move ... as if you've got music in your soul. And you've got the most beautiful eyes.'

Winifred felt the colour rising in her cheeks. No one had ever spoken to her like that before. He was older than she was, with a lean, strong body and a suntanned face, and she felt his grey eyes gazing into hers as if he could read her thoughts. She felt tongue-tied, not knowing how to answer.

'Can I walk you home?'

'But it's only across the paddock to the house.'

'We'll go the long way,' and he laughed, seeing her confusion, then undid the blue ribbon she had tied around her hair and tucked it into his pocket. 'Wait for me out here.' Then he went back to the makeshift stage where the people crowded around eagerly waiting for the music to begin again.

She remained where she was, listening to the music and gazing across the paddock to where hurricane lamps glowed on fence posts. The night had begun to close in and it looked like rain. Mrs Williams came to the door. 'There you are, my dear. They've finished their supper. Would you help me carry the things back to the house. There's some cakes left ... the children will have a feast tomorrow.'

Winifred did as she was asked and was in bed when she heard the sound of horses leaving and people saying goodbye. She wondered if the young man had waited for her on the verandah; she felt a little disappointed, yet was glad that she had come back early, not sure what he had meant about taking her the long way home and sensing that Mrs Williams would not have approved.

Winifred stayed on at Jondaryan after the dance, knowing she was welcome, the days lengthening into weeks, not admitting to herself that she was hoping to meet the young man again.

Mrs Williams was glad of her help and gave the girl an old riding habit which she had altered to fit, then told the stablehand to find her a quiet horse so that she could go riding with the children.

It was a blissful time for Winifred as she rode through the paddocks in the early morning, once going down past the shearers' huts that lined the river bank in the hope of catching a glimpse of the young man from the dance. Instead she was embarrassed to see so many men sitting naked to the waist with their shaving mugs and razors, trimming their beards. And further out in the river she could see men swimming, and fancied they were naked. She heard one man say, 'That's a fine filly,' and wasn't sure whether he was talking about her or her horse. She turned and flicked the reins and her bay mare cantered away.

That night over dinner Mr Williams said, 'There's a young man in the woolshed asking after you.'

Winifred felt her colour rise and concentrated on eating her slice of baked jam roll.

'His name's Charles Steger. I think he's sweet on you,' Mr Williams laughed. Then, seeing her confusion, he changed the subject and began to talk about the wool clip.

The next day her father sent over a message that he needed her at home.

* * *

Winifred missed the comforts of life at Jondaryan and the sound of the children's voices as they clustered around her bed in the morning, hoping for a story. Now she had to fend for herself, make her own bread, eat a solitary meal with only the crickets for company and the sound of cattle moving through the grass. Her father had bought a mob of cattle. He wanted her to look after them while he was away working in the far north-west. He had also bought two horses so that she could muster the cattle and ride into town for supplies.

She had objected bitterly when she found out her father was planning to leave her there to manage alone. 'I know nothing about cattle!' she cried.

'You don't need to know anything. All you have to do is to watch that they don't get out. I'll be back when it's time to get them to the saleyards. It's been a good season. There's plenty of feed. If I can make some money I can improve the property.'

It was a hard and lonely life for the young girl. She was afraid of the cattle and found the horses were difficult to look after. Sometimes she tethered them on a long rope, afraid to let them loose in case they swam across the creek that bounded their property on one side, or got caught up in the prickly pear that had taken over the back of the land. She knew that if one of the sharp spikes of the pear penetrated the horses' kneecaps they would go lame. Then there would be nothing to be done except wait for the spike to work its way out the other side, and that could take months.

Her father sent her money from time to time so that she could buy chaff for the horses to supplement the grass, which was over her head in some places, though the cattle soon ate it down to a stubble — then she had to move them to another part of the property until the grass grew again. The slight young woman found it difficult, seated on a horse that had a mind of his own, to move the beasts, many of them wild cattle that had escaped into the prickly pear and found their way onto the road. Unlike the horses the cattle were impervious to the prickly pear because of their thick hides.

Each night before she turned out the kerosene lamp Winifred would thank God that she was still alive. Once a bull calf went berserk and charged her horse, grazing him on the side. The horse gave a dreadful whinny of pain and bolted towards the house. He cleared the sliprail in one bound and went galloping along the dirt road while she pulled on the reins, calling, 'Whoa! Whoa, Ginger!' until the horse ran under a low-spreading tree and she was thrown off. The horse came to a halt about a hundred yards away. When Winifred had recovered from the spill she limped to where Ginger was standing, foam around his mouth and a deep red gash in his side from the horn of the bull. Weak and trembling, Winifred led him along the road and back into their property, where she put him in the stable and filled his nosebag with chaff, wiping the sweat from his coat and shooing away the flies that were worrying the open wound. Then she went into the hut and returned with a handful of dripping, which she spread on the horse's flank to cover the cut, not knowing what else to do.

The incident frightened her and made her angry because her father had left her there to cope alone with fences that had gaping holes, a mixture of tame and wild cattle which she had no hope of controlling, and two stupid horses that were impossible to ride. When she went inside the hut to make herself a meagre meal that night, she put her head on the table and wept tears of frustration and rage.

Her father came home on Christmas Eve. She had made no special preparations, not expecting him, and was surprised when she heard him call out, 'Come and open the sliprails. I've got a surprise for you.'

The surprise turned out to be a dingo pup. He handed the pup down to her from the sulky and she took the small creature in her arms. He was thin, with yellow eyes, and she regarded him with mixed feelings. She would have preferred something small and fluffy like a kitten.

'He's from a wild litter. I got him from one of the natives where I was working in exchange for a few twists of tobacco. He won't need feeding. He can fend for himself, there's plenty of rabbits.'

Winifred put the dog down and he ran round in circles, sniffing the ground. She began to laugh and her father joined in. 'I thought you might be lonely here by yourself. The dog'll be company and he can keep the cattle in order.' He took a length of rope out of the sulky and fastened the dog to a tree near the hut. 'He can stay there until he gets used to the place, otherwise he might run off.'

The girl picked up an empty tin from the pile of rubbish behind the hut and filled it with water from the tank. As soon as she put it beside the dog, he began to lap thirstily. 'There's a star called after a dog … But Sirius is too big a word for a little scrap like you … I'll call you Star,' and she bent and patted him.

Then she followed her father into the hut where he unpacked his swag. First he put a pudding tied in a cloth on the table. 'A plum duff the cook made, and here's a shoulder of smoked bacon from when they killed a pig. And I picked up some chops from the butcher on the way through. We'd best eat them tonight before they go off in the heat. The dog can have the scraps.'

As she listened to her father Winifred thought he seemed happier than she'd seen him for a long time. Once they had eaten he carried two chairs outside where it was cool and lit a little fire downwind, piling on green leaves so that the smoke would keep the mosquitoes away. And then he lit his pipe and lapsed into silence.

To Winifred it seemed as if they were the only two people in the world as she sat listening to the ripple of sound from the bush, the once alien calls that had now become part of her life. A frog croaked in the water tank. An owl hooted in a gum tree, the horses stirred in the barn. The only new sound was that of the puppy which began to whimper when a dingo howled in the distance, until he finally settled back to sleep.

Wilfred blew a cloud of smoke from his pipe. 'Things have been hard for you here on your own. It won't be for much longer. I'm making good money and in a little while I'll be able to build a better house. But first I need to fence in another paddock and get some dairy cows — now that the cheese factory's opened there's a good market. They tell me they're sending cheese to England.'

'It's a long way. Won't it go bad?'

'Not as long as it goes in the coolroom.'

'Would you like to go back to England?'

'No, there's nothing there for me.'

'What about my mother?' Winifred was surprised at her temerity. 'Why didn't she come with us?'

Her father was silent for a while, drawing on his pipe and looking into the distance. 'She said … she said I was too much of a Don Juan for her. And she wouldn't take any more of it. That's what she said to me before she left the ship.'

Winifred saw him swallow and for a moment she thought he was going to cry. 'I don't understand.'

'She said I looked at other women, but I didn't, I loved your mother. She didn't love me. We only stayed together because of you.'

'Did she love me?'

Wilfred rose and went inside the hut, returning with a bottle of whisky and a glass. He poured some of the liquid into the glass and drank it down in one gulp. 'I don't know … I really don't know. She gave you life, perhaps that's all we should expect.'

That night Winifred dreamt she was back in London walking beside Mrs Watkins with her barrow. It was Christmas Eve and the shops were glowing with coloured candles and there was mistletoe. Suddenly an urchin ran up and kissed Mrs Watkins on the cheek and called, 'Happy Christmas!'

'Be off with you, you little rascal,' and she threw a speckled apple at him, which he caught and began to bite into while juice ran down his chin. Mrs Watkins walked on, laughing. And then Winifred saw her mother hurrying ahead. Her father caught up with her and tried to take her arm, but Louisa shook him off. Winifred could tell that she was angry.

When she woke in the morning her father was still asleep. She remembered that it was Christmas Day. She heard the sound of the puppy whimpering and ran outside, where she saw the empty whisky bottle lying on its side. She carried it around to the pile of rubbish and then ran over to the little dog and hugged him.

'Merry Christmas,' she said. 'You don't know anything about that, but there's a nice bacon bone for your lunch and a piece of plum duff.'

On New Year's Eve they were invited to Jondaryan to celebrate Hogmanay. Winifred dressed carefully, brushing her hair until it shone, and tying it with a red ribbon. She pinched her cheeks to put colour in them and bit her lips to make them red. She was filled with anticipation at seeing Charles Steger again, but she was disappointed. Someone played the pipes for dancing, and though she enjoyed the Eightsome Reels and the Dashing White Sergeant, without Charles the evening fell flat.

It was six weeks before Wilfred went away again. He spent the time repairing fences while Winifred tried to hold the wire taut as he hammered in small pieces of wire which he twisted into barbs with a pair of pliers, railing at her when the wire twisted out of her hands, until she would dissolve into tears and run back to the hut while he called after her, 'You're not worth your salt.'

Every day he made her take the horses for a run. 'You have to let them know who's boss. I can't afford to keep lazy beasts hanging around the paddocks all day, eating their heads off when there's work to be done.'

If she had a fall he'd make her get on again, until one day she said angrily, 'It's all right for you. You don't have to ride a horse. You drive around in your sulky like the King of England.'

He gave her a stinging blow on the leg with a stick. Instead of crying she stood and faced him. 'I may be your daughter but I am also a woman. I don't deserve to be hit. You have made my life hell. Taken me from a place I liked … Mrs Williams was kind to me. No wonder my mother left you.'

Wilfred stared after her as she went into the hut and came out dressed in her riding habit. She went into the paddock and caught Ginger and put the saddle and bridle on him, then led the horse to the sliprails while her father stood watching. 'Open the sliprails,' she said and he obeyed. Without saying goodbye she kicked the horse's rump and Ginger went cantering down the road in the direction of Jondaryan.

Later she marvelled at her actions and how Ginger had obeyed her. She reasoned that it was because she had been so angry, too angry to be afraid of the horse, too angry to be afraid of her father. She could earn her own living, except that he needed her to look after the cattle for him. It was always what she could do for him. He had never considered her needs — to go to school, to have books to read and people to talk to.

They never mentioned the quarrel again. She returned home the next morning wondering if he would still be there. When he heard the sound of her horse outside he came out of the hut, opened the sliprails and helped her to dismount. 'We're out of bread,' was all he said. 'There's some damper if you're hungry. The fire's going and the billy's on the boil.'

She changed into her working clothes and made some tea, carrying it down to the paddock where her father was working, calling to Star to follow her, though he went streaking in the opposite direction after a rabbit instead.

Before he left her father said, 'I don't know when I'll be back. It's a long way to where I'm going. Way past Charleville and I can't drive the horse too hard ... There's a good job waiting for me. There'll be odd jobs to do and I'll be helping the manager hand out the rations and doing the ordering. I'd take you with me if you weren't needed to mind this place. If you want anything you can always ride over to Jondaryan. But you mustn't leave the place, not overnight. The dog'll keep you company.'

Winifred stood at the sliprails, holding the lantern as her father drove through and onto the dirt road, with Ginger tethered to the sulky. 'Because I need a spare horse,' he had said.

She kept quiet, knowing that he always did what suited him, without any thought for her, angry that he had taken her best horse.

Now he paused and, leaning down, touched her lightly on the head with the handle of his whip. 'Be good,' he said and then he called to the horses and they went trotting down the road and out of sight.

She heard Star growling and whistled, and the dog came bounding through the bush and lay panting at her feet. Winifred bent to pat him and he licked her face. 'You're all I've got now, Star. You mustn't run away and leave me.'

He followed her down the path to the hut, where she tied him up beside the door. Then she went inside. The sun had risen and she blew out the lamp and put it on the table beside the remains of her father's hurried breakfast. Instead of washing the dishes, and putting the bread away, as she normally did, she threw herself on her bed and, seething with rage and resentment, began to weep bitterly.

II

FALLING IN LOVE

THE NEXT WEEK WINIFRED RODE INTO town on Topsy, the horse her father had left her. Winifred knew it would be a slow ride because the old mare would travel in circles and go down on one leg if they met anyone on a horse. When she had asked her father about Topsy he had said, 'I got her for a song. She was trained in a circus. The owners had a soft spot for her and threw the saddle in. She'll do — you just have to learn how to handle her.'

The horse was in a docile mood and they met no one else on the road. By the time they got to town Winifred felt very relaxed and she patted the old horse as she tied her to the hitching post in front of the post office. She was hoping for a letter from Shaw Fitchett. But she was disappointed. She had sent in a story about her life with the cattle. It was the first piece she had written for a long time because she had been kept so busy. Now, with the fences mended the cattle no longer strayed, and she occupied herself by writing, finding that it helped her overcome her feeling of isolation.

As she was leaving the building she paused to read a notice advertising a dance at the local hall on Saturday. She read it a second time. The idea of going to a dance tempted her. Except for riding into town to check the mail and buy supplies, she met no one. She knew her father would not approve of her going alone to a dance, but she put that thought out of her mind. He was far away and would never find out.

When she arrived at the dance she felt sorry she had come. Standing alone at the door she felt shy and awkward, trying to pluck up the courage to go in. And then she saw Charles Steger. He was playing the accordion and her heart began to beat faster. He looked up and smiled, and beckoned to her to come in. With heightened colour she skirted the dancers until she was beside him. There was a vacant chair and she sat down until someone asked her to dance and she joined in.

Later Charles asked if he could ride home with her and so they set off, her horse going down on one leg whenever they met a horse coming the other way, until Charles took the reins and pulled savagely on Topsy's bit. He brought his horse to a halt and lifted Winifred onto his mount's back then set off again, Charles holding Topsy's reins in one hand while Winifred gripped him round the waist. Each time Topsy went down on one leg he struck the horse with his whip, making Winifred flinch.

'It's the only thing they understand. You've got to let them see who's boss,' he said.

When they reached Winifred's gate, Charles let down the sliprail and led Topsy into the stable, where she lashed out with one leg and narrowly missed him. '*Mein Gott*, that horse's not fit to ride!' he said. 'I'll come over some time and give it a lesson it won't forget.'

Then he lifted Winifred down and she was assailed with the raw male smell of him — of sweat and tobacco and horseflesh — as he held her to him briefly. 'Next week I'll call for you in the waggon. I'll ask my father to lend it to me.'

She whistled to Star who came bounding through the paddock and began to dance around her legs until Charles put out his hand and the dog drew back and snarled. 'Where did you get this vermin?' he asked, kicking out with his foot. 'I've a good mind to shoot it.'

Winifred bent and put her arms around the little dog. 'My father gave him to me, he's mine.'

'Your father should have known better. Dingoes are no good. They kill sheep, goats, chickens. The government pays people to shoot them, and there's a dingo fence to keep them out. You won't have him long. You'll find his scalp hanging on someone's belt.'

Winifred stared at him, a stricken look on her face.

'Don't worry. As soon as he's old enough he'll run off to join the pack.' He bent and kissed the tip of her nose. 'I can see there's a lot I have to teach you.' He walked out the gate, closing it behind him, and jumped on his horse. With a flourish of his whip and a wide grin he went galloping down the road.

The dances in the district continued, with Winifred a familiar figure at Charles's side, until she soon became known as Charlie's girl. The first time she heard it her heart swelled with pride.

At first he said goodbye at the sliprail, until one night there was a heavy storm. He drove the waggon through the gate and ran with Winifred into the hut to take shelter from the rain. She made some tea and sliced some bread while he waited for the thunder and lightning to abate.

It was still raining an hour later, the sound of thunder combining with the noise of rain on the tin roof, the little hut lit by sheets of vivid lightning one minute and then only the flickering light from the candle the next. A wind sprang up and a shutter blew open. Winifred jumped onto her bed, struggling to close the shutter until Charles leant across and pulled it tight. Then he turned her to face him and she found herself in his arms. She made no attempt to free herself, feeling the heat rising in her body as he began to kiss her face, her throat, her hands. Then he pulled her down onto the bed and she felt powerless to resist as he undressed her, whispering, 'I love you. I love you. I love you.'

When she woke the next morning he had gone and she wondered if she had dreamt it, until she saw her clothes lying in a puddle of water on the floor where the rain had trickled in under the door. She looked outside. Steam was rising from the ground as the sun drew up the moisture and the grass glistened with dew. She put on her riding habit and went to the barn to saddle the horse. Then she rode to the bottom boundary where she could hear Star worrying the cattle, her heart singing as she remembered the night before and the sound of Charles's voice whispering, 'I love you.'

Winifred was to see Charles twice more when he came to call for her in the waggon to take her to a dance. She had made up her mind not to ask him into the house again until they had made plans for their wedding, but when he stopped by the side of the road and held her in his arms and kissed her, before laying her down on blankets in the back of the waggon, she was unable to resist, knowing that she wanted him as much as he wanted her. She had fallen hopelessly in love, and her whole life centred around Charles and how soon she would see him again.

And then, without any warning, he stopped coming. She waited for him by the gate, running out each time she heard the sound of horses' hooves; she even enquired after him at the store, where she was told that he had gone away with a team to prepare for shearing. Though she refused to admit it to herself, she could not block out the thought that he had deserted her.

Weeks went by and she began to feel sick in the morning, putting it down to her disappointment that Charles had not written. But then her waistline began to thicken and she was seized with terror. She knew that she was going to have a child and, even worse, her lover had abandoned her. She wondered how she could have been so foolish. She had done wrong and now she was going to be punished.

She remembered hearing snatches of whispered conversations between her mother and Mrs Watkins and she tried to remember the remedies they had talked about. She'd heard of a man in Lambeth who fixed women up and how a girl who worked at the steam laundry with Aggie had been to see him and died and they found her body floating in the Thames.

Winifred had no one she could go to for advice. She had not seen her Aunt Lydia since she and William had left her father's house. And in any case she would be too ashamed to show herself, knowing that Uncle William would find out and sneer at her. There was Mrs Williams at Jondaryan, but she knew she could never face her. The only other person was the postmistress who had cashed her cheque, but she was a gossip who couldn't keep a secret.

She became a recluse, letting the cattle wander at will, living on tea and damper when her supply of tinned goods had run out. She still nursed the hope that Charles would return once the shearing had finished and they would be married and all would be well, until one night she woke from a vivid dream. She had been on her bay mare, flying high above the trees, her hair streaming in the wind. Far below she could see the cattle standing in her father's paddock, the smoke curling lazily from the chimney of their hut, and beyond it the creek, brown after rain. As her horse carried her higher and higher she laughed, feeling an incredible sense of lightness. She was free. Behind her she could hear Charles on his black stallion and she glanced over her shoulder, her eyes sparkling, daring him to catch her. She heard his laughter and the crack of his stockwhip. Then she felt an incredible pain as the whip snaked around her waist. The next thing she was falling. She woke with a feeling of unease, wondering how she would manage if Charles didn't return.

Winifred was seven months' pregnant when her father returned home. She was lying down in the hut when she heard the sound of horses at the front gate. For a moment she imagined that Charles had returned. Charles who had told her she was beautiful ... words that touched her heart because he loved her. She thought back to her pride when she had heard people say, 'That's Charlie's girl,' knowing herself to be wanted and loved. Everything was going to be all right. He had come to get her.

She smoothed her hair and took off the apron made of sugar bags which she had wrapped around her spreading figure, feeling clumsy and awkward, wondering how he would react when he saw her and whether he would still love her. She hesitated in the doorway. She had lost the slim waist he had admired. Her hair was matted and she had grown out of her dress that was stretched tightly across her stomach. She did not know whether she could bear to face him looking the way she did.

Suddenly she hated him, hated him for what he'd done to her. He had said he loved her and then had gone without a word. Just then she heard her father's voice. 'Winifred, will you come and open this blasted gate.' She looked around with a feeling of terror, wondering where she could hide, but there was nowhere. Her father had been away a long time. He did not know about her and Charles. If only Charles had come, they could have faced her father together.

Winifred heard her father call again. She grabbed a blanket from her bed, wrapped it around her like a shawl and went to meet him.

As she opened the sliprail and dragged it back so that her father could drive through, the blanket slipped. But her father was intent on unharnessing the horses and unpacking a roll of fencing wire and a few supplies for the house. It wasn't until she said, 'I'll put the billy on,' and she turned to go into the hut that he really looked at her. She had grown heavier and there was something different about her gait. He grabbed her by the wrist and spun her around to face him. He took in the distended stomach with a look of shock. 'You filthy slut! You've been with a man!' And he forced her to her knees. 'Who was it? I'll kill him!'

Winifred crouched there, hiding her face, until he brought his whip savagely across her shoulders. She screamed and made an effort to rise, but he held her fast. 'I'll find out his name if I have to beat it out of you.'

She began to cry. Great gulping sobs, holding him around the knees, her face hidden, until he pulled her up and helped her into the hut. Bit by bit he dragged the story out of her. Later, his face like a thunder cloud, he forced her into the sulky and drove her to the Steger farm at Evergreen, where Barbara Steger and her daughters were in the kitchen making *knockenbrot*. Wilfred stepped up to the fence and called out, 'Come out, you German swine, and see what your son has done to my daughter. He'll marry her or I'll shoot him.'

The women came out, hands covered in flour, and the older woman sent Kate running to fetch Vater Carl. Winifred sat in the buggy, tears streaming down her face, wishing she was dead, while Charles's mother and sister stared at her with undisguised hostility.

PART TWO

12

THE GERMAN CONNECTION

IT WAS A MONTH BEFORE CHARLES STEGER could be located and 'persuaded' to return home to marry Winifred. There was a bitter little ceremony in St John's Church of England, Dalby, which the groom's family refused to attend. Wilfred Oaten and the wife of the presiding minister, the Reverend W Maitland Woods, were the only witnesses.

Winifred wore a voluminous black dress her father had brought home 'to hide her shame'. She hated it. It reminded her of the dress she had worn to her first dance at Jondaryan when everyone had laughed at her. Black was the colour of death and she wondered if this was an omen. She had often imagined her wedding dress and thought of something soft and light, a dress that floated around her slim figure, not this outsized black bombazine that made her look old and ugly.

The minister had interviewed Winifred when her father brought her to meet him before the wedding. She had felt affronted when he said, 'You have sinned, my daughter, like a woman taken in adultery. The child will be a constant reminder of your fall from grace, but like a loving father God will forgive you if you truly repent. Your father tells me that the father of the child is Charles Steger and that he will marry you. Will you promise to be an obedient wife, looking to your husband for guidance and being faithful to him?'

Winifred had felt her cheeks burning with indignation. She hung her head, afraid that the tears filling her eyes would spill down her cheeks. She wanted to scream, 'I did what I did because I was in love. I don't want to get married to a man who doesn't love me.' Instead she remained silent, biting back the words, knowing that she had not been wanton, only weak. It was her father's fault. It was he who had taken her from a good situation where she was respected and cared for, he who had gone away and left her alone. If he had looked after her properly this would never have happened.

When the minister asked her age, her father had answered for her. 'Nineteen. Old enough to be married.' Lying to suit himself. The truth was that Winifred was barely seventeen and her bridegroom twenty-eight when she was married off on 7 December 1899.

Winifred had not seen Charles for months and when he came and stood beside her at the altar she averted her gaze, wondering whether he still cared for her or whether he was angry. But when he took her hand in his and said, 'With this ring I thee wed,' and she felt the warmth of his large work-roughened hand, she raised her eyes. He returned her gaze but there was no love there, only a look of undisguised contempt. A wave of nausea swept over her and she thought she was going to faint, until the minister's wife put her arm around her shoulders and led her into the vestry where she was able to rest for a few minutes while they signed the register.

Outside the church her father gave her a perfunctory peck on the cheek. 'Well that's done and you're a married woman. Good luck in your new life.' He pointed to a bank of dark clouds. 'I'd best be getting home. If the creek rises I might be stuck.' He nodded to Charles. 'See that you take good care of my daughter.'

As Wilfred turned to leave, Winifred took him by the arm. 'Can't I come home with you?'

'Don't be so stupid. You're a married woman now. Your home is with your husband,' and he ran to his sulky, climbed in and called to his horse, which took off down the main street at a smart trot.

Winifred stared after him and then back at Charles, who was leaning on the fence. 'I don't want to get a soaking, I'm off. Suit yourself whether you come or not,' and he started to walk towards the waggon.

She followed him clumsily, knowing she had no choice. He pushed her up into the waggon and leapt up himself, then drove off hard over the unmade road, slashing the horses with his whip. At each blow she flinched, certain that the anger was directed at her.

They reached the farm and the shelter of the house as the storm broke. The family was already seated at the table when

Charles led his bride into the dining room. Thunder rumbled and sheets of vivid lightning lit up the little room and the paddocks until it looked like daylight.

Winifred was conscious of Charles's mother, who looked at her coldly and waved her towards a long wooden form that ran the length of the table. She sat down clumsily, supporting her back with both hands, and lowered her eyes, biting back the tears. Someone pushed a plate in front of her with some cold sausage and a slice of black bread. She felt she would choke if she tried to eat. The noise of rain on the iron roof drowned out all other sounds. No one spoke.

When the meal was over the women rose and carried the plates and food into the kitchen while the men stood in the doorway smoking, all except Charles who strode out into the yard and rode off on his horse.

The storm passed and the men went outside. Winifred could hear them talking. She walked to the door. It was cooler now. The rain had brought relief from the heat. It was a black night and there were no stars. She stood breathing in the smell of wet earth and listening to frogs croaking. Then she returned to the table and sat alone until Charles's sister Kate came into the room carrying a lighted lamp.

'Mutter said to bring in your things.'

'What things?'

'Your linen … your blankets … your cups and saucers.'

'I have no things. Only my clothes.' Winifred's voice was barely audible and she wondered if Charles's sister had understood, but then she heard her voice in the kitchen. 'She has no things, only what she is wearing. These dom Britishers. We work hard. That man … her father … is feckless. His fences fall down, his crops fail and now he has wished his daughter on us and he sends her with nothing ... *Mein Gott,* how do we know Charles is *die vater* of her *kind*? It could be anyone's.'

The family prepared for bed and the house became quiet and all the while Winifred sat there. Then finally she was forced by her bladder, to stumble out to the privy in the backyard, feeling her way over the wet path until her eyes became accustomed to the light. She was sitting on the back doorstep when Charles rode in. He unharnessed his horse and hobbled it and almost fell over Winifred. '*Gott im himmel*! What are you doing out here?'

'I didn't know where to go ... I have no blankets.'

He helped her to her feet and led her inside to where a length of hessian hung in a corner by the stove. He moved aside the curtain to reveal a stretcher. 'This is where I sleep when I'm home. You can have the bed.'

'But where will you sleep?'

He took one of the blankets and spread it on the floor, then lay down. 'There's a slab hut ... It's where Mutter and Vater lived when they first came from Germany. Vater says we can have it.' Then he turned over, grunted a couple of times and began to snore.

Winifred lay on the narrow bed, trying to get comfortable and listening to the night noises. The frogs were still croaking and there were mosquitoes buzzing, and somewhere inside a bed creaked. She heard the murmur of voices but couldn't make out what they were saying. There was a clock ticking on a shelf in the kitchen and outside a cow was bellowing. She recognised the sound from the time she had been at Mrs

Smith's. It meant that the cow needed a bull. She fell asleep some hours later and woke to hear a rooster crowing in the yard.

It took her a few moments to realise where she was and then she looked down to where Charles had been sleeping. His blanket had been folded and there was no sign of him. She pulled on her black dress and boots and stepped into the kitchen. The table was set for breakfast and the kettle was boiling on the stove. She realised how hungry she was and cut a piece off a loaf of black bread, eating it as she walked to the door and out into the yard. There she saw Charles's sisters cleaning out the dairy, with the cows ambling back to the paddock, while Vater Carl was harnessing the horse to the waggon, which was filled with gleaming milk cans.

Winifred saw him looking at her, then he said something to his daughters in German and the young wife picked out the words 'dom Britisher'.

As Carl Steger drove out of the yard, the milk cans rattling in the waggon, Kate called out to Winifred, 'Vater said, "*Gott im himmel*, what have we done to deserve this dom Britisher. We work hard … dom Britishers, their fences fall down and their cows go unmilked." Vater says, "In this house you only eat if you work."' She pointed to Winifred's stomach, 'Look at you, you're useless.' And she picked up a pail of milk and carried it into the house.

Winifred didn't reply. She realised, as if for the first time, that this would be her life from now on, living with Charles's family on a small block of land with neighbours so close that if you walked to the end paddock you could throw a stone onto the roof of the next house. She wondered how long her new family would go on hating her and whether she would ever be accepted.

Her husband was nowhere to be seen. She had no idea whether he worked on the farm or for someone else and there was no one to ask. She could feel the child kicking in her womb and she put her hand on her stomach, thinking that it was all her own fault. She had believed Charles when he said he loved her. Now she was certain that he hated her because her father had made him marry her. And yet he had treated her with some kindness, letting her sleep in his bed. Perhaps when they moved into their own place things would be better.

And then Charles's mother emerged from the privy, saying, '*Guten morgen*. There's no time to stand and stare.' She gave Winifred a hard look. 'After *frühstück* you can make *das brot*. You do know how to make *das brot*?'

Winifred looked at her, puzzled. 'I'm not sure what *das brot* is.'

Barbara made a gesture of impatience. '*Das brot … das* bread.'

Winifred nodded.

'*Gut*,' and the older woman went into the kitchen while Winifred followed. She handed her an apron, then pointed to the table. 'Sit. Last *nacht* you took no food. You must eat … for the *kind*.' She lifted a piece of smoked bacon from the meat safe and cut off a slice. 'Here … it is *gut mit brot*. After go to the dairy and get a cup of milk. Once *das brot* is set you can feed the fowls and there's whey to give to the pigs.'

'What shall I call you?' Winifred asked.

'Mutter Barbara,' she said as she bustled off to make the beds and tidy the house, while Winifred sat in the kitchen with an aching back, hardly able to walk for the pain in her legs, knowing that there was no chance of escape until after the child was born. She was terrified of what lay ahead and yet afraid to ask questions because she knew she was only there on sufferance. It was as if she had wished herself on Charles and that it was all her fault that she was having a child. She was married to the man she had once thought she loved and it was nothing like she had imagined.

Later, with the bread set to rise, she went out into the yard where Vater Carl had come rattling back from the cheese factory with the whey from the separated milk. She gazed helplessly at the heavy buckets, knowing it was beyond her strength to lift them from the cart or carry them over to the pigsty.

As Winifred stood there without speaking, Vater glared at her and with a bucket in each hand went striding across to the pigs. She thought about unharnessing the horse and putting it in the stable, but even that was too much effort. All she wanted to do was to lie down somewhere quiet on her own.

She made her way across the paddock to where she could see a tumbledown house of iron and slabs almost on the border of the farm next door. The door was hanging on one hinge, and she pushed it open. She could tell by the cobwebs, the thick layer of dust on the furniture and the grass growing on the dirt floor that it had been a long while since it had been lived in.

There was a broom in the corner and she picked it up and began to sweep the dust off the furniture. As she worked, she made up her mind that she would move in and help herself to what she needed from her in-laws' place. Even if they hated her she had a right to her food and keep, and if she was out of sight they might not resent her so much. At least she would have privacy and somewhere to have her child, and perhaps when things had settled down Charles might forgive her. She would ask him to build her a fowl run. She could sell the eggs and, once the birth was over, start a vegetable garden and make herself independent.

She remembered the bread and returned to the kitchen. She lifted the damp cloth with which she had covered the dough and punched it down, putting it by the stove so that it could rise again before she cooked it. Then she took a dipper of water and found a bundle of old rags and went back to the slab hut. There she wiped the furniture, then sprinkled the water that was left onto the floor before sweeping it. She thought that perhaps she might find some cornsacks in the barn, which she could unpick and lay over the dirt floor.

The hut had two rooms with threadbare hessian to cover the window openings. There was a stretcher in the bedroom made of wire netting tied to four posts sunk into the ground. She would have to gather some bracken fern from the creek to make a mattress. In the kitchen there was an old stove and a table with one leg missing, which was supported by an upturned wooden box. Boxes also served as chairs. On a shelf over the stove was a candlestick with a stub of a candle, plus a black-iron pot and pan, a cracked teapot and some tin mugs. An old iron tank with a door cut in its side served as a toilet. Remembering how she and her father had slept in the prickly pear when they first arrived in Australia, she thought she could live here very well. The main thing was to get some food.

Winifred returned to the main house and put the bread in the oven. She had opened the pantry and was looking around to see what she could find to take back to the hut when Mutter Barbara came into the kitchen. 'Make the tea,' she said. 'The cows will be coming in from the paddock and there's milking to be done.'

The family sat around the long table drinking tea with slices of Mutter Barbara's gingerbread. Vater Carl drank noisily and he and his wife carried on a conversation in German. The daughters were silent the whole while, eating quickly before returning to the milking shed. Winifred carried the dirty cups and plates to the sink, waited until her mother- and father-in-law had finished and then washed up.

She was feeling unbelievably tired, as well as completely out of place in the household, so she went outside and picked her way through the long grass to the little hut, where she lay down on the makeshift bed. It was here Charles found her when he returned from a day spent haymaking on a neighbour's farm. 'Mutter said you must come and eat.'

'I want to stay here,' Winifred replied. 'They all hate me.'

'You must eat.' He took her by the arm and pulled her off the bed, then, with his arm around her waist, forced her back to his parents' house.

That night they returned to the hut with bread, eggs, tea and sugar and the blankets from Charles's bed. When he blew out the candle he tried to take her in his arms, but she moved away, turning her back to him, and he cursed under his breath. Later she heard him rise and the sound of his horse as he cantered out the gate. She slept fitfully, plagued by mosquitoes and unable to get comfortable on the wire netting. Towards morning she heard Charles returning and pretended to be asleep when he climbed into bed. But he made no attempt to touch her this time and lay with his back to her. Later she heard him snoring.

It had been a long, hot summer and Winifred found the last few weeks of her pregnancy almost unbearable. Her legs were swollen and she had trouble turning over in bed. Her one consolation was that she did not have to face the undisguised hostility of Charles's family. While she remained in her own little place she felt safe. Though she knew she would soon give birth, she did not dwell on it, as if she was somehow immune from the pain and suffering it would involve.

Charles worked away but came home most nights. Winifred gathered kindling, chopped wood, fetched water and made bread as she had done for her father. There was always fresh milk and eggs, and sometimes a cabbage or a few carrots from the vegetable patch by the main homestead. She did not ask permission but took what she needed as being her right. Charles had told her that he received no payment for working for his father, only payment in kind. If he wanted money he had to work away from the farm, and even then his father expected him to pay money into the household.

Charles was away harvesting and did not return home the night Winifred went into labour. The pain woke her and she lit a candle and lay there wondering how she could cope on her own. She had hoped Charles would be here to help. Now she felt clammy and afraid, knowing nothing about childbirth except what she had heard in whispered conversations.

Mutter Barbara found her the next morning when she brought her a jug of milk. She lifted up the young wife's nightgown and felt her stomach, then told her to get up and walk around.

It was three days before Winifred gave birth — three days in which she screamed in agony, while her mother-in-law cursed her for bringing disgrace to the family. Then on 22 February 1900 a son was born. Mutter Barbara wrapped him in a shawl and took him to show her husband.

Charles paid her a brief visit while she was lying in. She thought he seemed pleased when she showed him his son, but he did not offer to hold him. Mutter Barbara had already told her that the child was to be called Charles. It did not worry Winifred as long as his second name was Wilfred after her father, and she filled in the paper her husband had brought so that the child's birth could be registered. To avoid confusion with his father, the child was to be known as Fred.

Winifred's experience with babies was limited to the few weeks she had spent helping Mrs Smith. She had watched her breastfeeding and once Winifred began to hold the child to her breast, her milk began to flow. Holding the small bundle in her arms, she was overwhelmed with joy. She would kiss each perfectly formed pink finger and lay the hands on her breast while she held him against her shoulder to try and bring up his wind as she had seen Mrs Smith do.

Charles stayed one night, going out as soon as they had eaten some cold sausage and sauerkraut his mother had brought over. He returned later and Winifred heard him tripping up the steps. She sat up in bed, saying, 'Ssshhh, don't wake the baby.' Ignoring her, he dropped his boots one by one on the floor, spread his blanket by the stove and lay down. He was breathing heavily and began to grunt and toss and turn in his sleep, and she sensed he had been drinking. Winifred lay awake in the dark. The baby was in bed beside her and she listened to his gentle breathing, reaching out to touch his face to make sure he was warm. She could hear a noise on the roof and wondered if it was a bird or a rat, or even a snake. She knew there were snakes around. She had climbed into the loft in the barn to fill a bag of potatoes one day when she saw a huge snake curled up. 'It's harmless,' Vater Carl had said when she went running out of the barn, her baby on her hip and her bag of potatoes in the other hand. 'They kill the rats.' But Winifred had been frightened. Now she was uneasy, remembering a picture she had seen of a python that had swallowed a goat whole. She thought that if a snake could swallow a young goat, it could swallow a baby. She wondered if she should wake Charles but she was afraid to disturb him in case he became angry.

She lay awake for a long while worrying, afraid to sleep. Then she thought about the wedding and how she had stood at the altar crying, feeling ashamed in her black dress. And then a feeling of guilt possessed her as she remembered how she had prayed that her baby would go away. And now here he was, her son, a being created within her own body, something of herself to love and to love her in return. Charles might be the father, but the child was hers. No one could take him from her. And thinking of this, she fell asleep.

It was still dark when the baby woke and began to cry. Winifred reached over and put him to her breast. As her eyes became accustomed to the light she saw Charles had already left for the harvest and a feeling of angst gripped her. She knew he had not forgiven her.

She did not know how she could endure living with a man who did not care for her, and she made up her mind that once her baby was old enough she would find somewhere else to go, somewhere she could have her child with her.

But the child was fractious and cried a lot, so that the young mother had little sleep. This, combined with being alone with no one she could talk to, sent her into a deep depression. Long after her three-week lying-in period had finished, she still spent her days in bed with the baby by her side, breastfeeding him when he woke, unable to do anything but weep.

When Mutter Barbara came bustling into the hut as she did each day and took the child without asking, Winifred became anxious, fearing that Mutter Barbara planned to keep the child and send her back to her father. Then one day she plucked up courage to say, 'I don't want you to take my baby away.'

Mutter Barbara's eyes flashed. '*Mein Gott*, I have done everything to help you, you ungrateful girl. Do you think I wanted this? But this is Charles's child and I have to see that he is cared for.' She looked around the little hut with its layers of dust, the unwashed mugs, the food scraps. 'This place is like a pigsty. When I had my *kinder* I did not lie around crying, there was work and more work, all day work, and yet I went on … I had ten *kinder* and you have only one.' And she picked up the child and took him over to the main house.

Though Winifred tried to talk to the midwife, Mrs Christerson, when she came to examine her six weeks after the birth, she could not make her understand. Mrs Christerson made Winifred get dressed, then boiled the kettle for tea and produced a Dundee cake she had made. 'Your bairn is bonnie,' she said as she smiled at the baby asleep in a makeshift cradle made from an empty butter box. 'Ye musna fash yourself, lassie … Ye must pull yourself together and take good care of the wee babe. Bairns are a gift from God. Next time it won't be so hard.'

The thought of having another child appalled Winifred but she kept quiet, knowing that it was unlikely because of the way Charles felt about her. She did not tell the midwife that she planned to leave as soon as she could. She wondered if she could go back to her father, but he had not been near her or sent a message since the wedding. She wondered if he even knew about the baby, and if he did, would he care enough to come and see his new grandson? Though she was accustomed to his indifference she had always felt that deep down he loved her.

As the weeks went by her mood changed. Fred would smile at her and make baby noises, and as she walked around the yard holding him in her arms she would point out a crow on a fence post or a rabbit scurrying into the long grass, saying 'moo' when they saw a cow. On a warm night she would stand near the door and look at the vast expanse of star-filled sky that arched overhead and say, 'God is out there somewhere, small one. He will watch over us.' And she would kiss the baby on the top of his head.

She no longer felt quite so lonely. Now when Mutter Barbara came to take little Fred over to the main house she would let him go, walking over later to carry him home. She sensed that the old woman's mood had softened towards her and Vater Carl would say, '*Guten morgen*,' when she went to the dairy to collect the milk.

But the sisters were still hostile and scarcely spoke to her. She knew it was because she did not help with the milking or the butter-making. Once she heard Kate complaining to Vater Carl about her taking the milk. He replied sharply, 'It's not for her. It is for *die kind*. In a few years he will be big enough to help with the milking. Let her have the milk.'

Hearing this, Winifred smiled to herself, wondering what they would say if she told them she and Fred would be far away by then.

It was the quiet moments that Winifred cherished. She would spend them immersed in writing stories, thinking that if she could sell some she could begin to save money until she had enough to leave Charles. As soon as she heard Mutter Barbara talking to Fred as she carried him across the paddock she'd rise hurriedly and hide the paper and pencil, throw a cloth over the dirty plates and mugs and pull the covers over the bed. By the time Mutter Barbara arrived at the door with the child, Winifred would be sitting at the table with a sheet of newspaper on it to catch the potato peelings as she prepared a simple meal.

Charles arrived unannounced in May when Fred was five months old. Winifred looked out the front door when she heard the sound of a horse and saw him dismount to open the gate. He waved to her and led his horse over to her. He flung his swag on the ground at her feet, saying, 'There's some washing to do,' and continued towards the stable.

Winifred picked up the bundle and emptied it onto the ground, extracting some dirty shirts, socks and a pair of trousers. Tomorrow she would light a fire and boil them up, and if it was windy she would be able to get them dry and ironed. She had no idea how long he intended to stay but thought she would wait until she was told. She gathered some kindling and went into the kitchen to stoke up the stove so she could put the kettle on. It was boiling when Charles returned and he sat at the table while she made the tea and produced a loaf of bread and a piece of cheese, which he ate rapidly. She sat there watching in silence, waiting for him to speak.

'I was hungry,' he said when he finally pushed his chair back from the table and stood up, filling his pipe as he walked to the door. 'Where's my son?'

'With your mother.'

'Work finally cut out. I've been weeks on the road. It was a good harvest. And I picked up some fencing work. Helped clear some land. I've been all over. Still, there's plenty to do here. I promised Vater I'd fix the fences. And there's a paddock to plough for a winter crop.' He went to the door. 'I'll go and see Mutter.'

'Bring Fred when you come,' she called and watched him stroll across the paddock towards the house.

As she filled the round tub with water and soaped his dirty clothes before putting them in to soak, turning the socks inside out and looking in the pockets of a pair of work trousers to make sure they were empty, she thought about his return. It would be the first time they had really been alone together since Fred's birth. She wondered if he would sleep on the floor as he had last time, or whether he would climb into bed beside her and try to take her in his arms. The thought alarmed her. She was still breastfeeding and wondered if she could use that as an excuse.

As she rubbed the clothes on her washboard she had a sudden memory of being at the Cut with Mrs Watkins and seeing a woman selling herrings. A young ragamuffin had been running along beside her and as Winifred watched, the child began to jump up and claw at her mother. The woman sat on an upturned butterbox and, taking the child on her knee, unbuttoned her shirt-waist to reveal two huge pendulous breasts. The child had clawed at one breast and, holding it to her mouth, began to suck lustily.

Mrs Watkins had laughed. 'She shouldn't be having titty-bottle at her age. She's old enough to work.' Then she had looked serious and leaned towards Winifred, a drop of moisture trembling on the end of her nose. 'They say you can't fall while you've got one on the breast. It makes you safe if your old man decides he wants to give you a poke. Women don't have much choice in this world. If you says no, he's likely to give you a poke in the eye instead.'

Winifred had puzzled over that conversation for a long time. Now she understood and was relieved that she was still breastfeeding. It would stop her from having another child if Charles wanted to make love to her, though she knew that love didn't enter into it. He only wanted a woman, and she wondered if he had found another young girl like her while he had been away. If he had, perhaps he would leave her alone.

She only had a few potatoes for tea and she peeled them and put them at the back of the stove in the black-iron pot, ready to bring them to the boil when Charles came back. She had not had meat for a long time and pride prevented her asking his mother.

It was getting dark when her husband returned with Fred on his shoulders. They were both laughing and Winifred had a pang of jealousy, thinking that if they got too close Charles might take Fred from her. 'He's a real tiger,' he said. 'As soon as he's old enough I'll show him how to use the clippers. I can just see him on the boards, beside his old man.'

'I want him to go to school.'

'All he needs is to be able to write his name and add up a few figures. School doesn't mean a thing when you're in a shearing shed.' He ruffled the child's hair, saying 'We'll be a real team, won't we, son?' and handed him to Winifred.

She put the child on the bed, unbuttoned her blouse and lay beside him, conscious that Charles was watching as the child kicked his legs and then fell off the breast to gaze around before latching on again. Later she sponged the child's face and hands and changed his napkin; then, wrapping him tightly in his shawl, she put him to sleep in her bed.

She boiled the potatoes and served them, giving the larger portion to Charles. 'Where's the meat?' he asked.

'I have no money to buy meat.'

'There's always sausage at the house, or bacon … I work hard for Vater. All I get in return is the use of this place and my keep. Anything you want you must ask Mutter.'

'Did you bring any money?' she asked.

'You don't need money.'

'I need things.'

'What things?'

'I need a new dress — the one I had for my wedding is too big — and I'd like some material to make curtains and a tablecloth.' She did not tell him that she wanted money to buy stamps to post off her articles.

'I have no money for such things … As for a new dress, you don't go anywhere. If you want money you'll have to find it yourself.'

'But where?'

'Do as my sisters do. They make butter and take it to market. Mutter makes preserves and cheese. When Vater kills a pig they make bloodwurst and smoked bacon. Other women sell eggs. I'll build you a fowl house and get you a goat. The cows dry out in winter. You'll need milk.'

'But who will milk it?'

'You dom Britishers, you've never learned to work. My sisters milk ten cows twice a day.'

Winifred did not answer, thinking of the years of hard work she had endured from the time she was a child. And now she had a child of her own to care for and was always tired. She wanted to ask what he had done with the money he earned but was afraid. Instead she rose to make the tea.

Her eyes were full of unshed tears as she washed the plates later, and then she became conscious that he was standing behind her. She felt him take off her apron and turn her to face him. He put his arms around her and pulled her towards him so that her head rested on his shoulder. 'Once,' he whispered, 'once I told you you had the most beautiful green eyes.' She could feel the heat rising from his body as he pressed himself closer, until he pulled her down and she was lying with him on the kitchen floor.

He went out later that night. When she asked him where he was going he said, 'To see a man about a dog.' And soon she heard the sound of his horse trotting along the path. She lay in bed with little Fred by her side, her feeling of unease growing. She had not meant to give in to him so easily. But at least she was safe. She knew that while he was home she must continue to breastfeed her child, then she would leave as soon as she could.

13

HOUSEHOLD DRUDGE

IT WAS AUGUST WHEN CHARLES LEFT to go shearing. He had been home long enough for the young couple to establish a relationship of sorts. Winifred had got into the habit of carrying him a billy can of tea and some bread and cheese in the middle of the day when he was working on the farm, and would sit on a cornsack with Fred propped up by her side, sharing his simple meal and watching while he ploughed the paddock.

One day she took down his lunch and found him working alongside a group of men who spoke German. They were fencing a paddock, and though they glanced at her sitting there, they ignored her, laughing and joking as they worked. She waited for a while and then returned to the hut, noticing a few bottles of liquor lying unopened in the shade of a tree as she passed. Late in the afternoon she heard singing and the sound of men's voices.

Charles came stumbling up the steps later that evening, his face flushed, holding his accordion in one hand. He stopped when he saw her sitting at the kitchen table which was set for a meal. 'Why are you still up?'

'I kept your supper hot … I waited. Why are you so late?'

'What I do is no concern of yours. No one asked you to come spying on me.'

'What about your supper?'

Instead of answering he leaned forward and swept the plates, the bread and cheese off the table, then without taking off his boots lay down on the bed fully dressed.

Winifred picked up the food and wrapped it in a towel, then she put the dishes and knives and forks in the tin dish she used for washing up. Then she moved the pot of soup off the stove and sat at the kitchen table with her head bowed, trying to stop the tears that flowed down her cheeks. Later, when Charles had begun to snore, she took off her apron and dress, pulled on her nightgown and crept into bed, where she lay awake staring into the darkness.

After that she kept her distance when he was working on the farm, always preparing something for supper in case he came home, never sure of his movements and too afraid to ask. She was worried that her milk might start to dry up over the winter and she was tense whenever he came near her, relieved when he went out in the evening so that she could pretend to be asleep when he returned. She had come to recognise the signs that he had been drinking heavily, his words slurred, his eyes red and wild-looking, and she tried not to provoke him, fearful of his temper and resentful of the way he squandered his money while refusing to give her any.

With the coming of winter, life on the farm had slowed. The cows were drying out as the grass died, and they looked emaciated, their ribs sticking out as they chewed their winter feed of straw or a barrow-load of broken pumpkins — enough to sustain them until spring when they would fatten up and later give birth to their calves, their udders filling with milk. As soon as the calves were old enough they would be taken from their mothers, the males separated from the heifers and sent to market, with one butchered to provide veal for the table and delicious sausages which were laced with herbs and smoked, then hung in the coolroom.

Mutter Barbara and her daughters spent the winter indoors by the huge fuel stove in the kitchen, sewing shirts and work trousers for the men and shirt-waists and skirts for themselves, darning and patching, making quilts from scraps of material and knitting woollen socks. Winifred kept away, isolated in the small hut with her child.

When spring arrived the women emerged again, being needed to work outside. The daughters rose at dawn to see to the cows, while Mutter was busy with her sausage-making, her cheeses and her vegetable garden. She grew herbs and cabbages to replenish her stock of sauerkraut which had been used up over the winter, and Vater Carl sowed corn, pumpkins, melons and potatoes in the paddocks Charles had ploughed.

Charles had also prepared a vegetable garden for Winifred beside the hut, turning over the dark soil, digging in barrow-loads of cow manure. Here Winifred planted corn and spinach, cabbages and potatoes. Beside the fence a plum tree had sprung into bloom. Gazing at it she thought it looked like a queen in its dress of delicate pink, and she felt bereft when she saw how the blossoms lay on the ground after the first spring rains. She consoled herself with the thought of the fruit that would follow, wondering how she would keep away the birds, remembering the way they had stripped the corn on her father's farm.

There was a feeling of rejuvenation, as if the world had come alive. New grass was pushing up through the earth and along the road the acacia trees were in bloom. Winifred would pick a bunch, being careful to avoid the bees that clustered on the yellow blossom, and put it on her table in an empty tin, gazing at it with a sense of joy as she ate her simple meals, almost as if she had reconciled herself to life on the farm.

She had Fred, so she did not feel lonely. And tethered near the house where it could keep the grass down, but beyond the reach of the clothes line which was tied between two belah trees and held up with a wooden prop, was the goat Charles had brought home. She had christened it the Princess Royal. As she fed it a clump of thistles or potato peelings, or sat beside it on a wooden stool milking it in the early mornings and afternoons, she would talk to it as if it was another human being, imagining the answers it might give and writing them down when she had a few spare minutes while Fred was asleep.

The chooks, too, were her friends. Charles had arrived home one day with six white leghorn hens and a red rooster. Each day she let them out to scratch and forage among the weeds and grass, calling them by name when she shooed them back into their pen at night so that they would be safe from dingoes. She had matured a lot from the seventeen-year-old girl Charles had reluctantly brought home as his bride, and her resolve to leave when Fred was old enough had hardened.

She talked to Fred as if he could understand, reading aloud what she had written, as he sat on her knee at the kitchen table, and making up stories about the Princess Royal, putting her in Buckingham Palace, a place she only knew from walking by the back gate with her father when they went to Victoria Station.

Her corn crop was growing and her fowls were laying and she had raised some chickens from settings of eggs, giving her a new-found sense of self-worth. Every week she would rise before it was light and milk the goat, filling the water dish and moving the creature to a patch of fresh grass, then opening the door of the pen so that the fowls could forage once it was light. She would pour herself a mug of milk and then wake Fred, feed him and carry him over to Mutter Barbara before she set off for the market with her basket of eggs. Mutter Barbara would give Fred his bath, while Winifred would pour herself a cup of tea from the pot beside the stove and cut herself a slice of bread and cheese, putting it in her pocket for when she wanted to have a rest later.

She enjoyed these early mornings just after sunrise. She felt free. And with the freedom her thoughts turned to the stories she would write. As she trudged along in the dust she would watch the green ants running up and down trees, or stitching leaves together to make a nest. Sometimes she surprised a mother quail out walking with her chicks and was moved to see how the bird gathered her young under her wings before speeding into the undergrowth. Other times she would watch a herd of wallabies bounding across the plain. Or there would be ducks swimming in the creek and skimmer birds diving down to drink or snatch insects off the surface.

At that time of the day, before the heat drained the life out of the bush, everything seemed fresh and new. But once she reached the markets there was no time for daydreaming. Buggies, sulkies, horses and waggons would be converging from all directions and Winifred would have to keep her wits about her to get the best price as she stood by the road with her basket of eggs.

She was always relieved when she had the money safely in her pocket, sometimes buying a little treat for Fred, like a coloured leather ball. Occasionally she bought something for herself, such as a length of serviceable material to make a dress, or some needle and thread. One of her first purchases was some red checked gingham for curtains and a tablecloth to brighten up the hut. Once she bought herself a new hat. It was a leghorn straw hat trimmed with field flowers in a fashionable sailor shape. She couldn't resist it when she looked at herself in a piece of cracked mirror the stallholder handed her, justifying the expense because she had no sun hat and her face was becoming weather-beaten. But as she neared the farm she began to worry, hoping she could sneak it in the door before Mutter Barbara saw it and told her she was being extravagant.

Charles returned home in October and for once he praised Winifred when he saw the crop of corn swaying in the breeze, and though he didn't comment he seemed pleased when he entered the hut and saw the changes she had made with curtains at the windows and a matching tablecloth.

Basking under his praise she experienced a feeling of happiness that she had not known for a long time, but it was not to last. By the time he left again in November he had begun to drink heavily, coming in late and refusing to eat the food she had cooked, throwing the plates onto the floor and once gathering everything into the tablecloth and hurling it out the door. Winifred found the remains of the cloth the next day when she went to milk the goat. The Princess Royal had chewed holes in it to get to the bread and cheese.

When Charles left to work as an offsider to a contractor who was travelling west to sink wells, Winifred was relieved that her life would settle down into some form of routine again, and she would have some measure of peace, free from the abuse Charles heaped on her when he was drunk, and free from the demands he made on her once he was lying by her side in bed.

By the time Fred was eighteen months old she was always tired. She was constantly chasing him around the paddocks when he climbed down the back steps, fearful that he would disappear into the long grass and be lost in the bush or wander down to the creek and be drowned. She remembered a girl of four who had been lost in the prickly pear after she had been sent to bring in the cattle. The men had searched for her through the night, until they came across her beside the creek with a group of Aborigines who had found her and fed her duck soup. Winifred had seen the mother's anguish as she waited for news of her daughter. She knew that she could not bear it if anything happened to Fred.

When her milk began to dry up Winifred weaned Fred onto goat's milk, arrowroot biscuits and bread in a dish of warm milk, noticing how her breasts had begun to sag, the nipples prominent, surrounded with an aureole of matching brown. She accepted the fact that her figure had thickened, despite the hard physical work on the farm, and that she was no longer the young girl with stars in her eyes who had fallen in love with Charles Steger.

On her husband's infrequent visits home she was unable to avoid his advances. When he was sober he was good company and would pick Fred up and throw him into the air while the child squealed in delight. Later he would carry him around the paddocks on his back while Fred clung to his hair. She was no longer jealous when she saw them together, knowing that as soon as Charles left, Fred would turn to her again.

Fred was two months short of his second birthday when Winifred began to feel off-colour in the mornings. At first she failed to recognise the signs that she was expecting another child, until her waistline started to thicken and Vater Carl, handing her a jug of cream when she was in the dairy, said, 'For *die kind*.' She could no longer ignore the changes taking place in her body and was filled with rage at her predicament, blaming Charles, forgetting that there were times when he had been kind to her and she had lain willingly in his arms, starved for affection and wanting him to love her as he had once done.

As the months went by, her rage diminished. By the time she was five months pregnant she had accepted the fact that the farm would be her home for a long while to come, and she sensed the approbation of Mutter Barbara and Vater Carl, though the sisters were as hostile as ever.

On 11 June 1902 Winifred gave birth to her second son, John Henry, to be known as Jack. Charles was home but it was two days after the birth before he came to see how she was. His brothers were also home at the time and they had taken Charles to the hotel to get him out of the way. They stayed there drinking until Vater Carl fetched them home in the waggon.

Winifred was in bed, the baby asleep by her side, when Charles came up the steps of the hut and stood looking at her with a pleading, hangdog look. His hair was dishevelled and he had a two-day beard shadowing his face. Mutter Barbara approached him and Winifred heard her say something to him in German. She could tell the older woman was angry by the way she spoke, but Charles did not answer. Winifred motioned for him to come closer and he did so, gazing down at the small scrap of humanity at her side until he burst into tears and covered his face with his hands.

He stayed home for three months — three months in which he got to know his elder son, who followed him everywhere. Winifred would watch them hand in hand as they walked around the paddock. Sometimes Fred would have a handful of thistles for the Princess Royal, or some weeds for the fowls. He would help his father hunt out the eggs they sometimes laid in nests away from the main pen and help him weed the vegetable garden, or carry into the house a few potatoes his father had dug for their supper.

For Winifred it was an idyllic few weeks as she recovered from the birth, which had not been as harrowing as her previous experience. She had begun to feel more settled, as if this was where she belonged. Two days before Charles was due to leave to join the shearing team, where he had the job of cook, she asked him to kill one of the roosters she had raised from a setting of eggs. She plucked it and cleaned it, putting the feathers to one side until she had enough to make a pillow, hanging the bird upside down in a cool place, planning to cook a special meal as a surprise the night before Charles left.

She set the table carefully, putting on the checked tablecloth she had made to replace the one the goat had eaten, and placing a handful of early acacia blossom in a jar in the centre. She lit a candle, leaving the curtains open so that he would see it as he approached the house. The small room was warm from the fuel stove, and the smell of roasting fowl, baking potatoes and pumpkin filled the air. The lid of the black-iron pot jiggled and steam rose as a jam roly-poly simmered. In a jug at the back of the hob was an egg custard keeping warm. Winifred had been filled with a sense of housewifely pride, remembering Mr Jackson and her pleasure in seeing row upon row of pies that she had helped to make. Now through her own efforts she was able to feed her family and she glowed at the thought of Charles's surprise when he came in the door.

She gave Fred a bowl of bread and milk and put him to bed, then breastfed Jack and sat there to wait. Outside, the wind had risen and she thought that perhaps there might be a late frost. She looked out the window. It was a clear night with no moon and the stars seemed almost close enough to touch.

She was still waiting when Charles opened the door and a blast of cold air blew out the candle. The fuel stove had long gone out and she had hacked a leg off the fowl and eaten it in her fingers with a piece of potato and pumpkin, then wrapped the rest of the meat in a cloth and placed it in the meat safe. She kept her eyes averted, afraid to look Charles in the face in case he became angry.

'You still up?' he said. 'I had a bite to eat with Mutter and Vater. I won't be home for a while and there were things to talk about … the farm.'

Winifred did not reply. She knew he was lying. She could tell, and she could smell the alcohol on his breath. She bent and lifted the baby out of his cradle and, unbuttoning her dress, lay down on the bed and began to feed him. Charles spread his blankets on the floor, took off his boots and outer garments and lay down. Before he went to sleep he said, 'I'll be back after shearing. In a couple of years' time Fred'll be old enough to come with me.'

Winifred did not reply, determined that come what may she would see that her sons went to school so that they could be educated and get a job, anything other than follow in their father's footsteps with weeks of hard work followed by weeks of drinking, then arriving home almost penniless. She thought that her boys could get a job on the railways. Most of all she wanted to make sure they didn't end up drunkards like her uncle or their father. In her heart she knew that Charles would never change. Charles would ruin her sons if she let him. She was determined to see that it didn't happen.

14

THE BREAK-UP

THE YOUNG MOTHER FELT VERY isolated that winter, shut up in the small hut with two young children to care for. She was constantly worried about what Fred was doing while she fed the baby. Once he had pushed a box over to the door, stood on it and opened the door before she was even awake. She had been frantic when she found he was missing, afraid that he might have wandered down to the creek, until Vater Carl came striding across the paddock holding the little boy in his arms. Fred had taken off the shirt he wore to bed and was naked. Sometimes he would lie down beside her while she told him another adventure in the life of the Princess Royal. She knew he was jealous of his little brother and once she caught him giving Jack a pinch. She slapped him and he went into a flood of tears until she picked him up and held him close, weeping herself from sheer exhaustion.

She thought of tethering the child to the clothes line near the goat but was worried about snakes. Once she had seen a king brown slithering across the path to the dairy then disappearing into the long grass. Vater Carl had searched for it with his shotgun but there was no sign of it. He told her that snakes were only dangerous at mating time, but she was never sure when that was. She asked a man to whom she sometimes sold live fowls at the market. 'Snakes is like birds,' he said, 'they stake out their territory. If you sees one, best not tangle with it. Ye need stout boots and a stick. Most of 'em won't attack. Just keep still and stamp yer feet, most times they'll go. They ain't got ears but they can sense the ground moving.' Even though he told her snakes hibernated in the winter, she still felt uneasy.

She thought that if anything happened to her children, she would die. It would be more than she could endure, and she wondered where this love came from for children she had never wanted. She thought that Charles was proud of his two sons but he did not love them as fiercely as she did. Perhaps men were different. They went away and came back when they felt like it, and nothing had changed except that their children had grown.

That year Winifred had been too busy to plant corn but she had kept her vegetable patch going, so that she was able to pick a few leaves of spinach and a cabbage and there was a box of potatoes in the kitchen which she had dug earlier. That, with eggs from her fowls, kept them in food.

She put Fred to work fetching the eggs as soon he was old enough, showing him how to place them gently in a basket lined with bracken fern picked from the banks of the creek.

At first he had been terrified of the rooster because it flew at him with its comb standing back and its mouth open as if it was going to bite. 'Don't be silly. They don't have any teeth,' she told him. 'And they need sharp claws to dig in the earth and grip the perch. You mustn't be a cry-baby. You're much bigger than it.' She showed him how to pick up a stick and call out 'Shoo!' if it tried to attack him. She felt guilty because he was so young, but she had no one else to help.

One morning she heard a commotion in the fowl yard and ran out of the house to find a snake curled up in one of the nests where a broody had been hatching a setting of eggs. Now the eggs were gone and the hen was petrified, too afraid to move. Winifred ran for the axe and struck at the snake until the body was a bloody pulp. She picked it up on a stick, carried it outside and put it on an ants' nest. But the incident unnerved her, even though she knew it was a harmless green tree snake. After that she told Fred to keep away from the fowl shed.

Once Jack was old enough to be left with Barbara, Winifred resumed her weekly trip to town. Now there were two children to be minded, the sisters resented her even more because it meant they had more work to do.

Winifred would take a basket of eggs and a few vegetables to exchange with the storekeeper for flour, tea, sugar and golden syrup, and sometimes citronella to protect the children from the mosquitoes that bred in the goat's dish, the water for the fowls and in the pools of water left by spring rains. The children were often badly bitten and Fred scratched the bites so that he was soon covered in sores that began to fester. She made a paste of bicarbonate of soda and water to cover them and told him he looked like a snowman.

The days when she could daydream by the clothes line or follow the wind-drift of clouds were over. When she looked in her mirror the face reflected back at her was red from the sun, the mouth turned down, tired lines around the eyes. Every evening, as soon as it got dark, she gave the children a bowl of bread and milk, ate a few boiled vegetables with a slice of bread and syrup and fell exhausted into bed, waking in the night to feed Jack and carry Fred into her bed when he had a bad dream.

When Charles came home the routine changed and Fred would become his shadow, leaving Winifred free to concentrate on Jack and his needs. Charles being home also meant preparing a proper meal and waiting until he came home, as well as having to judge when to stop waiting and eat by herself because he had gone to the hotel and would stay till closing. She always made sure she was in bed when he lurched into the hut, stumbling and swearing as he tripped over boxes. She would lie still, making no sign that she was awake, praying that the children wouldn't start to cry because it made him so angry. Once he had punched Fred because he was making a noise. The child had screamed and run to her. She had turned on Charles, 'He's only a baby.' He had raised his fist at her while she stood facing him with Fred in her arms, a look of terror in her eyes, until, with a muttered curse, he flung himself out the door.

Her milk supply had begun to dry up when Jack was seven months old and though she tried to persevere, by nine months he was fully weaned and she found herself pregnant again. It was a time when her fowls had stopped laying, the goat was dry and her vegetable garden was overrun with weeds. Overwhelmed with morning sickness she was unable to do anything but lie down, depending on Mutter Barbara to care for the children until the late afternoon when they would return with their father, bringing food from the main house. She would struggle to prepare an evening meal, retching as she smelt the bacon frying in the pan.

She had recovered by the time Charles left to go shearing. It was a relief because he had begun to beat Fred, often for some trifling misdemeanour. And this particular day was no exception. When Charles was home he kept his things in a tin box. This included his accordion which no one was allowed to touch. When he left, he took the box with him. Winifred was in the yard doing the washing when Fred opened the box and took out his father's accordion, attempting to play it. When she called him to help lift the clothes out of the dish so that she could hang them on the line, he left it on the floor. Later she replaced it in the box, shutting the lid.

The two children were asleep, Jack in his butter box cradle and Fred on the floor on a straw mattress, when Charles returned home. 'Who's been at my box?' he asked when he went to take out his accordion.

Winifred was at the stove stirring the soup for their supper, and without turning around said, 'You know I never touch your things.'

'If it wasn't you, it must have been Fred.'

'He didn't mean any harm.' She put a bowl of soup on the table. 'Come and eat.'

Ignoring her, Charles took off his belt. He bent over Fred, pulled off the cornsacks which served as blankets and shook him roughly. The child stirred and, still half asleep, looked at his father looming above him. 'I'll teach you to touch my things.' He brought his belt down hard and the child screamed as he felt it bite into his bare legs.

Winifred dropped the serving spoon. 'Don't hit him, he didn't know it was wrong.'

'Keep out of this or you'll get some too. Children are like horses. They need breaking in. They're my sons and I'll deal with them as I see fit.' He buckled on his belt, picked up his accordion and walked out the door.

She bent over the small boy, cradling him in her arms. 'Don't cry. Daddy's angry because you went to his box. You must learn to leave his things alone.'

That night the child woke with a bad dream but Winifred didn't go to him as she normally did, because Charles had returned and was lying by her side and she was afraid to provoke him.

Fred and his father resumed normal relations, almost as if the child did not remember the incident. He followed Charles around the farm as he always did, walking over to Mutter Barbara's to see if he was there, and sometimes looking in the dairy. Once he returned with blood streaming from a cut to his head. When Winifred asked him how he did it he said, 'Aunt Kate hit me with the dog chain. She told me to go away.'

Before he left, Winifred got Charles to plough her corn patch and turn over the vegetable garden, and when her fowls came into lay again he took her eggs to town, returning with staple items for the house, such as tea and sugar, but never any money. She suspected that he put it in his own pocket and it irked her, but there was nothing she could do.

* * *

Fred was old enough to start school at the beginning of 1905, but instead of sending him as she had planned, she kept him home to look after Jack and do odd jobs on the farm. She had given birth to her third son, Peter Andrew Stuart, on 30 December the previous year. Charles had come home briefly and then gone again, leaving Winifred to manage as best she could. It fell to Fred to fetch the water, tend the vegetable patch, watch his younger brother and look after the fowls. As soon as his hands were strong enough she planned to teach him to milk the goat.

She tried to make up for keeping him home from school by teaching him to read from jam tin labels as she had done as a child. And she told him stories she remembered from her own school days. By now she had put all ideas of leaving home from her mind, knowing she had no way of supporting her children. She had accepted that she was locked into life on the Steger farm until she could fend for herself. Any feelings she'd had for Charles had diminished.

Her dreams of making money from her writing had been shattered. She had sent some stories to *Life*, the magazine which had printed some of them before. When months went by and she heard nothing she wondered if the magazine still existed. But it did not stop her putting her thoughts on paper, being careful that Charles did not find out. But he surprised her one day as she was sitting hunched over the table, a stub of pencil in her mouth as she pondered over what to write, finding release in pouring out her unhappiness, her love for her children and describing life on the farm. She tried to hide what she was doing but it was too late. He grabbed the stack of papers from under her hand, his face black as he read what she had written. 'You … you dom Britisher. No one asked you to come onto my father's land, now you sit here wasting time while cockatoos eat the corn, while Mutter and my sisters do the work of men because … because I am away earning money to keep body and soul together.' She had watched helplessly as he threw her stories into the fuel stove, steeling herself not to cry, biting back the angry words that rose to her tongue. She was always relieved when Charles left to go shearing. She felt only loathing when he reached out to pull her towards him, rolling onto his side of the bed once he was satisfied. Afterwards she would rise and stand at the kitchen door gazing out into the night, crying quietly and wondering how much longer she could go on.

Her eldest son was six when Winifred found herself pregnant again. The years of neglect and hard work had taken their toll and the young mother was certain she was going to die. As the time for the birth drew near, she begged Mutter Barbara to find her Aunt Lydia, whom she had not seen since her father and uncle had quarrelled. Vater Carl located Lydia and brought her to the hut where Winifred was awaiting the birth.

Lydia arrived wearing the same elegant brown dress she had worn the first time Winifred met her. The boys came running in to tell their mother there was a lady outside when they saw Vater Carl handing her out of the waggon. Winifred was in bed when Lydia walked in, taking off her brown kid gloves and putting her hat on the table. She stepped lightly across to her niece and, taking her face in her hands, gazed at her. 'My dear child, if you only knew how I have missed you.

I had no news of you, no one told me. It is very sad. William and your father are still estranged.'

She turned to the boys. 'Are these your children? My, what fine, strong boys they are,' and she kissed them, then opened her basket and took out a white apron which she put on. She bustled around the kitchen making tea, producing a plum cake and cutting the boys a slice before sending them outside again, so that she could talk to their mother.

She carried a cup of tea and a piece of cake across to Winifred and sat by the bed holding her hand.

Winifred looked at her with tears in her eyes. 'I've thought of you so often, had conversations with you in my head. Will you stay with me?'

'Of course … that's why I'm here. I'll help you have the baby —'

'And after that?'

'We'll see, I can't stay forever. I have to get back to your uncle.'

'Aunt Liddy, it's been so hard … I already have three children and I don't want any more.'

'Which of your children would you send back?'

Winifred looked at her, surprised. 'I want them all.'

'Well then, be thankful that the Lord has blessed you. I would have given anything to have been a mother.'

'You don't understand … the family hate me.'

'Surely not. Mr Steger is a very nice man. He told me how he and his wife came as shepherds, living miles from anywhere in a little hut until they got some land of their own. He's so proud of your sons. And now you must rest. I'll give you a cool sponge bath. It's so hot in here. Not a breath of air.'

Winifred watched as she went to the stove and rolled up her sleeves. Her aunt pushed her hair back from a forehead beaded in perspiration, and Winifred noticed the sprinkling of grey hairs. It had been so long since she had last seen her and now here she was, as beautiful as ever with her lovely clothes and her gentle kindness.

The young woman looked around at the rusted tin walls, the three-legged table, the boxes that served as chairs, and felt ashamed that her aunt had come to such a place. And as Aunt Lydia pulled back the blankets and saw the calico bag filled with straw that served as the mattress, Winifred began to cry, wishing she could have managed better — made some sheets, bought blankets for the children's beds, forced Charles to get her some real furniture. But there were always more important things for the farm ... always the farm. And last time she had some money she had bought herself a pair of strong boots, boots she needed when she was in the corn patch or weeding the garden, and for the long walk into town. As for the children, they went barefoot, sometimes spiking their feet on old fencing wire that had been thrown into a paddock and covered with long grass, or treading on a nail that someone had left to rust in a piece of discarded timber. When they came limping home crying, she would make a poultice of bread and hot water and make them lie down with a rag over the wound until the infection had gone down.

Now her aunt dipped a cloth in a dish of lukewarm water and gently sponged her face, then lifted up her nightgown and rubbed her swelling stomach gently, laughing when the baby kicked. 'Don't cry, little one. Life is hard. Things will improve.' She patted Winifred dry with a towel and wiped her eyes, then held out a corner of her apron, 'Blow,' she said and Winifred blew her nose.

After she had emptied the water onto the vegetable garden, Lydia came back with an armful of kindling for the stove. 'What time does Charles get home?'

'He doesn't always come home.'

'Is he working away?'

'Not now, but he goes ... he goes to the hotel ...' And she began to cry again. 'I have nothing. He drinks everything, even my egg money. No matter where I hide it, he finds it.'

'Oh, my dear ... Do you want me to speak to him about it?'

'It will only make him angry.'

Winifred's waters broke that night and Aunt Lydia woke the older boys and sent them to tell their grandmother, who came over in her nightgown and white cap, a shawl draped around her shoulders, holding a lantern. The boys stayed behind with their grandfather. On 2 February 1907, eight hours after she had gone into labour, Winifred gave birth to a baby girl, whom she named Winifred.

'The image of you. A beautiful child,' said Aunt Lydia as she put the child in her arms, bending over to kiss her niece on the forehead.

It was a week before Charles came to see his new daughter, a week Aunt Lydia spent sleeping on the floor of the little hut, tending to the mother and child and getting to know the children. She baked bread and girdle cakes and cared for two-year-old Peter, walking him round the farm so that Winifred could rest, going to the dairy to talk to Vater Carl and sometimes to the main house to have a cup of tea with Mutter Barbara.

She tackled Charles when he was leaving the hut one morning. 'Mr Steger, I am concerned about my niece. She needs things, things which are the right of every woman. She worries because the children do not have proper blankets and there are no sheets for their beds. She does not want them to grow up like savages. There is the egg money ... most women have the use of it to buy things ... things for the house ... but my niece ...' She hesitated, gazing into Charles's eyes.

For a moment he held her gaze and then he looked away, an angry flush rising in his cheeks. 'No one asked you to come prying into my affairs. I decide how the money is spent in this house. My wife and children want for nothing. There is milk from the goat, vegetables and eggs, cheese and meat from my parents that we have earned by hard work. I know how to look after my own, and now you, a dom Britisher, dare to tell me what I should do in my own home! You are not welcome here, madam, stirring up trouble. The quicker you are gone the better. Tomorrow, when he goes to the dairy, my father will take you back where you belong.'

'You are no gentleman, Mr Steger,' Lydia called after him as he went striding across the paddock. She was sorry she had spoken and looked across to where Winifred was lying with the child by her side.

'It's all right, Aunt Lydia, I'll manage,' Winifred said. She tried to smile but dissolved into tears, feeling like a child again as her aunt took her in her arms and held her close.

The next day Vater Carl stopped by with the waggon as he was going to the dairy and Winifred bid her aunt a tearful farewell.

'I'll write,' said Lydia. 'It's time I went home. William has been too long alone. He needs me. He's not cut out to be a farmer.'

By the time Winifred's fourth child was one year old Jack and Fred were both at school. In addition, they had taken over a lot more of the work. Fred milked the goat, chopped wood, dug potatoes and helped Vater Carl with the hay-gathering. Jack looked after the fowls, weeded the vegetable patch and chased the cockatoos off the ripening corn. It made life easier for Winifred, until Charles returned home during harvest and took the boys with him to help out on a neighbour's farm.

Once again the bulk of the work fell to her. She came to the realisation that this was how it would always be. Her two older sons had gone from her. Charles had taken them. And she knew that if she was not careful he would take Peter too. Of all her children he was the one she loved the best because he reminded her of her father. She was determined not to let Charles spoil their relationship. Now it was Peter who fetched and carried for her when she was feeding her little daughter. It was Peter who listened to her stories and who handed the pegs to her when she was hanging out the clothes. And though he followed his older brothers around when they were home, at other times he was like her shadow, working with her as she bent over weeding the garden, or shooing the flies off his little sister who was sleeping in the butter-box cradle beside them. Now when she resumed her walks into town Winifred left her baby daughter with Mutter Barbara, who had become attached to the little girl, and took Peter with her, walking slowly and taking rests so that he did not get tired, determined to build a strong bond so that he would not want to leave her.

Her relations with Charles had not improved. She was only happy when he was away, and when he was home she was glad when he stayed at the hotel so that she did not have to resist his sexual advances.

That Christmas the plum tree had a particularly large crop of fruit. Winifred had watched it carefully to make sure that the birds did not get at it, encouraging the older boys to rise early one morning to pick the plums, promising that she would bring them back something special from the market. Jack coveted a pocketknife like the one Vater Carl had given his older brother. She asked Charles to go with her to the market because she could not manage the heavy load on her own.

Jack was hanging on the gate waiting expectantly when his parents returned. He cried bitterly when his mother produced a bag of boiled lollies and told him to share them with his brothers. His father began to unbuckle his belt saying, 'Stop crying or I'll give you something to cry about. You're lucky to get anything.'

Winifred watched, unnerved, unable to tell her son that Charles had taken all the money, even though she had been expecting to keep it and buy the children some little treats for Christmas, because, like the fowls, the plum tree belonged to her.

Baby Winifred was a year and ten months old when Winifred came to breaking point. Charles was home again and she had resisted all his advances, turning her back on him when he tried to take her in his arms. She knew that if she gave in it would mean another child and another, until she would be like Mutter Barbara. One evening, instead of swearing at her as he usually did, then rushing angrily out of the hut, when she told him to leave her alone, using all his strength, he pushed her out of bed. She fell heavily to the floor and lay there, stunned. Later she crawled over to curl up beside Peter, and lay awake in the dark, knowing that she could no longer live under the same roof as her husband.

Her older boys were away when she made her preparations for leaving. Charles was still home but was working on a neighbour's farm. Winifred left her little girl with Mutter Barbara, saying she was taking Peter into town. She had saved up her egg money for weeks, hiding it in a new place where she was sure Charles would never find it. She thought she would catch the train to Towoomba and ask Mr Jackson to give them a bed until she could find something to do, planning to send for her daughter once she was settled.

She was never sure how Charles had found out she was leaving. She thought later that the sisters might have seen her put a bag outside the hut. She was writing a note to tell Charles she was going, but he returned before she had finished. She looked up guiltily, trying to hide the paper, but he snatched it out of her hand and read it.

She stood staring at him with defiance, holding Peter by the hand. 'I'm going. Don't try to stop me.'

'I never wanted you in the first place. Your father wished you on to me. You may be the mother of my children, but you are *shiete*. Just *shiete*. If you leave now you can never return.'

He had raised his voice and Winifred could see the veins standing out in his neck. He stood between her and the door. She had to walk past him if she wanted to leave and was afraid of what he might do to her if he lost his temper. 'I was going to put the kettle on before I left,' she said, hoping to calm him. If she could get him to sit down at the table she could get her treacle tin of money from where she had hidden it under the steps. If she went without it, there would be no money for the train and there was no way she and Peter could walk to Toowoomba.

She felt sick, knowing that her plan had backfired. Miraculously Charles came and sat at the kitchen table. She lifted down three mugs, filling one with milk for Peter and putting a loaf of bread and some cheese on the table. Then she took the teapot outside and emptied it, glancing quickly under the steps where she could see the lid of the treacle tin, wondering how she could get it without her husband noticing.

As he drank his tea he appeared calmer. 'Things have never been right between us. If you must go, then go, but take Winifred. She is a girl and needs her mother. You will be able to give her things that I can't. Leave me my sons. Wait here and I'll fetch her.'

As soon as he had gone, Winifred ran outside and pulled out the treacle tin, carrying it into the kitchen where she prised off the lid with a knife. The tin was empty. She slumped down, feeling ill. He had known about her hiding place all along. Now she had nothing.

She saw Charles running across the paddock, Winifred on his shoulder. He was holding a rifle in his hand. She stood and told Peter to hurry, then ran down the steps.

Charles called to her, 'You're not taking Peter.'

She was trembling, 'You have taken my other sons. Peter is mine.' And she held out her arms to the small boy.

'I will not let you have my sons!' He was level with her. He put the baby girl down and turned to Peter. 'Take your sister by the hand and go down to Mutter Barbara. She will give you a slice of bread and jam.' The child looked at his mother and then back at his father. 'Do as I say,' his father said and the child obeyed. Holding his sister by the hand he began to walk down the path.

Winifred stared after them helplessly, tears running down her face. 'You have ruined my life. You have taken everything from me — my girlhood, my father, my writing, even my egg money ... And now you have taken my children. You are worthless, a drunkard. I have hated you for a long time.' She swayed and clutched at the wooden railing of the steps for support.

He glared at her, his face livid, froth coming out of the corner of his mouth. Then he raised his rifle and pointed it at her. 'Get off my father's land before I put a bullet in you.' He kicked the bag she had packed out of her reach. She stared at him, his words sinking in. He was holding the rifle steady, his eyes fixed on her, glowing like hot coals. And then she turned and ran, while he followed, pointing the gun at her until he had driven her out of the gate.

15

THE FUGITIVE

WINIFRED WOKE IN THE MORNING after a fitful sleep. Her hair was damp with dew, her dress crumpled and soiled. She had no idea where she was except that she knew she had been heading west, walking until she was exhausted. Finally she had settled down under a tree in a paddock with some cattle. It had been a long night and at first the mosquitoes had kept her awake until she pulled her dress up around her ears, pulled her petticoat over her ankles, unfastened her hair to cover her face and curled herself into a ball.

It took her a few moments to realise where she was now, and then a sharp pain assailed her as she went over yesterday's events, knowing she had lost her children. The thought that she might never see them again went through her mind but she dismissed it. There had to be some way of getting them back. She was their mother. She had rights. It was her, not Charles, who had suffered to bring them into the world. For the moment they were safe. Mutter Barbara loved them. She would care for them until Winifred could send for them.

Her immediate situation was desperate. She had only the clothes she stood up in and was hungry and thirsty. Her last meal had been a cup of tea and a slice of bread and cheese at lunchtime. She thought about the night before. Everyone within earshot would have heard Charles shouting. Yet no one had come to her aid. Perhaps they were glad to see her go, otherwise someone would have followed her in the waggon and taken her back to the farm. In her heart she knew that even after nine years and four children she had not been accepted — always the outsider.

Smoke was coming from a chimney in the distance and Winifred thought about going to beg for food, but then if she did someone might tell Charles and he might come after her with the gun. She didn't want to return to the same old arguments, the same drudgery; the nights when Charles came home drunk and forced her onto her back, when he lay astride her as she stifled a scream of rage at her powerlessness, listening to him say, 'You're my wife. I take what is mine.' If she returned it would mean total submission. It was unthinkable.

And yet she knew she had been foolhardy, thinking she could leave home without making any plans. She could go to her father, but he had abandoned her after she married. She had only seen him once in nine years. She did not even know where he was. Thinking about her plight she began to cry, rocking backwards and forwards, sobbing until she had no tears left. When she calmed down she blew her nose on her petticoat — she had no handkerchief or handbag.

The tears proved a release and hardened her resolve to go on alone, accepting for the moment she had no way of getting her children back.

She stretched. The sun was rising and the bush emerged from the shadows of the night, as if the world was waking up. Magpies warbled in the tree over her head. A crow flew onto a branch and stared at her. As she stood there the thought came into her mind that she had been given the gift of a new day, as if it was the first day of her life. The past was dead. She had to learn to accept it.

The cows were ambling in single file to the dairy to be milked as she crossed the paddock to the creek. There she knelt and, cupping her hands, scooped up a draught of water which she drank thirstily. Then she laved her face and hands, the cool water refreshing her. When she had smoothed her hair and straightened her dress she made her way back to the road, planning to hail any passing vehicle for a lift to the nearest town.

She was sitting by the side of the road later when she heard the unmistakable sound of horses, and soon a team of horses pulling a dray came into view. She ran alongside until the driver brought the dray to a halt. Holding the reins loosely he leaned down. 'Where did you spring from, mavourneen? You look as if you've been in the wars.'

'My horse bolted.' Winifred tried to smile but failed dismally. 'I slept out all night. My clothes … everything I own was in my saddlebag.'

'Where're ya bound?'

'Somewhere where I can get work,' she said, and without waiting for an invitation she climbed up beside the driver. He sat there for a few seconds looking at her. He was about her own age, with a mop of light red hair, a long unkempt beard and a pair of penetrating blue eyes. She became conscious of her bedraggled state and looked away in confusion. Then he cracked his whip and called, 'Move along, me spalpeens,' and the horses were on their way, clip-clopping along the dirt road in a swirl of dust.

They continued in silence until the driver turned to her and held out his hand. 'I'm Michael Flanagan.'

'My name's Winifred,' she said as she took the outstretched hand, wondering whether to use the name of Steger or make up another name.

But it didn't seem to matter because the next thing he said was, 'Ye hungry?'

She nodded and he brought the horses to a halt. 'We'll stop here and make some tea.' He took a loaf of bread, a tin of treacle and some tin mugs out of a box in the back of the waggon. A black billy can and a battered frying pan were hanging from the side of the dray which was packed high with boxes and bundles. 'You look as if you could do with a feed? Fancy a fresh egg?'

Winifred gathered some kindling and a dead branch from the side of the road and placed them in a little clearing. 'You've done this before,' her companion said, and the kindling blazed into life as he struck a match. Winifred leaned closer, trying to warm her hands. She felt cold, even though the sun was shining.

The water in the billy can came to the boil and Michael Flanagan lifted the lid. As steam poured out he dropped in a handful of tea leaves, replaced the lid and put the tea to one side while he melted some dripping in the frying pan. Winifred's eyes widened as he broke in twelve eggs, tossing the shells into the fire where they hissed, then blackened and disintegrated.

'If you look in the box you'll find some tin plates and a knife.' She did as she was bid and then watched as with a deft twist of his wrist, he tossed the eggs high in the pan to turn them over.

She cut two slices of bread and put a slice on each plate while Michael served the eggs, dividing them evenly so that they had six each. In later years Winifred often thought of that meal. It was one of the best she had ever eaten, sitting by the side of the road with a stranger and yet feeling completely at ease as if she had known him all her life.

When they had finished he took a piece of newspaper and wiped the plates and frying pan clean, then rinsed the knives and forks and the mugs in the water left in the billy can, then packed them back in their box. With Winifred sitting beside him he flicked the whip and the dray was off again.

She woke with a start some time later; the movement of the horses and the fact that she had not slept much the night before had made her drowsy.

'Feeling better?' Michael asked.

She nodded and instinctively put her hands to her head to smooth down her hair, thinking she must look a fright.

'We'll kip down for the night before it gets dark. I know a place,' he said. 'It's a bit off the beaten track. There's a clearing with some feed for the horses and plenty of wood. I'll light a fire and we can have a bite of bread and cheese and a mug of tea with a drop of whisky to keep the cold out.' And he continued on his way until the sun started to sink lower in the western sky.

He turned off the main road and made his way along a track until he came to a clearing. He brought the dray to a halt and jumped down to release the horses from between the shafts, hobbling them before filling their nosebags with chaff and pouring some water from a canvas bag into a large tin dish. Then he filled the billy can and made a small fire in a circle of stones. 'This is my secret place. Even the mozzies don't know about it.'

It was dark by the time they finished eating and a chill wind had sprung up. Michael put a log on the fire and then spread a blanket for Winifred in the back of the dray, lifting out the bales and boxes so that she could lie down and putting them underneath the dray to prop it up. He spread his blanket on the ground alongside. 'Don't forget your prayers, mavourneen. My mother taught me to pray when I was only knee high to a grasshopper. "You can always talk to Our Lady when there's no one else," she'd say.'

Winifred thought about his words as she lay looking up at the stars, listening to the sound of him breathing and occasionally grunting in his sleep. She thought about Sister Angela and Sister Beatrice on the ship to Australia all those years ago. They had talked to her about God and his angels. God … it was almost as if He had sent Michael when she was so weary from walking that she could no longer put one foot in front of the other. Thinking about it, she pulled her blanket tighter and, with her head resting on a bundle of papers, fell asleep.

In the morning they stopped by a creek and Michael Flanagan handed her a towel and a piece of soap. 'I'll light the fire while you have a bathe. Wash your clothes ... I'll lend you some duds. Your things will dry in this heat by the time we're ready to leave.'

Later she returned to the camp fire, her wet hair hanging loose, her wet clothes over her arm, feeling clean and fresh from the cool water and wearing the shirt and trousers Michael had lent her. He grinned when he saw her. 'Begorra, if it weren't for your hair I'd swear it was me little brother.'

He took the wet towel and Winifred heard him splashing in the creek, and then he began to sing, the notes rising over the twittering of hundreds of coloured finches that were perched on the branches of a gum tree that shaded the creek.

He came back not long after, wearing a pair of trousers and holding his wet shirt over his arm. He slung it over a low-growing bush, close to where Winifred had spread her clothes to dry. He was naked to the waist, and she stared at the thick mat of red hair that curled over his chest and sloped down his navel, where it disappeared into his trousers, which were tied with a piece of rope. Then, feeling his eyes on her, she looked away, her cheeks flushed, and put the tea in the billy can which had come to the boil.

Later, with a mug of tea cradled in his hands, Michael Flanagan pointed across the water to where wild ducks were feeding among the bed of reeds. 'If this was Ireland there'd be green hills that run down to the sea ... and white swans. Did you know, mavourneen, there's no snakes in Ireland? Not like this place where you pick up something that looks like a stick and it bites you and you're dead afore you know it.'

Winifred tipped the billy can and filled his tea cup and then her own, her grief momentarily forgotten as his rich Irish brogue carried her to his homeland.

'It was St Patrick himself who drove them away. We lived in a little cottage with a dry stone wall and outside a little path barely wide enough for a donkey cart to pass. And then my da died, God rest his soul. My mither tried to manage with a few fowls and a patch of taties and a pig that slept in the house alongside of me bed. But some foul plague got into the ground … Father Murphy said it was the work of the devil and he tried praying, but 'twas no use. My little mither tried putting out a dish of milk for the leprechauns but that didn't work either … The fowls got some disease, the pig died and the taties rotted in our little patch … It weren't the first time it happened.'

He looked at her and grinned, leaning across to the fire to toast a slice of bread on a stick. 'Don't mind me going on. My little mither, God rest her soul, said I must have kissed the Blarney stone. But when I'm on the road for so long with no one to talk to, it's kinda lonely like.' He looked sideways at her. 'You English?'

'I grew up in London.'

'Well, it weren't your fault, so I'll forgive you. You never heard tell of the potato famine in Ireland?'

Winifred shook her head and spread some treacle on her toast, brushing off the flies that seemed to have appeared from nowhere.

They were packed up and on the road again when he said, 'You see, the English … well the English owned all our land, but they didn't live there. It didn't matter a tinker's cuss to them that their brothers on the other side of the Irish Sea were starving.' He looked at her. She was sitting beside him in her borrowed clothes, a tweed cap he had lent her covering her hair, her shoulders hunched, a sad dejected air about her. He patted her on the shoulder. 'I can see you got troubles of your own. Well, Michael Flanagan ain't the one to go pokin' and pryin', so I'll shut up now.' He took a tin whistle out of his pocket and began to play an Irish jig that set the horses almost dancing along the road until Winifred began to laugh.

'I had a horse once … It used to go down on its knees if it saw anyone coming along the road.'

'Not the horse that bolted on you?'

'No, that was a different horse.'

'Where were you going when your horse bolted?'

She was tempted to tell him the truth, but something restrained her. Instead she said, 'Looking for work.'

'There's a few homesteads where I drop off supplies … Most are as lean as Paddy's pig … they could do with an extra pair of hands but can't afford a brass farthing in wages. You'd be up at sparrow's fart milkin' cows, diggin' turnips, and no one to talk to from one day t'other … You're not hiding from the law, are you? Not that it's any business of mine.'

'I haven't committed any crime.'

'Well then, I know just the place for you, if you can bear with me for a few more days. There's a hotel at Morven where I stop off when I'm passing … I think you'd get along right well. Mrs Dawkins, well now, she's a fine woman and generous — she can afford to be. She'll pay you good wages and be glad to have you. It's hard to get a decent white woman out here. Always plenty of t'other sort. And Aboriginal women, afore you can say a Hail Mary they're off. I don't blame them, it's their country and they don't have to work for white folks … You been to Morven?'

Winifred shook her head.

'Well now, it's a place where roads meet, with lots of folk going backwards and forwards. It used to be called Saddler's Well after a waterhole on Hamburg Creek. It was here folks stayed when they couldn't face going any further, and built a store or a hotel. You'll like it there.'

16

SANCTUARY

WINIFRED ARRIVED AT MORVEN JUST before Christmas 1909. Michael Flanagan took her to a hotel on the western edge of the town. She often wondered what Mrs Dawkins must have thought when she first saw her in a crumpled dress, her face burned from sitting in the open dray in the sun without a hat, her hair like a birch broom in a fit, and her fingernails broken and black with grime.

He drove the dray around the back and left Winifred sitting there while he went in to talk to Mrs Dawkins. Winifred had no idea what he told her but later she felt it wouldn't have mattered, because Mrs Dawkins was beside herself trying to cook breakfast for fifty people.

The kitchen staff had run off, so Winifred went into the kitchen and washed the stack of dishes piled up from the night before and cleaned the kitchen. Mrs Amelia Dawkins, the owner of the hotel, was overjoyed and offered her a pound a week and her keep if she'd stay, and gave her five pounds in advance so that she could get herself some clothes.

After breakfast was over, Mrs Dawkins sat with Winifred and Michael while they ate sausages, eggs, bacon and fried bread and washed it down with cups of tea.

'All the rooms are full,' she said to Michael. 'I can make you up a bed in the stable.'

'I'm not staying. There's a lotta little spalpeens out west who'd wake up disappointed on Christmas morn if there wasn't a dolly or a tin whistle in their stocking. I'll take a couple of bottles of whisky from the bar in case someone asks me to share a slice of pudden.' He put a pound note on the table. Then, with a wave of his hand, he went out the back door and into the yard where his horses were waiting.

The hotel was quiet now and Mrs Dawkins told Winifred to have a hot bath. She lent her some clean clothes and led her to a little room off the verandah. 'As soon as you're ready, come through. There's beds to make and the bar opens at ten o'clock, then there'll be lunch. You've got half an hour,' and she went bustling off.

Winifred gazed around the small room with its door lock and a key on the inside, its black-iron bedstead with a white counterpane and its clean white sheets and a soft pillow. She had found a haven. For the time being she had a home. Then, thinking back to her flight from Charles and her lost children, she was overcome with grief and began to weep.

The work was demanding, but Winifred was no stranger to hard work and her employer treated her fairly, sharing the workload and treating her as an equal. As she got to know the town she was to discover that Morven was a big trucking centre for sheep, cattle and horses which were loaded onto the railway that travelled via Toowoomba to Brisbane. Cobb and Co passenger coaches also travelled from Mitchell to Roma in the east, through to Morven, Charleville and places beyond. There was a steady stream of people passing through, which kept Mrs Dawkins's hotel very busy.

Morven had a mixed population, with a police station, a school and four hotels. Aborigines camped below the main settlement, drawing their water from the dam on the edge of town. And gangs of Chinese were employed as itinerant workers to poison prickly pear, which was still a problem.

There was plenty of work to be had and for the first time in her life Winifred knew that she would earn a proper wage for what she did. That knowledge gave her a lot of satisfaction. She swept and dusted, made beds, took cups of tea to the men in the morning, learning to evade their groping hands, emptied chamber pots as she had done years before for Mother Sybil, served meals and washed up. It was a clean, well-run hotel and the men left tips in their saucer when they had finished eating. She began to save money, having little to spend it on once she had bought herself some new clothes, a hairbrush and mirror, a pair of good leather shoes, some stockings, some chemises and drawers and a knitted woollen shawl for when the evenings got cool.

Mostly she kept to herself, walking along Main Street to one of the market gardens on the edge of the dam where she chose the vegetables for lunch, stopping to chat to an old Chinaman. In broken English he talked about his family in

China, to whom he sent money every month, and she learnt how he had come to Australia hoping to find gold, only to discover that Chinese were not allowed on the goldfields. They could not work at other trades — they were not allowed to become a member of a trade union because of their race. He missed his family and she sympathised with him, though she could never bring herself to speak of her own situation and how she yearned to see her children. He would follow her to the gate and call out, 'Goodbye, missy.' Once he gave her a pot of preserved ginger as a gift. She did not know why, except that he said, 'Special day,' and she thought it might be his wedding anniversary or someone's birthday.

Sometimes when the weather had cooled in the late afternoon and the hotel wasn't busy, she would go for long walks, but always by herself, afraid to trust any of the men she met. To the north and north-west of the town was plain country, and to the south, hilly, scrub country with sandalwood, ooline and mulga trees. She would watch the kangaroos and wallabies grazing quietly until a sudden movement sent them leaping away. And there were flocks of bright birds that swooped in to eat the grass seeds and others that chased insects in mid-flight. Other times she walked to the top of one of the hills and stood facing the Downs, trying to imagine that she could see her children. She would talk to them as if they were there, telling them how much she missed them and that she still loved them. Later, she would dream of holding them in her arms. When she woke she would weep bitterly, until it was time to get up and make early morning tea.

Mrs Dawkins never commented on Winifred's tear-stained face, though she was always gentle with her in the mornings, until later in the day when the hotel got busy. Then her temper would flare and she would begin to scold if Winifred was slow making the beds or took too long fetching the vegetables from the market garden. 'For heaven's sake, woman, get a move on. Otherwise the customers will go somewhere else and then we'll both be out in the street.' But later she would make it up to Winifred by pressing a ten-shilling note into her hand and saying, 'I don't know what I'd do without you.'

Two years had passed and Winifred felt more settled, as if she had never lived anywhere else. The hard work and the company of the men in the bar diverted her mind from her grief over her children, and though she did not intend to stay at the hotel forever, she had no immediate plans to leave. Occasionally Michael Flanagan turned up on his way through, and he would play the tin whistle in the bar while the men sang and danced an Irish jig, clumping around in their clodhoppers until the two women collapsed with laughter.

It was during a quiet time in the hotel that Winifred began to write again.

12 January 1911. For once I know the date. I managed to get a notebook and a pencil and now I can write. It's been a long while since I've put pencil to paper. The urge to scribble left me but now it's coming back.

Sometimes I have no idea of the date or the day of the month. I go into the bar and look at the calendar. Or I ask one of the men. Sometimes they look at me as if I'm daft. But the days go by so quickly and there's always so much to do that I just fall into bed exhausted.

Yet I can never go back. Not after what happened. Sometimes I cry, and it helps, but it won't change things or bring back my children. Today is a glorious day. Mrs Dawkins told me to stay in bed. She brought me a cup of tea and some toast and honey. She said, 'You've earned a rest.' It's true. I was run off my feet over Christmas, so many men came in for a week, men without homes or families.

The luxury of lying back in clean white sheets and a soft pillow filled with feathers, white curtains at the windows and a view across the acacias to the distant mountains. In the mornings the trees are festooned with green and red parrots and I close my eyes and imagine that I am in Arabia. Then at night the birds squabble and squeak as they fight for a place on a branch. I have to laugh watching them ... not that I get much time to stop and stare. I like to look across to the mountains. It's a long way off. Too far to walk.

I like to imagine that I'm there all by myself in a little white tent. No beds to make, no sheets to wash, no washing-up, no cooking or cleaning. Just me sitting quietly writing stories for myself. I am the queen of the mountain, with kangaroos and possums as my subjects. I live on nuts and berries and drink from a waterfall that flows down the mountain like a fine veil, crystal drops dancing in the sunlight as it sparkles against the side of the cliff.

22 February 1911. For the first time this morning I didn't cry when I woke up. I feel as if part of me is healing. I'm tired — so tired. So much washing to do here at the hotel. My hands

are red raw by the end of the day. I rub mutton fat and sugar on them. And my legs ache — the veins. Some days I'm so tired that all I want to do is to lie down with my legs wrapped in wet towels. Yet I found myself singing the other day, a silly song the men were singing in the bar called 'Waltzing Matilda'. Someone came in with an accordion and played all night. It was like a party. Even though I'd been up since dawn I joined in. I don't drink but there were some sore heads in the morning. Rusty, the rouseabout, hosed down the verandah — but the smell of vomit! Still, it was good for business. Mrs Dawkins gave me an extra pound. And some of the men gave me tips. I'm saving money. I won't have to stay here forever.

30 March 1911. Nights here are strangely quiet once the drovers have left. I think of the nights as velvet. The days are like gauze with a fine film of dust that shimmers in the heat. The sun sets very quickly. The birds quieten down and the night noises take over. A horse whinnies, an owl hoots and sometimes I hear the beating of its wings as it swoops through the air to seize a mouse. Then there are the dingoes that howl to the moon. Everything is white in the moonlight and the stars disappear. I try to pretend that it's snowing outside so that I can snuggle under the sheet and get back to sleep. The air is so hot, without a whisper of a breeze — except the mozzies fanning the air. I tried sleeping under a net but I found I couldn't breathe and even so one found it couldn't live without me and had a fine feed. I was covered in red welts when I woke.

Now I burn cow dung in an empty jam tin — it keeps them away. Sometimes my hair reeks of it when I go into the

226

bar, but I don't care. I've no time for men. They want to dance with me, ask me to go for a walk or a ride on the back of their horse. But I know where that will lead. I don't want to get caught again. Still, they're good to me. I got so many tips over Christmas and Michael Flanagan gave me a piece of opal potch. You can see the fire in it if you turn it to the light. He said it wasn't worth much — just a keepsake. I put it in the box under my bed. I've saved almost fifty pounds.

1 August 1912. Sometimes I write a letter to my children but I never hear back. The first time I wrote, the page was wet with tears. I didn't write again for a long while after that, but I don't want them to forget me. I wonder if they ever see my letters. Sometimes I think I might just as well walk to the creek and put a letter in an empty lemonade bottle, seal it with a marble, pull the wire tight around the neck and toss it in when the water's high. A fanciful thought. I don't think Hamburg Creek meets up with the creeks on the Downs. It would be funny if it did and the lemonade bottle bobbed up in the creek near Evergreen.

15 November 1912. It's my birthday today and I'm thirty. Almost middle-aged. I don't know why I remembered. No one else ever did, except Aunt Liddy. She made me a cake once. That was when they were living with us. I wonder where she is now. Uncle Bill kept us apart. She told me she wanted to come when Fred was born, but he wouldn't let her. Still, she was there when I had Winnie.

I wrote a letter to little Winnie to let her know I still love her. I wrote to Peter on his birthday too. I sent him a copy of

Huckleberry Finn *which one of the men left in the bar. But that was three months ago and no word. I keep hoping. Charles was so angry with me for leaving. I can't understand why. It's not as if he ever loved me. Once I thought he did. It was just because I was lonely. I was weak and foolish. I needed someone.*

When he took me in his arms and said he loved me, I believed him. When anyone comes this way from the Downs I ask about the family, hoping for some news. I've heard nothing since I left. I'd just like to know that my children are alive and well, especially my darling Peter. He was always my favourite. He used to put his arms around me and hug me. Little Winnie was too young to remember me. And she had her grandmother — that hausfrau. *I think she hated me because I was British. Fred and Jack. I wonder how they turned out. Jack was a bit too much like his father. Sometimes I wonder if they'll walk into the bar one day and I won't know them.*

10 July 1913. I dreamed of home last night. That I walked across the cornfield and in the back door. The family were seated around the long bark table — Vater Carl at one end and Mutter Barbara at the other. He had his stockwhip by his plate so that he could lash out if anyone spoke out of turn. His gun was in the corner by the door. There were fourteen plates set. As I stood there I was conscious of heads turning and fourteen pairs of eyes staring at me. I was hungry and there was an enormous loaf of black bread on the table. I leaned across to take a slice but Vater Carl said, 'Nein. We have fourteen mouths to feed already. In this house you have to earn your brot.' I wanted to explain that I was expecting a child — Charles's child, but then I woke and found I was crying.

I never wanted to be like Mutter Barbara. Twelve children and one that died. She wanted me to be the same. She hated me from the first. Blamed me for what I did to her son. It was what he did to me. I was glad when I woke. The dream unsettled me.

1 September 1913. There's no meaning in my life. Every morning I get up at five o'clock to light the fire. I carry cups of tea to all the rooms, listen to men grunting and breaking wind, smell their foul breath from drinking too much, dodge their hands when they try to drag me down to the bed. I've had enough of men to last me for life.

I'm saving a little money. Perhaps one day I can escape.

24 December 1914. I washed up for fifty today. So many men came in for Christmas. They slept out in the yard, on the verandah, every room was full. Yesterday the cook had a fight with Mrs Dawkins and left on the train. She promised me another pound a week if I can manage until they get another cook. I've never cooked for so many before. I was up to my neck in flour, and the heat from the stove. It's hard not to let the meat spoil. Someone said it was 140 degrees. I had to scrape the maggots off the mutton before I cooked it.

It's a luxury to go to bed at night. Clean white sheets and a soft pillow filled with down and a clean woollen blanket — when I think of the cornsacks we used at Evergreen. And no husband to come home drunk.

Winifred often wondered how a refined Englishwoman like Mrs Dawkins came to be running a hotel. Even after so many years Winifred felt that she did not know her well enough to ask personal questions. Though the two women often talked as they worked, it was always general conversation about men who came into the hotel, or whether it would be a good drying day for the washing, or what to cook for lunch the next day. At night when the work was done Mrs Dawkins would retire to her private quarters. All Winifred knew about her was that she had relatives or friends in England because she wrote letters which she asked Winifred to post. It was not until her employer received a cable from England that Winifred heard the full story.

The two women were at the clothes line unpegging the sheets, which Winifred had risen at dawn to boil up in the fuel copper, stirring the clothes with a pot stick until the sweat poured down her face and from under her armpits. While Winifred had been busy in the washhouse, Mrs Dawkins had been flat out in the kitchen, cooking for a team of drovers who were heading out west after having a few days in town over Christmas and New Year.

It had been a busy time, with the men carousing in the bar till the early hours and the two women almost run off their feet. Business had been brisk, and the men had been generous with tips, but now the two women were looking forward to a break. There was still work to be done, though. The rooms had to be thoroughly cleaned from top to bottom, cobwebs removed with a long-handled broom, brass doorknobs polished, windows cleaned and windowsills wiped down, wooden floors scrubbed, mattresses aired and sulphur burned in treacle tins to fumigate rooms against bedbugs and fleas.

The rouseabout helped with the heavy work, lugging the mattresses out to the backyard, climbing a ladder to polish the top-storey windows, mending the wooden railing to the front steps, replacing rotting wall timbers, touching up the paintwork in time for the next onslaught at Easter.

There were also chutneys, preserves and jams to be made from the summer fruits. The rouseabout trundled the wheelbarrow to the general store to collect a bag of sugar, while Mrs Dawkins brought the glass jars to the boil in the copper to sterilise them, and Winifred cut up the fruit.

Now the women were in the laundry pulling the sheets into shape, walking towards each other as they stretched and tugged, before folding them and putting them in the linen closet.

'I've had a cable from England. My sister Annie has died,' Mrs Dawkins said.

'I'm sorry to hear that.' Winifred took the folded sheet and put it on the table.

'I won't be able to go to her funeral. It would take me weeks to get home.'

Winifred lifted another sheet out of the basket. 'Where's home?' she asked as Mrs Dawkins took the other end and began to pull it into shape.

'A little place called Makir, in Cornwall. I was the eldest of ten daughters. When my mother died, my father took it for granted that I would keep house.'

'Was that hard?'

'It wasn't the life I wanted.'

'And yet you ended up here.' Winifred lifted another sheet off the line and put it in the basket.

Mrs Dawkins leaned against the washtub and wiped the sweat from her face with a towel. 'I had a friend, she married a man in the Indian Army. There were not enough eligible young men in our village. She invited me to India, introduced me a friend of her husband. By the end of the season I was engaged.'

She sat down at the table and took a needle and cotton out of her workbasket, and threaded it and began to sew a patch on a worn sheet. 'I went back to England. When he came home on furlough we were married.'

Winifred held up a pillowslip to the light to see if it needed patching, 'Did your father mind?'

'Oh no. Annie took over when I went to India. He was glad to get rid of me. We were as poor as church mice. We used to turn our dresses when they faded. Remake our bonnets. Put newspaper in our shoes when the soles wore thin. Still, the bishop's wife was kind. She gave me some piece goods and bed linen so that I didn't go into the marriage a pauper.'

'But why did you come to Australia?'

'It was my husband's dream. They used to buy horses from here for the Indian Army. He thought he could get rich if he could breed his own horses. So he shipped out of the army and we set sail. I thought it would be like being in India — card parties, balls, servants ... It wasn't like that at all. And Mr Dawkins knew nothing about horses except how to ride them.'

She put down her needle and thread and gazed out the door to where the bees, with a loud humming sound, were clustered thickly on the acacia blossom. 'We should get some good honey … We always had a beehive in the garden. Father used to rob the hive. Once he got so badly stung he was in bed for a week.'

Winifred put the pillowslips on the ironing table. Then she sat down and began to sew a button on a blouse. She was only half listening to Mrs Dawkins, her mind going back to the Darling Downs. She thought it must be the acacia blossoms. They reminded her of Evergreen and how she used to pick them to put on the table. It seemed like a different life. Then she heard Mrs Dawkins say very quietly, 'And then he shot himself.'

Winifred stared at her, not sure what to say, then she stood up. 'I'll put the kettle on.'

'It's all right. It happened a long time ago. You get over things. Just the same, a cup of tea would be nice. Cut some plum cake.'

Winifred went into the kitchen, stoked up the fuel stove and came back a few minutes later with the teapot and cups and two slices of cake on a tray. 'It must have been hard,' she said.

'It was. It was … It wasn't just his dying. There were bills to pay, bills for feed going back years … his whisky. It was all right when he was alive, but when they thought I couldn't pay they threatened to foreclose. And then where would I have been? That's why I started the hotel.'

Winifred sat slumped in her chair. She felt unbearably tired and still had a mountain of ironing to do. She'd be up till all hours. She felt sorry for Mrs Dawkins but it had all happened a long time ago. At least now she owned the hotel and had money.

'If you only knew how I yearn for the sight of the sea. The fishing boats coming in … baskets of fresh mackerel and herring laid out on the beach. Our house looked over the churchyard where my mother was buried and my father alongside, a little brother and now Annie. In the spring there's daffodils and jonquils. If I have to spend another summer here I'll die of longing. As soon as I can I'll sell out and go home.'

As her words sunk in, Winifred thought, 'She's going to tell me I'm no longer needed,' and a feeling of panic went through her.

She was relieved when Mrs Dawkins said, 'I want to ask a favour of you. Could you … Could you possibly run the hotel for a while? I want to go to Brisbane. I'd like a change and I need to see an agent about selling.'

The following week Mrs Dawkins caught the train to Brisbane and left Winifred in sole charge, with the help of the rouseabout and an Aboriginal girl.

Left to her own devices Winifred found she could manage very well. She left the lighting of the stove to the rouseabout; it also fell to him to take the early morning teas to the rooms and to empty the chamber pots. At first he did this with bad grace, until Winifred made it plain that he either knuckled under or found another job. She had a protective feeling towards the young Aboriginal woman and kept her working in the kitchen and laundry, out of reach of the men staying in the hotel.

Often she had to rewash the plates and scour the pots or throw a few buckets of water over the sheets on the line but she didn't hold this against the girl, remembering how she was at the same age and also that the girl had not grown up in this kind of household and knew nothing of housekeeping.

Winifred had helped in the bar before, but this was different. She was in charge. It had always worried her that men came into the bar at the end of shearing and squandered all their money on drink. She remembered how Charles had come home empty-handed after being away, and understood now how it happened. Men went into a hotel, after a long, hard season of work, looking for company, a comfortable bed and a hot meal before they returned home. But under the influence of drink they soon forgot.

Now she was going to try to change things. When men came in with their pay cheque she put it on a spike behind the bar and made sure there was something left to take home. When she thought a man had drunk too much she told him to go to bed. If he refused, she simply ignored his requests to fill up his glass. It was something Amelia Dawkins had never done and at the first the men accused Winifred of trying to run a Sunday school. But although they might stay away a couple of nights in protest, she noticed they came slinking back. She was never sure whether it was the clean beds or the food that attracted them. It never occurred to her that many of the men had a genuine affection for her because she made no demands on them, except that they behave in a decent manner. They liked the way she looked them in the eye, and there was something about her that reminded them of home and of their wives and sisters. She only had to look at a man who was behaving badly for him to quieten down, though there were exceptions.

She was cleaning the bar one morning when she heard a knock on the door. When she didn't answer it she saw a burly man with a shaved head peering in the window. Seeing her there he began to shake the door violently until she opened it a crack and said, 'We don't open till ten.'

Before she could close it he had pushed his way inside and walked to the bar demanding whisky.

'You'll have to come back in an hour. The bar isn't open yet.'

'I want a whisky, you fucking bitch.'

Winifred felt her temper rise. 'I don't allow that sort of language here.'

'And who's going to stop me?' He reached over the counter and attempted to help himself to a bottle of whisky.

There was an empty bottle on the floor and Winifred reached down and picked it up. She swung it around her head and brought it down hard, fetching the man a glancing blow on his temple. He lost his balance and fell sideways, striking his head on the side of the bar before falling to the ground unconscious.

The rouseabout was in the yard cleaning the stables when she ran out screaming, 'Quick, I've killed a man!'

He followed her back into the bar and then laughed. 'That's Big Swede … You couldn't kill him if you tried.'

He grabbed the man by the feet, dragged him out into the yard and threw a bucket of water over him from the horse trough. Winifred stood watching from the safety of the door, certain she'd killed him. She was relieved when she heard him groan. He staggered to his feet, fell against the fence, vomited and then, holding his head, lurched along the dirt road until he collapsed in a heap under a gum tree. Later, before she opened the bar, she peered out the window and was relieved to see that he had gone.

The news of her exploit spread and men she had never seen before came into the bar to look at her. They were surprised to see a slight, handsome woman in a printed cotton dress, with dark hair and a determined look in her grey–green eyes, who refused to be drawn when someone said, 'Is this the hotel where Big Swede lost a fight with a sheila? They say she king-hit him in the first round.'

Mrs Dawkins did not return to the hotel. Instead she wrote to say that Michael Flanagan had offered to buy the hotel, and asking Winifred to stay on until he took over. She was returning to England.

It was some weeks later before Michael arrived with his dray. She saw him from the window and watched as he unsaddled his horses, wiped them down, saw that they had water and feed, and led them to the stable.

He came into the kitchen where she was busy filling the salt cellars for breakfast. 'Mrs Dawkins tells me you're buying the hotel,' she said.

'Well, not quite. It depends on certain things.'

Winifred went on with her work.

'I'd like to talk to you, mavourneen.'

She looked at him.

'Not here. Will you walk with me to the waterhole when the bar is closed?'

'Why can't we talk here?'

'There's too many ears.'

'I'm always so tired,' and she looked at him, wondering what was on his mind.

'Just this once, mavourneen,' he asked, and she agreed.

That night she was conscious of being watched as they left the hotel. There was a new moon and Michael pointed to it. 'If me mother was alive, God rest her soul, she'd be turning over the few coppers in her purse for luck. "Never look at the new moon through glass. It's unlucky," she'd say. Brother Henry would chide her for being superstitious. "Bridget Mary," he'd say, "there's only the blessed Virgin and our dear Lord her Son. Pray to them for what you want. There's no such thing as luck." But then he'd never seen a leprechaun or found a four-leafed clover.'

His face crinkled in a grin. 'Do you believe in luck? I do. This is going to be my lucky night.'

Winifred stood beside him, looking at the water, wondering if he intended to ask her to marry him, knowing that no matter how much she was tempted she must refuse. And even if she was free to marry again, she wondered if it would end up with Michael drinking and her working hard to support them both. And yet there was something so engaging about him. She remembered how she had been stirred when she had seen him coming bare-chested from the creek.

'Mavourneen, I've knocked about a bit. Done things I'm ashamed of, but deep down I'm a decent man. Before I left Ireland I promised my mither I'd find a little Irish colleen and marry her and call our first girl Bridget Mary. Well, I'm still looking for that girl and my mither's dead, God rest her soul. You and me ... we could make a go of it. You could run the hotel and I could keep on with my work.'

His face was glowing as he spoke, his lips parted. She wondered what it would be like to feel his arms around her, his lips on hers, and was tempted to hold out her arms. But she resisted.

'What do ye say, mavourneen. Do you want me to go down on me bended knee?'

She shook her head. 'No, Mr Flanagan. It's not possible. I can't marry you.'

'Don't say that. We can make something of the hotel. Of course things will have to change. You're too easy and that's the way to ruination. In a few years we can sell out and I'll take you back to Ireland and show you my mither's grave.'

'I'm sorry,' she said softly. 'Truly sorry, but it's not possible.'

'Without you I can't run the hotel. It's so hard to get good staff.'

As his words sunk in she thought, 'I know. Now I get a wage. If I was your wife I would be working for my keep.'

'No, Mr Flanagan.'

He tried to take her by the hand. 'Mavourneen, I'm tired of being on my Pat Malone.'

She pulled her hand away. 'I told you, no.'

'By why, mavourneen? I'm making you a fair offer. You're not a silly girl. And I know me own mind. This might be your last chance. I'd treat you fair. I promise on me mither's grave. If you marry me you won't regret it.'

She looked at him standing there, his eyes shining in the half-light, his voice low and pleading. She wanted to go to him, to feel his body pressed against hers. To run her fingers through his red hair. She could feel her body trembling. She told herself it was madness. It took all her willpower to turn away. Without looking back she hurried back into the hotel and went straight to her room, leaving the rouseabout to close the bar.

Michael had gone in the morning without having breakfast. She felt guilty, wondering if she had misjudged him and he really cared for her. But it was impossible while she was still married.

Michael Flanagan did not buy the hotel. It was quickly sold to a Yorkshireman, Jack Dyson, who asked Winifred to stay on. He turned out to be a hard-drinking man who skited to her about the money he'd made gambling. She did not take to him. Now she was kept out of the bar at night. He brought in a woman with hennaed hair called Molly, who sat on the bar with her legs crossed. She had a room upstairs among the men and at night Winifred would hear whispered voices and doors opening and closing. One night the handle of Winifred's door turned and she heard a voice calling softly, 'Let me in, Moll.' She lay quietly, knowing that the door was locked and she was safe, while her mind travelled back to Mother Sybil's. She knew she could no longer stay at the hotel.

Now there were arguments, and fights with broken bottles. Sometimes in the morning there would be men lying in the yard in their own vomit, while the rouseabout hosed around them as if they were nothing better than a lump of wood.

The atmosphere in the hotel changed. The new publican encouraged the men to spend their cheques, so that there was nothing left to take home. When Winifred protested he said, 'This isn't the Salvation Army. I didn't come to Australia to preach, but to make money. I had to struggle to get where I am and I'm not giving it away.'

She was certain her employer was serving adulterated liquor, but he made sure she stayed out of the way in the kitchen. And once when he had been drinking and saw her looking at him, he said, 'Your face would curdle a mother's milk.'

His words wounded her and she began to ask passing drovers if they knew of any other jobs. When she heard that they needed a cook at a hotel in Mungallala she gave notice. Jack Dyson was angry, and told her that she was leaving him in the lurch.

'It's your own fault. You told me I was sour. It's the way you run this place that's soured me, taking men down for everything they have and leaving nothing for their wives and families. If you need someone to cook, then put that fancy piece with the red hair in front of the stove. It'd do her good to do an honest day's work.'

She regretted her words later because when she left he owed her five pounds, which he refused to pay.

PART THREE

17
FALLING IN LOVE AGAIN

WINIFRED HAD BEEN SEPARATED from her husband Charles for seven years when she met Ali Ackba Nuby, who ran a general store in a disused hotel at Mungallala. It was owned by Mrs Elizabeth Corbett of Victoria Downs Station, who also owned the Mungallala Hotel where Winifred now worked. In that seven years she had been unbearably lonely, missing her children, though the first sharp pain at their loss had dulled and she had come to accept that she might never see them again.

Now she felt shut in as day followed day, the same routine of cooking and cleaning, talking to men who passed through, saving money but with no clear plan for the future. The thought that she might spend the rest of her days doing the same dreary work terrified her.

She found it difficult to plan ahead, thinking that once she had saved enough she could start something for herself, perhaps a place where she sold food to passers-by, but then she knew she would have to offer grog with it and she didn't know whether she could stand the drunkenness and the fights. It would mean employing a man and she was reluctant to do that, certain that whoever it was would exploit her and end up bringing her grief.

She was still writing down her thoughts, finding solace in putting words on paper.

10 March 1915. There's a hawker who calls here … an Indian. His name is Ali. He comes into the kitchen and I make him a cup of tea. He's one of three brothers … His older brother came here in 1884 and stayed for eighteen years and then he went back to India and Ali came to take his place. He's been here for thirteen years. He drives a horse and cart and hawks things around. I can tell he's lonely. They're not allowed to bring their wives with them. He comes into the kitchen and I make him a cup of tea and we talk.

I bought a dress length from him. It's sprigged muslin. I made myself a new dress on the treadle machine. I patch the sheets and do the mending for the hotel. And I do little jobs for the men — sew on a button, turn a collar, patch a pair of pants. They pay me for it. I'm saving more money. There's nothing much to spend it on here.

11 March 1915. Ali came in again today. He has the most beautiful brown eyes and white teeth. He calls me mem-sahib and treats me with respect. He gave me a length of hair ribbon to match the dimity. He speaks English but with an accent — not like Vater Carl with his thick guttural voice, but in a lilting tone. He talked about his home in India and his little mother and his brothers and sisters. I had tears in my eyes listening to him. He doesn't go into the bar with the other men.

I watch him sometimes from my bedroom window. He is a Moslem. He prays, kneeling and prostrating himself on the ground. He always comes to the tap in the yard to wash himself first.

Sometimes he wears a turban and baggy pants and a waistcoat. He looks different from the drovers in their moleskin pants and shirts. Some of them don't like him and call him 'that bloody Afghan'. He is gentle-looking and smells of curries and spices. He delivers vegetables in his horse and cart, and spices and fancy goods. He keeps them in a tin trunk. When he stops outside the hotel he lets down the side of the cart and everything is on display. There is a smell of sandalwood and spices. Often I smell it in the air long after he has gone, and imagine that I am in Arabia with date palms and desert, with a full moon turning the sand to silver. I pretend I'm waiting for a lover, listening for the sound of horse's hooves.

Next time Ali comes I'll buy myself a lace camisole. He has such pretty things. I bought a little red wooden top to send to Peter for his birthday. He would be eleven now. I didn't hear back so I don't know whether he got it or not. There is no news. It's like another life. It's strange to think that on the other side of the world there's a war on. Some of the men have gone off to fight the Germans. There used to be a German

man who came into the bar. He stopped coming after a fight out the back. I don't know why there has to be a war. The men argue about it and about conscription. Sometimes they get heated and I have to say, 'Calm down now, boys. You're not in the trenches. How about a song?' And someone gets out the accordion and they start to sing and forget the war.

I hope the war ends before my boys are old enough to fight. They're half-German. They could be fighting cousins they've never met. Ali doesn't know I'm married. He thinks I'm a widow and my husband was killed in the war.

It was September 1915 and the hotel was short-handed. Winifred was in the kitchen up to her arms in dirty water, her hair like rats' tails falling into her eyes, and her face running with sweat. It was the end of shearing and the hotel was full. Though she could hear laughing and shouting in the bar she had made up her mind not to go in. Her ankles were swollen, her head ached and she felt exhausted. For a week she had been run off her feet. 'I can't go on like this,' she told the barman when he came into the kitchen for his evening meal. 'I'm expected to cook and clean all day and then help out in the bar at night. Once I've finished here I'm going to bed.'

He was so angry that he got up and stormed out, leaving his plate of Irish stew half-eaten. He had been left in charge while the owner was away. Winifred resented the fact that she was expected to help out in the bar and yet the barman never came into the kitchen to see if she needed help. And when she'd asked the rouseabout to bring in the wood for the stove he had said, 'Get it yourself. I've got better things to do.' Winifred knew she was being imposed on but until she could find another situation she had no option but to put up with it.

She was still washing up when she heard the sound of a horse and cart. She knew it must be Ali, and wondered why he was coming to the hotel at this late hour. He had already been once that day with the vegetables. She finished the last of the pots and dried her hands. There was a piece of cracked mirror above the sink and she glanced in it. 'I look a fright,' she thought and took a comb out of her pocket. She combed her hair, wiped her face on her apron, then grabbed the bottle of lemon essence from the pantry and dabbed a few drops on her forehead to hide the smell of sweat.

Winifred turned as his shadow fell on the kitchen wall and she saw that his arms were filled with yellow paperdaisies. She took the flowers and put them in a jug of water on the kitchen table, conscious that he had come closer. She turned to face him. He leaned forward and took off her apron and hung it on the nail behind the door. 'Come,' he said, holding out his hand.

'I'm too tired to go for a walk.'

'That's not what I mean. Come with me and be my wife.'

'But I can't. I can't just walk out like that. Who will do the work?'

'They'll find someone else. I have watched. You have worked too hard. You must come to me. I have waited a long time.' He folded her in his arms and she began to weep. 'Come,' he said, and led her out the door. 'I will fetch your things tomorrow.'

Winifred hesitated, glancing back at the flowers that glowed on the table beside the lamp, hardly knowing what was happening. In her heart she knew that she wanted to be with him. He saw her gazing at the flowers and took her hand and put it to his lips. 'There will be other flowers.'

Later, she was to remember the night breeze, cool on her skin, and the clip-clop of the horse's hooves on the hard-baked road. The moon had not yet risen. She had nodded off and woke with a start when he stopped the horse outside his shop. He got out and lifted Winifred down, holding her close for a few seconds. She could feel her heart beating faster as he released her. He spread a blanket in front of his door and said, 'Wait here, beloved, while I tend to my horse.' Then he unhooked the hurricane lamp from the side of the cart and hung it on a nail outside the shop.

She watched as he unsaddled the horse and led it into a shed, then returned holding a tin trunk which he opened, spreading the contents on the blanket. There was a pair of baggy white silk pants and a black waistcoat embroidered with red and yellow flowers. 'My wedding garments,' he said. And then he handed her a dress of soft white silk. 'First we must bathe and then ask Allah to bless our union.'

Winifred went into the kitchen and in the darkness sponged her body with cool water; then she pulled the dress over her head, marvelling at the softness of the silk against her naked body. There was the aroma of sandalwood and the air smelt fresh and clean. For a while she stood there, listening to the noises of the night — a frog croaked in the creek, a cricket chirped and a bird called as it flew overhead. The enormity of what she had done overcame her. She had run away with a man she hardly knew, a man who might be unkind to her, a man who might not really love her.

She went to the door of the shop. Ali was standing there beside the lamp looking into a mirror as he wound a length of white silk around his head to form a turban. He had changed into his wedding garments and she thought how handsome he looked. He moved towards her, holding out a string of gold coins which he fastened around her neck. Then he took a length of shimmering cloth embroidered with gold thread and draped it over her head and shoulders, covering her face. 'My little bride,' he whispered. 'You are more beautiful than life itself.' He took her by the right hand and led her to the blanket which he had decorated with yellow and white paperdaisies. Around it he had placed lighted sticks of incense, one at each corner, and wisps of smoke curled lazily upward. The breeze had dropped and the air was still and warm, fragrant with sandalwood.

Ali spread the prayer rug beside the blanket. The lamp hanging on the wall cast a circle of light and beyond it stretched the bush, dark and mysterious. Winifred had the feeling that they were the only two people in the whole world. He stood beside her and with his arms raised above his head called, '*Allah akbar.*' Then he gently pulled her down until she knelt beside him. She watched as he prostrated himself, calling aloud in words she did not understand. When he had finished he turned and took her by the hand. 'Allah, I thank thee for giving me this woman. I will care for her and guide her in the true faith so that she becomes a true daughter of Islam.'

He rose and extinguished the lamp. In the darkness she sensed him moving towards her. '*Salaam alaikum,*' he whispered and lifted her veil.

She was to remember that night with wonder. She had given birth to four children and been married for eight years, yet had never experienced such tenderness. For the first time in her life she felt herself truly loved.

The moon rose sometime in the night and she woke and raised herself on her elbow to gaze at Ali, her husband. He lay beside her, sleeping gently, moonlight shining on his face. She bent and kissed him softly on the forehead and he stirred in his sleep but did not wake. Suddenly she was afraid. She knew that if she ever lost him it would be more than she could bear. 'Allah,' she whispered. 'Keep my Ali safe.'

For Winifred life with Ali was a tranquil existence. For the first time she was living with someone who loved her and whom she loved in return. Ali was always up before dawn to recite his prayers as the sun rose, spreading his prayer rug on the damp grass and turning to face Mecca, while she lay in bed half asleep, dozing until she noticed that he was not beside her. When she heard the sound of splashing she knew that he was washing himself before he began to pray, and she thrilled to the sound of his soft lilting voice as he prayed aloud, thinking that it sounded like music with the birds singing in the background. The only word she understood was Allah. But she was learning to say the prayers, disconcerted when Ali told her that men and women did not pray together.

'If we lived in my country you would stay behind the curtain with the other women. Only the women of the household and your husband would see your face. If you went to the market you would wear a yashmak and someone would go with you.'

'But I wouldn't like that,' she frowned.

'It is a matter of honour.' Seeing that she was disturbed, he took her hand in his and held it to his lips. 'Once you become a Moslem you will understand.'

She was in love and submitted to his will, writing in her diary:

Ali says that if we lead a good life we will find paradise. But if we are bad we go to hell. He doesn't like the way Australian men behave — drinking and swearing. He says that it offends Allah. He told me of Mohommed's vision of the angel Gabriel with feet astride the horizon who said he was the apostle of God. And how Mohommed's wife told him he had been visited by an angel and that Islam owes a lot to women.

Now I have learned to recite the First Pillar of Islam in Arabic and one night we knelt together facing Mecca while I said the words he taught me. 'I testify La Ilaha illa Allah. Mohammed rasul Allah.' *Which means there is no god but Allah and Mohammed is his prophet. I found it easy to become a Moslem, though if I had not married Ali I would be as I had been before: with no religion except my own instincts which tell me that there is an eternal being who cares for us and who has created a beautiful world for us to live in. There is ugliness too and this is something I have never learned to understand. All I learned was acceptance. Life is to be lived and there's no use complaining. But with the help of Ali I have learned to put a face, a name, to a God I can believe in.*

Ali was very moved the night I became a Moslem. He prayed for a long time, sometimes in a loud voice, calling on

Allah, and at other times silently. When my knees began to ache, and my back, from prostrating myself, I stood and very quietly went back into the bedroom and prepared myself for bed. I woke to find myself in his arms and when I put my hand to his face I found it wet with tears.

'Why are you crying?' I asked.

'Because now we are truly blessed. You have become a daughter of Islam and my heart is overflowing with joy.'

I think it was that night our son was conceived.

Ali was gentle and kind, showering her with gifts — silk undergarments and elaborate embroidered scarves to cover her hair. 'In my country a married woman does not allow another man to gaze on her hair. It is for her husband's eyes alone,' and he would gather a long strand of her hair and wind it around his wrist, trying to pull her towards him.

She would laugh and free herself, tossing the scarf from her head. 'It's too hot … and in any case my hair is my own affair.'

He would hold her close, twisting her hair around his neck and kiss her on the lips. 'When I take you to India, then we shall see.'

'India? When are we going to India?'

'One day,' he would say as he resumed his work, loading his cart while she stood looking at his strong hands, hands that could be so tender, thinking how much she loved him and wondering what it would be like to live the shut-in life of an Indian wife. And whether she could bear it, knowing in her heart that wherever he led she would follow.

Each day he would go on his rounds, leaving her to look after the shop, to ladle out sultanas and currants from the two large sacks that stood at the front door, or a few spoonfuls of spices — turmeric, cinnamon and cardamom. She would lift down tins of condensed milk from the shelf, measure up lengths of ribbon and count out buttons, and help select cottons to match dress lengths of printed Indian cotton or brightly coloured silk. When there were no customers she would sweep out the shop and tidy the shelves or spend time making flowers out of coloured tissue paper which Ali sold door to door. There were no fresh flowers except the yellow and white paperdaisies which sprang up after rain and the acacia blossom in spring.

The building they rented had thirteen rooms but they used only four. Winifred found it unbearably hot because of the tin roof. She and Ali would sit outside in the cool of evening and listen to the crickets chirping in the long grass and the wild ducks squabbling in the reeds that lined the banks of Hamburg Creek, which ran past their shop.

As her pregnancy advanced, she found herself constantly tired, spending most of the day lying down until she heard the sound of Ali's horse, when she would rise and prepare a simple meal of curried vegetables with dhal or rice and a dish of sliced cucumbers if they were in season, excusing herself from praying by his side because of her difficulty in kneeling.

He returned home one afternoon just before dusk to find her lying outside under a belah tree because it was too hot inside the shop. She had had niggling pains all day and knew that the birth was close. Winifred tried to reassure her husband but he became alarmed. He got her to her feet and tried to bundle her into the cart so that he could take her to the hospital. The harder he tried the more she laughed, until she leaned against the side of the cart with water trickling down her legs, not sure whether her waters had broken or she had wet herself. When he finally got her into the cart he whipped up the horse which began to gallop wildly, the cart rattling along behind it, bouncing over ruts, sparks flying as the horse's hooves struck ironstone, until they pulled up at Ridge View, Milton, the horse's nostrils flaring, its flanks quivering.

Winifred often thought of that wild ride, imagining that the jolting did her good because her baby was born a few hours later. This time she had a doctor and nurse in attendance. They had told Ali to go home and come back the next day, but he shook his head. He was still there in the morning. Winifred looked out the window at dawn and saw him prostrating himself on his prayer mat. He had unsaddled the horse and thrown its reins over the fence, where it was happily demolishing the hedge. The sight of it made her laugh, and she wondered what the hospital staff would say when they noticed.

She was holding her newborn baby to her breast when Ali came into the room. He bent and kissed her. 'Allah be praised,' he said, and Winifred saw that his eyes were full of tears. Then the nurse came bustling in. 'You must go now and let your wife rest. You can come back later.'

Winifred watched from the window as he harnessed up the horse and went trotting out the gate. Each evening after his rounds were finished he called to see her, bringing figs, dates and almonds, until, three weeks after the birth, he was allowed to take her home.

For Winifred it had been a blissful three weeks in which she had had nothing to do but feed her baby and rest. She could not help thinking back to her other pregnancies and how Charles had expected her to get up and milk the goat almost as soon as the birth was over, as if nothing had happened. Lying with her child in her arms she tried to recall how her other babies had looked, but she found herself lost in her new son, who was to be called Yusef Deen. It was the likeness to Ali that amazed her — the thick dark hair, the eyes and the tiny brown hands that curled around her fingers. He was so different from her other blue-eyed, fair-skinned children with their mixture of German and English blood. Now she had given birth to a dark-skinned child and she wondered whether life would be hard for him. She knew that people did not like Indians. And even though they were British subjects, the government tried to make them return to India every three years, and there apply to return to Australia. The idea filled her with panic because if Ali went he might not be allowed to return, and then what would happen to her and her son?

Later, when she went to Roma to register the birth, she left out details of the father's name and registered the child under the name of Joseph Deen Steger. She was still legally married to Charles and could always claim he was the father if the government tried to send her son back to India. It was all right to be German, even though they were the enemy and fighting the British. The Indians, who were fighting on the British side, were aliens. She found it hard to understand.

At the beginning of 1917, Goolamon Nuby, Ali's younger brother, arrived to take over the store. The family came from a small village near Lahore in north-west India, where periodic droughts caused by the failure of the monsoon meant famine. Thousands died of starvation, others from the resultant cholera. Llaneal Nuby, who had managed the store for almost eighteen years, had returned home fifteen years before, after the death of their father. Ali had taken his place, sending money to India to help support his mother and two unmarried sisters who needed a dowry before they could find a husband. Now, with a wife and child to keep, Ali had decided it was time to go further afield to where the real money lay — in running camel teams — and he had written for his younger brother to come and take his place.

Winifred and Ali were sitting outside the store in the cool one evening, with Ali bent over his water pipe which bubbled at his feet.

'Once my brother is settled in we can leave here. Soon the motorcar will replace the horse and cart and people will no longer want what we sell when they can get it from Toowoomba.'

'But where will we go?'

'To Broken Hill. Abdul Wade is managing the Bourke Carrying Company. I'll see if I can work for him until I can afford to buy my own camels.'

Often he took Yusef with him, the little boy wearing a jacket of black velvet with mirrors sewn on it and embroidered with red and yellow flowers, a pair of baggy silk pants and a little embroidered cap to match the jacket. Winifred would watch them go off together in the horse and cart, realising that a strong bond had developed between them. Yusef would prattle away in a mixture of English and Hindustani, with a few Arabic words thrown in because his father was teaching him the prayers and already he had his own prayer mat.

She and Ali had talked about the child's future and Ali had said, 'He must be good at English if he is to get on in the world. Even in my country those who can't speak English are the poor coolies. I want my son to be rich. Not like me, with nothing but one horse. We need to get our own camels. There's money to be made in cartage. When I own a camel string, Yusef and I will work together.'

'What about me?' she had asked.

'You'll live like a queen in a palace.'

Winifred wasn't sure whether she'd like this. She wanted to be with Ali, not left behind while her husband and son went off without her, but she kept her thoughts to herself.

The family settled in north-eastern New South Wales and there Winifred had two more children, Rhamat Hanaford in 1920 and Pansy two years later, both born in the Boggabri Hospital. They did not stay in the area long because the Bourke Carrying Company was in the process of being wound up in the early 1920s and there was no more work.

They moved to South Australia, where Ali had heard there was work carrying goods to isolated stations in the north. On the way they stopped over in Adelaide so that Ali could visit the mosque and have his sons blessed by the mullah. The family stayed in one of the adjoining tenements in Gilbert Lane which provided free accommodation for travellers. There was no furniture and they had to make themselves comfortable on their prayer mats. They stayed for three days, with Ali spending his time at the mosque with the other men while Winifred looked after the children, resentful when she found that she was not admitted into the mosque but had to remain outside in the small yard. When she asked Ali why he said, 'I told you, women pray at home. The men who come here are camel-men from the north. In fine weather they sleep in the open under the stars and when it rains they sleep inside. If they have a wife she stays at home.'

Winifred had one meeting with the mullah who prayed over her and the children in words she could not understand and then sent her and Pansy from the room while Ali remained behind with the two boys, whom Ali had dressed in white. Winifred had covered her head to please Ali. 'It is a matter of honour, beloved,' he had said. She had acquiesced, realising how much this visit to the mosque meant to him after all these years.

It was at the mosque that Ali found there was work at Marree and the small family joined the fortnightly train with its terminus at Oodnadatta. It was a long, three-day train trip and they carried their own food — dates, figs, oranges and fresh water, plus a bag of flour to make chapattis, which they cooked in a pan on a small kerosene stove when the train stopped for a change of crew. Sometimes the train came to a halt beside a bubbling hot spring so that the passengers could bathe, and Yusef would run wildly over the plains, kicking the small gibber stones, three-year-old Rhamat trotting along behind him. Or the two boys would wrestle, with Yusef always ending up on top of Rhamat, who would have to be rescued. It broke the monotony of the trip, as did the sight of small groups of Aborigines who stood watching in silence at isolated sidings, scrambling wildly with shrieks of joy when one of the passengers threw out an orange or an apple or a handful of boiled lollies. Then the train whistle would give a blast and the engine would gather speed again as it chugged along the narrow gauge track, travelling further and further north.

Now she found the landscape daunting, just mile upon mile of barren plains stretching as far as the eye could see, until towards evening there would be great herds of kangaroos and emus trying to race the train. The driver would blow the whistle, smoke pouring out of the funnel and cinders flying in the open window, while the boys screamed with joy, their heads hanging out of the window while their father hung on to their legs, afraid they might fall out.

Even before they arrived at Marree Winifred felt the strangeness and the loneliness of the country. At dusk she watched as shadows chased the daylight to the edge of the horizon, wondering what lay beyond.

As she looked across the stony plains that shimmered in the heat even though it was not yet noon, Winifred's first response to Marree was one of dismay. It came into being because of the need for a railway from Port Augusta to the copper mines in the Flinders Ranges and beyond. Though the country was arid, with sparse vegetation, there was a chain of springs where the water leaked from the periphery of the Great Artesian Basin. It was from here that the camel-men carried supplies along the Birdsville Track into Queensland.

The family walked from the station past the shops, school, church and hotel, conscious that they were the centre of attention because they were strangers. The men lounging under the verandah of the Great Northern Hotel, glasses in their hands, stared at them as Ali strode ahead in baggy pants, flowing shirt and waistcoat, his brown eyes fierce under his turban. An Aboriginal boy trotted behind with a wheelbarrow containing a large cane hamper with all their wordly goods, and a sugar bag with their pots and pans, their primus, an axe, a shovel and a tin dish for washing. Ali did not seem to notice when a man spat on the ground and said something that made the other men laugh.

Winifred strolled along behind, holding Pansy in her arms while Rhamat clung to her skirts. She called out to Yusef, who was running ahead to catch up with his father, not to fall over. The path was strewn with large gibbers and she did not want him to skin his knees. As she drew level with the hotel she raised her head and stared at the man who had spat, until he dropped his eyes and went back inside, the sound of laughter following him. She knew she had got the better of him. She had come to understand this type of man from her years serving behind the bar and knew that what bothered him was the sight of a white woman with a coloured man, when there were so few women to go round. Not many women were willing to give up the comforts of the city to live a lonely life in a humpy in the outback, or to watch their children die because there were no doctors within easy reach — no other white women for hundreds of miles.

Though she understood the reasons for the man's hostility, she could not excuse it. Women did not belong to men. They had a right to choose their own husbands. And her choice was Ali. She had been given away to Charles, and he had mistreated her. But now she had found love and respect and she knew that this transcended skin colour and race.

She was surprised to see Ali striding back to meet them, Yusef trundling along behind. 'Follow me,' he said. 'The mosque is on the other side of the line. That's where the camel-men live, near the camel yards.' Winifred turned and followed in weary silence.

She smelt the camels coming before she saw them. A swarm of black flies zoomed overhead and she stepped to one side, with Rhamat burying his face in her dress and Pansy screaming. They stood still as the camels were driven forward with shouts and screams until they reached the station where the train was being unloaded. A horse pulling a cart bolted along the road until it upturned into a paddock, throwing out its driver, a man in a bowler hat. He stood and shook his fist at the camels, before unharnessing his horse which was frothing at the mouth, and righting the cart with the help of some passers-by.

The man looked so comical with his bowler hat squashed and his face red that Winifred had trouble suppressing her mirth. She thought that perhaps horses were afraid of camels. She couldn't blame them. They looked like snakes with their long necks that twisted and turned this way and that, and she wondered whether she would ever have the courage to get close. Their coats were thick with dust and had patches of mange where the skin was bare. She thought of Jezebel, the old horse that pulled Mr Jackson's pie-cart, and how she used to brush her coat till it shone and how she would snuffle up to her and eat sugar from her hand. She felt certain that if she tried to do this to one of these creatures it would bite her hand off.

She crossed the railway track, keeping well away from the camels, and saw Yusef running to meet her. 'Baba has gone to the mosque. He says to wait here until he comes.'

The news irritated Winifred. It was hot and dry; the dust kicked up by the camels swirled around their heads, and flies were bothering them. All Winifred wanted was a place in the shade and a hot cup of tea. But Ali had gone off with the spirit stove and tea things. She thought about walking back to the station to get some water for the children to drink, but it meant going past the camels. Instead, she told Yusef to mind Pansy and Rhamat and set off to look for Ali.

Winifred made her way through the galvanised-iron huts with lean-tos in the front, where herds of goats roamed in the dust, conscious of peering eyes and yet not seeing anyone, until she came to a small mosque made of brush and iron set among date palms, where she could hear the sound of men's voices. She poked her head around the door. There were prayer mats hanging on the iron walls and men were sitting around cross-legged. But there was no sign of Ali. A man with a long grey beard and wearing a turban moved swiftly towards her, admonishing her with one finger before waving her away.

'I'm looking for my husband,' she said.

'Go home, woman. Your husband will return all in good time. You have no business here.'

Winifred could feel her anger rising, but then she thought that Ali had come here to find work and she mustn't provoke this man. He could be important. So she walked back the way she had come, her shoes sending up little eddies of dust. She could feel the heat of the sun biting through her thin cotton dress and she wished she had worn a hat, anything to protect her from the heat.

Pansy was fretful when she returned and Rhamat was crying. When he saw his mother he said, 'Yusef won't get me a drink and I'm thirsty.'

With Pansy on her hip, holding Rhamat by the hand and with Yusef by her side, she made her way back to the station where there was a tap. She turned it on and, cupping her hands, let Pansy drink before splashing the child's face with the brackish water. She did the same for Rhamat, then waited while Yusef took a long draught before helping herself.

They settled on the station to wait, watching the goods being loaded onto the camels. Two men were standing, one on each side, and they balanced the weight while the camels knelt snapping and snarling, trying to cast the load off until it was finally secured. Watching, Winifred wondered how she and Ali could possibly manage a camel team. She knew she did not have the strength to load a camel, let alone have enough courage to go near one. And Yusef was still a child.

When Ali returned he was angry because she had gone to the mosque. 'You have shamed me in front of my people. You must learn to be obedient.'

She was silent, even though angry words rose to her lips, and followed him to where he had found accommodation for her and Pansy in one house and for the boys and himself in another. She was not happy with the arrangements and protested about being separated. 'Be quiet, woman,' Ali said. 'There is no other way.'

His sharp words were too much and she began to cry until he took her in his arms. 'Hush, it's only for a short time. Be patient.'

'I'm afraid you will go off and leave us here alone.'

'It would be best if you and the two younger ones stayed where you will be safe, until I learn how to manage a camel string.'

She was silent, making up her mind that she would go with him come what may.

The next day, while Ali was at the mosque, she left the three children and went to the camel yards. She found the smell nauseating but knew it was something she would have to get used to. But it was the evil look of the creatures, with their large yellow teeth and saliva dripping from their mouths, that repulsed and frightened her.

There was a man inside the camel enclosure and she called out, 'Is there a quiet camel I could learn to ride?'

He looked up and walked over, staring at her.

'My husband will be working with camels and we have three young children. I need a quiet camel for them to ride. I've ridden a horse.'

'A camel is a horse of a different colour. They'll bite your hand off if you get in the way ... or your head. If two of them bull camels fight over a female, best keep yer distance.'

Winifred gave him a winning smile. 'I'll be careful.'

He pointed to a camel lying by the fence. 'Sheeba, now, she's expecting a calf and is as gentle as a lamb.' He called, 'Hoosta' and the beast rose to her knees. He lifted a saddle off the fence and fastened it on her back, then tied a long string through a peg in her nose. Winifred saw that the saddle reached almost to the tail of the beast and was nothing like the saddles she had seen on horses. She wondered how anyone could manage to stop falling off the back. Just the same, with the man helping, she settled herself on the saddle, her legs astride, and took the nose strings in her hand. She was conscious that her skirt had ridden up, exposing her knees. She wondered what Ali would say if he could see. She had always ridden side-saddle. She didn't think there were side-saddles for camels because only men rode them. She would have to manage the best way she could, perhaps borrow a pair of Ali's old pants.

She was relieved that the man didn't seem to notice her predicament. He was intent on opening the gate. 'Hang on,' he said and gave a low whistle. The beast rose in the air.

Winifred felt alarmed. She had only the flimsy strings to guide the camel and was a long way from the ground. She wondered how she could possibly manage to stay on. It was nothing like being on a horse. She dug her heels into the sides of the beast and the camel began a slow promenade, swaying from side to side down the dirt track, while the man walked ahead with a stick in his hand until they came to a patch of saltbush. The animal stopped and the man called, 'Hoosta' and as Winifred clung to the saddle the animal sank to her knees and began to chew at the bush.

Winifred slid off and turned to the man. 'Would you sell her?'

'Twenty pounds — two for the price of one.'

A week later Winifred and Ali were on their way to Birdsville where Ali had been offered work as a companion driver, with two borrowed camels and Sheeba. The camels were tied nose to tail in a string in case one wandered off, with Sheeba at the rear. Ali had agreed to work for rations, taking his pay in camels so that he could build up his own string.

Before they'd left Marree, Winifred had strolled across to the other side of the line and called at the school where she'd asked Harold Gale, the young schoolmaster, if she could get some books to teach Yusef while they were on the track. He gave her a copy of a reader that was missing its cover and told her to teach him his alphabet and multiplication tables. She had hoped for some story books but there were no spares, only the ones the teacher used. On her way back to ghantown she passed a general store and went in to see if they had any books for sale. But there were none. Instead the shopkeeper sold her a bottle of a castor oil. 'You can use it for sandy blight, if yer gits a stomick ache and to make a poultice if yer gits a boil.'

Winifred wrapped the blue bottle carefully in a piece of cloth and put it in her bag, evading the question when he asked, 'You new here?' She knew that the camel-men's wives never crossed the line to shop because they had their own shop in ghantown.

Before they set out the next morning at dawn, Ali went to the mosque to pray for a safe journey. When he returned to where they were waiting by their camel string, he said, 'We are going into a trackless waste but Allah will guide us.'

For Winifred, the first day was the worst, over rough gibber plains with no sign of human life except the trail of empty tins and bottles left behind by other travellers to serve as rough signposts. There were no houses, no smoke rising from chimneys, no paddocks, just a treeless emptiness that stretched to the horizon. Ali walked beside the lead camel which carried all their belongings, plus flour, tea, sugar, some salted beef wrapped in a cloth, a huge bunch of dates which had been a parting gift from the camel-men, jars of water, and firewood because there was no wood to be had on the track.

It was the most desolate country Winifred had ever seen. The camels plodded on and the sun rose higher. Rhamat complained of the heat, while Pansy grizzled as she lay awake in a basket which Winifred had fastened on the saddle behind her, with an umbrella for shade. All she could do was to give them sips of water, certain that she had made a mistake in bringing them and that they would never get through alive. She kept her thoughts to herself. Ali had warned her of the dangers but she had insisted on having her own way. If anything happened to the children, she had only herself to blame.

Ali stopped briefly in the middle of the day to pray. The camels sank to their knees to rest and Winifred spread a blanket in the meagre shade they cast. The family sat down and ate a handful of dates with a piece of cold damper, and a mug of water. Winifred would have liked the children to have had a chance to run around and play, but the heat was too intense, the ground parched and almost too hot to walk on.

They stopped at dusk by a small fringe of stunted bush. Winifred was so weary that she was afraid of falling off her camel, but first she had to see to the children, bathing their hands and faces and making them comfortable. Ali had lit a small fire, heated some tinned vegetables and made some chapattis on the hot coals and a huge damper for the next day. As they sat resting, the sky turned a fiery red, the sun like a huge red ball in the west until it vanished, leaving only a red glow on the horizon.

Ali had hobbled the camels and their bells tinkled as they moved off looking for food. Watching them Ali said, 'I hope they don't wander too far. Otherwise we may never find them again.'

Winifred looked at him, her gaze anxious, and he took her hand. 'Allah will guide us. We have nothing to fear. I will pray.'

With the setting of the sun a cool breeze sprang up, and with the coming of night the harshness melted into soft darkness. Winifred spread the children's blankets beside the goods they had unloaded, making a little wall. Pansy was already asleep when she put her down and Rhamat was nodding with exhaustion. She kissed them gently then turned to Yusef, who watched as his father doused the fire and then unwound his turban, preparing for bed.

She took the child's hand. 'Today has been a hard day — nothing to see, only plains covered with stones, not even a tree ... no tracks to follow.'

'How will we find our way?' the child asked, his brown eyes anxious.

Winifred touched him lightly on the head. 'The camels know. They understand this type of country. Now they are looking for something to eat. Tomorrow you and Baba must go and bring them back as soon as it is light.'

'But how will we know where to look?'

'Can't you hear their bells? There's nothing to worry about. We have the sun to guide us. We're travelling north-east. When the sun rises in the morning we know which is east. And at night there are the stars.' She pointed to the night sky that arched above, the stars like beacons against the blackness. 'Watch, and if you see a falling star, make a wish.'

He went to speak and she put her finger on his lips. 'Hush, you mustn't tell. Otherwise your wish won't come true.' She bent and kissed him on the forehead. 'May Allah bless you, my son, and give you pleasant dreams. Tomorrow we reach the sandhills, like giants' castles, so they say. They move with the wind. At dawn they will be tinged with red and turn to honey in the light of the day. At night they will be soft as velvet, full of purple shadows.'

'Does anyone live there?'

'Only lizards that take on the colour of the sand, and hopping mice and sometimes a bird.' She looked down. His eyes were closed and he was breathing deeply. She stood there gazing at her children. It was cooler now and they were sleeping peacefully, and suddenly her spirits lifted. They had survived the first day. Tomorrow would be easier.

She unfastened her hair and went to the tin dish where she washed her hands and face, then sponged her body before relieving herself in the sand. She walked across to where Ali was waiting beside their blankets. The stars glittered in the night sky, the breeze cooled her body in her white calico nightdress, and as she lay in Ali's arms her fears vanished. In some strange way the night seemed holy. She was at peace with herself and her world.

18

TRACKLESS WASTES

LOOKING BACK, WINIFRED WAS SURPRISED at how quickly the family adapted to the nomadic life, spending months away from civilisation, or civilisation as she had come to know it in the small Queensland country towns in which she had lived. But then she thought back to her first year in Australia after growing up in London — the isolation of living in the prickly pear with only her father for company, and the occasional meeting with an Aboriginal boy who sold them a wallaby for sixpence, or Mr McNab who tried to persuade her father to walk off his land. It was a marvel they had survived.

She wondered about her father, thinking of him with pity. She saw him in the lonely drunkards she noticed on the fringes of towns — morose, unhappy, given to fits of violent rage against anyone who tried to help, a rage that was really directed at themselves. Where her father was, or what had happened to him, she had no idea.

Her concerns now were with her children, their education, their health and her own need to be with the man she loved. She had lived so long without love that she could not bear to be parted from Ali. If she was being unfair to her children she put it from her mind. She forgot how she had yearned to go to school in the years she spent trapped with her father, telling herself that the life they were leading was richer and fuller. It was a chance for them to run free instead of being cooped up in a schoolroom, though she knew that sooner or later she would have to accept the fact that her children would need a proper education. And when that time came she would be confined to ghantown without friends, living the narrow, restricted existence of a Moslem wife. In her brief visit to Marree she had seen the way the women lived, not permitted to speak to any man other than their husband or male relatives. Not even allowed to cross the railway line to shop. Staying indoors while the men congregated round their fire talking, arguing and passing the water pipe.

When she had protested Ali had said, 'It's worse in India. If a woman speaks to a man other than her husband, both the man and woman are killed. It is a matter of honour.'

'Pooh,' she had replied. 'It's barbaric!'

Instead of arguing with her Ali had walked away in the direction of the mosque, leaving her with the children. She had vowed then that she would never surrender her freedom. She was a British citizen and had rights. Perhaps it was different for the Aboriginal women who married camel-men and had children. Their daughters were brought up in

Moslem ways, and if they had never known freedom maybe they did not yearn for it.

Later, when she wound her arms around Ali, pressing him close, feeling her pulse quickening as he kissed her eyelids and her throat, she knew he still loved her as much as she loved him. She thought that she was different from the other wives and he had come to accept it, loving her more in some perverse way because he could not control her.

She had asked him if children went to school in India. 'Only the boys. Girls are taught the things they need to know by their mothers — how to care for children, the home, to be good wives. Most boys only have a few years schooling before they start work. But now I can afford it I want my sons to have a good education.'

'When they are older,' she said as she twined her fingers through his beard and kissed him on the lips, 'I don't want us to be separated.'

Winifred developed her own ingenious method of teaching her children, so that by the time they started school they would know how to read. Winifred had acquired a small collection of books, including the Bible, which she read aloud to the children, encouraging them to learn passages by heart. She had been given a second-hand copy of *The Treasure of Heaven*, a romance by the popular English novelist Marie Corelli. Though she pored over the love story, identifying with the heroine, she knew it was not a suitable book for Yusef, so she read him only selected passages describing the scenery, to give him a taste of England. Jam tins and pickle bottles were another substitute for books and she taught Yusef and Rhamat to read by showing them how to make up words from the letters on the labels, as she had done as a child.

She taught them how to distinguish between east and west by the movement of the sun, and passed on her scant knowledge of the stars from what she had learned from Mr Smithers on the long voyage to Australia, pointing out the constellations of Orion and Scorpio, telling them about Sirius the dog star and the Southern Cross which pointed south. Without an atlas, geography became a game in which Winifred would send the children west to Africa to fetch wood for the fire, or point north to China where the camels were grazing on saltbush. She tried to instill in them the knowledge that across the sea, beyond the sandhills, the gibber plains, the unmarked tracks where they travelled with their camels, lay a vast world where people with different skin colours, languages and customs lived.

Ali had won a lucrative contract to deliver building supplies for a hospital being constructed in Alice Springs, so, with their own string of twenty camels, they travelled to Oodnadatta, a journey of six hundred miles. With them were two Aboriginal men to help with the saddling and loading of the camels, to guide them across the unmarked track and to lead them to soaks where there was fresh water. The Aborigines brought their wives and children, the women doing their own cooking with the rations of flour, tea, sugar and jam that Ali supplied. When they called at a station Ali would buy half a bullock which he would then share with the Aborigines. Other times they would hunt wild game.

At dusk, and in the first light of morning, Yusef and Rhamat would run wild with the Aboriginal children. They learnt to track the brush turkey, which sometimes weighed forty pounds, and could creep up on a lizard and grab it by the tail. Though they ate the brush turkey, Winifred made them give the reptiles to the Aborigines, who would toss them live onto the hot coals, skin and all. She was always sickened by the sight and would never allow the boys to eat at the Aboriginal camp, which was positioned away from theirs. Instead, she made them sit quietly while Ali prayed and read the Koran aloud, until Yusef knew long passages by heart, even though he could not understand Arabic. Then they would eat their simple meal together, including bread Winifred had made in the camp oven.

The life suited the children. The boys' faces had browned with constant exposure to the sun, so that sometimes from a distance Winifred found it hard to tell them from the Aboriginal children. She had to be careful with Rhamat because he had her fair skin and grey–green eyes. She was always chasing him with his straw hat. It was easy to keep a sunbonnet on Pansy, because of the ribbons tied under her chin. Yusef had a felt hat like his father, which Ali wore in place of a turban when he was working with camels to give him more protection from the sun.

With the new contract the family based themselves at Oodnadatta, the terminus of the northern railway. If Winifred had expected to see a grand railway terminus like Victoria in London she was disappointed. There were one hundred and fifty residents in the town, housed in forty dwellings. The railway workers lived in the fenced-off railway property. The post office was part of the railway station; nearby was the stationmaster's residence, a tennis court and a school.

There were general stores, a butcher's shop, a blacksmith, plus a number of dwellings known as shacks, which were maintained by the stations further out so that their staff would have somewhere to stay when they came to town. In 1911 the Australian Inland Mission established a hospital not far from the police station. There were few other services. The town only existed because of the railway and to service the sheep and cattle stations further out.

Oodnadatta had become the terminus of the Great Northern Railway by accident in 1891, when the government of the day decided that the railway workers were needed to help harvest a bumper wheat crop further south. Work on the railway, which was intended to follow the Overland Telegraph Line to Darwin, stopped, and was never resumed.

At first sight Winifred was disappointed. The town was built on hot dry gibber plains. The gibbers, which averaged the size of a man's fist, had been polished by wind and sun and reflected the heat. There was no relief from the sun, no distant mountain range to divert the eye, only mirages that shimmered in the heat, giving the impression of vast lakes of water. The tops of the Overland Telegraph poles took on the image of masts on yachts in some great inland sea.

Most years the area was completely devoid of vegetation because the average rainfall was only three inches per annum. People depended on galvanised-iron water tanks to collect rainwater. When they were dry they drew water from an artesian bore. This had been sunk half a mile west of Oodnadatta and flowed at about 250 000 gallons a day through a standpipe to serve the town, with a branch going to a communal shower room where people could bathe in the warm water. Excess water ran down a drain to where Ned Chong had a market garden to supply the town with fresh vegetables.

The camel-men lived apart in ghantown, which was north of the main settlement, and the Aborigines camped further out again. The young family made their home in a small iron hut, divided off with a hessian curtain. Close by were date palms, planted by the camel-men for shade, a crude mosque with a tap in front for ablutions, a bore drain for the camel yards, and goats that wandered around foraging for food.

Winifred and her family arrived ten days before the train was due to arrive with passengers and freight. Even though they were exhausted by the long trip from Birdsville there was work to be done, getting their team ready for the trek to Alice Springs. Camels had to be broken in and branded and saddles needed repairing before they could rest.

They were to discover that the town came to life on those Fridays the fortnightly train steamed in from Adelaide, six hundred and eighty-eight miles south. The European settlers treated it as a holiday. Dressed in their best they hurried across the dirt clearing to the railway station when they heard the whistle as the train crossed Stony Creek Bridge, a tributary of the nearby Neales River.

At the same time the camels, hundreds of them, were brought in to prepare for the loading, with a race to see whose team could be loaded and away first. There was fat and tar to be smeared on mangy hides, saddles to be adjusted while the beasts snapped and snarled. To add to the confusion there was a pack of dogs barking above the noise of the shunting train as the driver tried to get the loaded carriages as near to the goods shed as possible. All the while the dust rose in suffocating clouds.

Despite the camel-men clamouring for the unloading of their goods, the stationmaster refused to deviate from his usual practice, which was first to sort the mail and make up the mailbags for the outlying stations. Once this was done the stationmaster removed his shirt, and with a porter went in to check the goods against the consignment notes, before allocating a load to its particular camel train. Soon the packages overflowed out of the shed onto the dirt platform while tempers flared, with drivers yelling and young camels tossing off their loads. Disputes would break out as men argued with the stationmaster over their consignment notes. Winifred found herself pressed into unwilling service by Ali. 'Many of my countrymen cannot read English. I have told them you will help check their goods.'

It was this that gave her a special place in the Moslem community. She became expert at checking consignment notes and bills of lading and also helped with correspondence. The role was not an easy one because the camel-men argued about the cost of freight, refusing to accept what was written on their cart notes, expecting instead that she could calculate the freight by looking at the loaded camels. Ali never went to Winifred with his accounts. She was never sure whether this was to save her extra work, or because he did not want her to know how much money he had.

On that first day she was at the station from the time the train arrived until the last camel train pulled out. Their own loading was timber and iron for the Alice Springs Hospital. It was an awkward load and they were the last to leave. It had been a six-hundred-mile trek to Oodnadatta, and beyond lay Alice Springs, three hundred miles to the north.

Once the contract for the Alice Springs Hospital had been fulfilled Winifred and Ali ventured further afield, travelling far to the north and almost to the western border. Sometimes they could only spare enough water for a wash in the morning. Other times they came across lush tropical country with lily-covered lagoons where they could bathe and wash their clothes, spreading them on the camels' humps to dry. At Newcastle Waters there was a lagoon the colour of milk from chalky deposits in the soil, and yet it was fit to drink.

There were great waterways, like the Katherine River that flowed through Katherine Gorge. There were ferns, acacia trees in bloom, paperbarks with wild orchids in their branches, and other trees festooned with parrots like exotic flowers. It was dusk when Winifred saw the river for the first time and they made camp. She hastened to its banks, sitting there listening to the droning of flies, thinking back to the times she had sat by the creek when her father sent her to get water and how it had soothed her. She was still sitting there when she heard Ali's voice. 'There may be crocodiles. I've heard they crawl up onto the banks at night. And soon the wild buffaloes will be coming to drink. It isn't safe.'

Their life was not without incident. Once Winifred rode under a gum tree for shade and a snake fell, hitting her shoulder, before sliding down the side of the camel and biting it. The beast plunged wildly and Winifred was thrown to the ground. Fortunately, the children were with their father. Winifred was badly bruised but lucky, because the camel died. It cost them a precious three days, waiting for her to recover.

Sometimes they passed Aborigines bathing in a waterhole covered with pink lotus blossoms. Other times they would pause beside one of the termite mounds which rose higher than the camels, and which had two flat sides facing east and west so that one side was always in the shade. One she christened Canterbury Cathedral because it was formed like a church, with a steeple at both ends that towered over the Overland Telegraph Line.

Once they met a lonely trooper who came and sat at their camp fire. He was looking for a party of Aborigines with leprosy, who had run away when they heard on the bush telegraph that they were to be sent to the leper colony off the coast of Australia. Once there they would never be released. They were still at large later, because Winifred saw them on the return trip and was horrified at the sight of their misshapen limbs when they came up and begged for 'bacca'. The encounter alarmed her, especially as they had leaned close to her children. When she returned to Oodnadatta she wrote to the health department and was relieved to find that there was no risk of infection.

Talking to a group of stockmen around the camp fire she heard about a massacre of Aborigines who had tried to drink from a water trough on a station and had been shot by the manager. 'They say the cattle smell them and won't drink the water. He got rid of the evidence by getting his half-castes to chuck the bodies over a cliff,' the stockmen had said.

When Winifred tried to find out where it happened they refused to tell her. 'Best if you don't know.' They were drovers, and their livelihood depended on securing contracts to take cattle safely through to Oodnadatta. To interfere risked losing work.

Though Winifred never witnessed any of the atrocities she heard about, she was always wary when they pulled into a station, looking at the manager and wondering if he was the one who had shot the Aborigines, knowing it was not something she could ask about. She noticed that often there was no white woman on the property, no wife, only young black women who worked in the homestead, with light-skinned children running underfoot. And though they played with her children she never liked to ask who their father was. All she knew was that when she and Ali had dinner with the manager there was usually a young black woman, wearing a neat cotton dress, who waited on the table but never sat with them.

Gradually Winifred became aware of the conflict over white ownership of the land and the natives who had been dispossessed, their hunting grounds out of bounds and the herbs they used for medicine eaten by cattle. She was disturbed by the sight of the young half-caste women who were caught between two cultures, easy prey for predatory white men.

She also became aware that there were conflicts among the Aborigines themselves. One evening they had hooshed their camels down by a waterhole. In the distance they could hear an uproar from an Aboriginal camp. One of the women in their train belonged to the same tribe and had gone to visit. The next morning Winifred asked her what the uproar had been about.

'Oh big fella row, missus. Old man Gulliman want younger woman. He bin say old Nelly im bin too old, no good. Can't see go hunting no more. So im bin tell her clear off. Nelly, im bin yabber. So Gulliman bin beat her and throw fire sticks and by and by she get up and Gulliman chase her away.'

Later, Winifred heard that the old woman's body had been found by the river bank, where it was left to be consumed by crocodiles.

Another time two men rode up to their camp at midday and were served a mug of tea from the black bucket by the fire. They turned out to be the constable and his tracker from Horse Shoe Bend on the border of South Australia and the Centre. 'We're looking for a big half-caste called Billy Sticktight. He murdered old Lenin, his native missus and their son. He's got a gun. Watch he don't make off with your camels.'

That night Winifred and Ali kept watch but nothing happened. The following evening Winifred was frying some steak that the boundary rider had given her, when Billy Sticktight appeared. He speared a steak and began to wolf it down. What Billy Sticktight didn't know, however, was that the constable had not left the area. The wanted man was overpowered, handcuffed and tied to a tree. The next morning the police constable and his tracker set off on the long ride to Port Augusta to hand over the wanted man. He walked behind, a rope around his waist to secure him to the constable's horse.

By now Winifred was adept at handling camels. She was still wary, though, because no matter how kind you were to them, or even if you raised them from birth, they were never domesticated. She had seen how a bull camel on musth behaved, disrupting the camel train as he tried to get to the females. And she knew of a man in Western Australia who had tried to stop a camel fight and had had his head bitten off. So she was always careful.

And yet she admired the way the camels cared for their calves. She would put the newborn camel in a sack with holes for its legs and secure it on top of the loading where the mother could see it. Once the mother knew her calf was safe she would settle down and the camel train could continue. At three days the baby camel was able to walk beside its mother, dropping behind when it got weary. When the string was unloaded at night the bull would drive the females back along the trail to their calves, where the herd would feed, making a circle to protect the young from prowling dingoes.

Because of the distances they had to travel the camel train set off at first light, as soon as the camels had been brought into camp and loaded by the Aboriginal helpers. Their livelihood depended on delivering supplies to the station and picking up the order for the next delivery as quickly as possible. Ali had elected to do the long runs because they paid better than shorter trips. There was barely time for a quick prayer, a cup of tea and a slice of damper and treacle, travelling as far as they could before the sun got too hot. Even so they only paused briefly for prayers, a drink of water and a few dates in the middle of the day.

Though prayers were prescribed five times a day, they only prayed three times when they were travelling, except on *Juma*, which fell on Friday. On that day they said full prayers.

Before they prayed they changed into their prayer suits which were of calico. If there was no water to perform the ritual ablutions they substituted clean sand, which they heaped into a cone and blessed. Sometimes they spent *Juma* sleeping unless there were saddles to mend, or camels with sores or the mange which needed covering with dripping and tar. For a treat Winifred would soak some dried apricots and make an apricot pie in the camp oven.

She always enjoyed pulling into a station. The Aboriginal children would run to meet them and the station owner and his wife and children would be standing by the gate in the home paddock. It was a welcome respite to be warmly greeted and shown into a room with clean sheets on the bed, and lie in a bath filled with hot water from the black-iron fountain on the fuel stove. Later she and the woman would talk far into the night. Sometimes she came away with a stack of back issues of the *Ladies' Home Journal*, which she pored over, reading the gossip, looking at the latest fashions and the tips on how to preserve your looks. If she noticed her weather-beaten skin when she glanced in the mirror in the guestroom of the homestead, she ignored it. Once on the track again she forgot about it.

It never occurred to her that Ali noticed how she looked. Away from the Aboriginal camp, their children sleeping, Ali still held her, kissing her tenderly, putting her hands to his lips as he had always done, telling her she was the jewel of his heart. Stirred by her own passion she had no reason to doubt his love.

They had been away three months, journeying almost to the western border, and had arrived at a homestead along the route at dusk. The camels had been unloaded and settled for the night. The children were swimming in a lily-covered pond with the Aboriginal children, under the watchful eyes of one of the women. Winifred and Ali were talking to the owner of the property, a middle-aged man, when his nineteen-year-old wife appeared. She was wearing a white muslin blouse and long black skirt, her fair hair curling softly around her shoulders, her unlined face youthful and fresh.

Winifred went to stand beside the young woman and as she did so she saw Ali glance at the young wife and then at her. A look of disgust passed over his face and she became conscious of her unkempt appearance. Her hair was greasy and lank and there were buttons missing from the old blouse she wore over a pair of Ali's old pants, which were torn and dirty and held up with a piece of string. She could smell the fragrance of lavender water, and she stepped to one side, acutely aware of her own smell of sweat and camel. It was weeks since she had had a proper bath.

Winifred realised that she should have bathed and changed her clothes before they reached the homestead but she had not had time. She had been chasing a recalcitrant camel and riding another one hard. Now she felt mortified. That night as she lay in bed Ali stood over her wearing his turban. She had bathed, washed her hair and changed into a clean white nightgown. Now her hair hung softly and sweet-smelling around her shoulders as she gazed up at him. Instead of unwinding his turban as he normally did, he stood glaring at her, his brown eyes flashing as he hissed, 'Once I thought you beautiful. Now I am ashamed to call you my wife. Tonight you looked like some filthy tramp.'

Winifred looked at him stricken, and then she began to weep, thinking of how hard she had worked for him and the children, with no thought for her own comfort. She had raised young camels to build his string, learned to milk a camel to make sure the children had fresh milk, cooked meals, washed and mended, even though she was ready to drop. Never complaining. Because she loved him and he loved her.

She felt his arms encircle her, and she rested her head on his shoulder until her tears subsided. Then he put his hand under her chin and raised her head, gazing into her eyes. 'Forgive me. This life is hard for a woman. It would have been better if you had stayed in Oodnadatta with the other women.'

She leaned her head against his chest and whispered, 'I could not bear for us to be parted.'

The incident came as a warning and Winifred began to take more care of her appearance, though she could not undo the damage done to her skin by the sun. Still, she made sure she brushed her hair and sponged her face and hands and changed into a clean blouse and skirt when they were approaching a homestead. After rain, when paperdaisies and Sturt's desert peas sprang up almost overnight, she would pick a flower and put it in her hair before they sat down to their evening meal, then decorate their bed with flowers as Ali had done on their wedding night. He responded with renewed tenderness. Secure in his arms she knew that everything was right between them, as if the incident on the station had never happened.

The experience of travelling to the far north and north-west of Australia brought Winifred into contact with people on the land who owned holdings that stretched for hundreds of miles, with vast herds of cattle. She knew they were wealthy, that was clear from the nice furniture, the pianos, the shelves of books and the way the women spoke. Like her, they taught their children. The difference was that when their children were old enough they were sent away to boarding school.

Often their closest neighbour was five hundred miles away; which was why she and Ali were always made so welcome and urged to stay, 'just one more day'. But unless it was Friday they had no time to waste. There was no backloading of wool. It was cattle country.

As time went by Winifred felt herself growing into the land. It had been a time of good seasons, with plentiful and lush pasture. There was a vastness about the landscape and yet she never felt lonely. She was no longer the insecure woman full of doubts about her future who had fallen in love with Ali. Now she knew her future was here with her husband and children and that she would never want to change her life. This vast emptiness was their inheritance and she thought that when Ali had made enough money they might retire to a great cattle station, where the children could grow up in a comfortable home and travel south to be educated.

She never discussed her plans with Ali, certain that she could persuade him when the time came. There was vacant land as far as the eye could see. One day part of it would be theirs.

19

THE PARTING

WINIFRED AND ALI HAD BEEN WORKING WITH camels for a little over two years when, in between trips, they returned to Oodnadatta to find a letter waiting for Ali at the post office. His family were being put off their land and needed him home urgently. It came at a bad time because Ali had contracts to fulfill. He had plenty of work and his dream of becoming rich seemed as if it would come true. And yet he felt he had a responsibility to his family in India.

'It is my duty as a son,' he told Winifred. 'I must go to my mother. She is old and what if she were to die without giving me her blessing?'

They were sitting outside the hut they had leased in ghantown, watching the shadows creep over the land, the last rays of the sun glinting off the gibber plains.

Though Winifred was concerned for his family, overriding her concern was her excitement at the thought of going to India and she began to plan what they would need for the trip. Her excitement turned to disappointment when Ali said, 'You must remain here and see to our contracts. Otherwise when I return we will have nothing.'

'But you promised to take me to India.'

'It is not possible,' said Ali. He rose and went walking in the direction of the mosque.

Winifred stared after her husband with a feeling of foreboding. If he went alone he might never return. And then what would become of her and her children?

The heat was still stifling. There was no breeze. She seemed to feel it more confined to the small iron hut than she did when they were travelling under the hot sun with the camels. Perhaps it was because there was no shade outside their hut, and inside the heat from the stove and the sun beating on the tin walls and roof made it almost unbearable. She had planted two date palms but they were barely more than seedlings and needed constant watering if they were to survive.

She sat listening to Yusef and Rhamat squabbling over who was going to wash the dishes. She picked up a thin stick from the woodheap and, charging inside, began to hit them around the legs until the stick broke. 'Get to bed! Get to bed!' she shouted. With tears streaming down their cheeks they obeyed, while she poured some water from the kettle into the tin dish and washed and dried the dishes, banging the tin plates down on the table before putting them on the shelf over the stove.

Then she made herself a cup of tea and went and sat outside again. It was a dark now and a breeze was coming off the desert, cooling the air. Gradually she calmed down and felt ashamed of the way she had behaved. She went into the small room where Rhamat and Pansy were sleeping and bent and kissed them, tucking the covers around them. She turned to Yusef and saw his eyes glinting as he watched her. She sat on the edge of his bed and took his hand. 'I'm sorry. I didn't mean to get angry. But I'm worried. Baba is going back to India without us.'

'Will he be coming back?' the child asked.

She thought about his question for a few minutes before answering and then she put her arms around him. 'Of course he will. Now go to sleep and tomorrow I'll make an apricot pie.'

'Will we stay here?' he asked.

She nodded.

'Will I be able to go to school?'

She patted him on the head. 'I expect so. And Rhamat too.'

Although she realised it was time they went to school, she was not prepared to give up her dream of going to India so easily. She filled the tin bath with water and bathed by the light of a candle. Then she went to bed to wait for Ali, still hoping to persuade him, but she fell asleep before he arrived home.

A week later he was gone. The train had come in on Friday and he had arranged his new contracts, getting Winifred to check the freight charges and the loadings as she did for the other camel-men.

'I will be back by the time our camels return,' he told her.

The camel-men had given him a farewell party, feasting on goats' meat which they had spent the day preparing, adding onions, spices and vegetables, leaving it to simmer for hours before placing the pot on a tarpaulin, where the men sat round scooping up the curry with a chapatti and washing it down with strong black tea.

The sound of their voices had drifted across to where Winifred was eating with her children. She felt disgruntled, wondering why women were excluded from such gatherings, as if they were of no importance.

She had not waited up for Ali, but woke when she felt him beside her. He had reached out his arms to pull her close, kissing her on the lips and whispering, 'Oh my dear heart, the nights will be long without you.'

The camel trains had left and only the women and the old men remained in ghantown when Ali caught the train to Adelaide. Winifred did not go to see him off, sending Yusef instead because she could not bear the thought of people seeing her cry, too proud to let them see her distress.

Weeks went by and stretched into months and there was no word. Ali had left money for food but had taken the rest with him on his trip. Now that she was settled in one place she planted a small vegetable garden on which she emptied the teapot and the washing-up water so that she could pick a few leaves of spinach. When there were no vegetables the boys would go to Ned Chong's market garden on their way home from school and buy a cabbage for threepence. They had enough money for meat. And there were always dates to eat. But she was afraid her money might run out and she did not want to have to ask for charity.

She asked Goolam, who butchered the meat for the Moslems and who, though not a mullah, was the leader at the mosque, if he had any news. His answer was, 'Be patient, sister. All in good time. It is the will of Allah.' She suspected that he knew something she did not. She made a point of sending Yusef to meet the train in case Ali arrived, thinking that he may have written a letter that had gone astray. She would have liked to have asked the stationmaster if there had been a letter, but she knew he would tell his wife and she might pass it on to the fettlers' wives. Winifred knew they looked down on her because she had married an Indian.

Weeks went by and still there was no news. She confronted Goolam when he was coming from the mosque. 'If you have news of my husband, please tell me. I am sick with worry.'

'I can tell you nothing … except … except that there is cholera in his village and many have died. That is all I know.'

The news chilled her but she could not accept it. 'No, not Ali …'

'We have no choice if it is the will of Allah.'

'Allah … Allah. What do I care about Allah? It is my husband I care about,' and she clutched him by the arm, while Pansy, standing clinging to her mother's skirts, began to cry.

'Compose yourself, sister … Go home now and pray to Allah for forgiveness. I will send someone to help you.'

Winifred was never sure how she made it back to her hut, where she put Pansy in her cot and flung herself on the bed, unable to control her tears.

She was still there when there was a voice at the door. 'Goolam has asked me to come. You are in trouble.' It was the stationmaster's wife and she sat by the bed and took Winifred by the hand. 'Is there some way I can help?'

'It is my husband. I have heard nothing since he left and now I am told that hundreds have died of cholera in his village and he may be among them.'

'But you do not know for certain.'

Winifred shook her head.

'Well then you must not worry until you know. He may be perfectly well and on his way home.' She went to the tank, filled the old black kettle and stoked up the fuel stove. 'I'll make a cup of tea.' She picked up Pansy who had woken up and was shaking the sides of her cot demanding to be let out. 'Hush, little one,' she said, and sat down with the child on her knee.

Later, at the kitchen table drinking tea, Winifred said, 'My boys are at school. I don't want them to know. I must go to Adelaide to the mosque. That is the only way I will be certain.'

'Do you want to leave the children with me?' the woman asked.

Winifred shook her head. 'No, where I go my children must go.'

Thinking back later Winifred was surprised at the kindness she was shown. All her life she had had to fend for herself, friendless and alone until she met Ali. The woman helped her pack and gave her a hamper of food for the train.

Winifred was subdued on the long trip to Adelaide, unable to rest, one minute certain Ali was dead and the next full of hope. She watched her children curled up asleep and when they were awake tried to act normally. Yusef had been excited about the trip, telling Rhamat that they were going to meet their father at the ship. Winifred did not disillusion him. If his father really was dead he would find out soon enough.

They left their luggage at the station and walked to the mosque. When the mullah saw her standing outside his office with dark circles under her eyes, her face pale, her mouth downcast, he called one of the visiting camel-men and asked him to look after the children. 'Buy them some milk and cake. Take them for a walk. I need to talk to their mother.'

Winifred remembered sitting in his office. Later someone brought her a cup of tea and a biscuit. She was so tired she could hardly speak. She knew from the way the mullah looked at her that it was bad news. For one crazy second she wondered if she should leave, thinking that she would rather not know. But that would solve nothing. She felt better after she had drunk the tea and steeled herself to find out the truth.

'I have come here for news of my husband. Goolam tells me that there has been cholera in his village. Is my husband alive?'

The mullah rose and walked to her side. 'Sister, you must be brave for the sake of your children. Your husband is dead.'

'No!' Her voice rose. 'I do not want him dead!'

'It is the will of Allah.'

'But we loved each other.'

'Then you must cherish his memory.'

Winifred heard the children returning and looked anxiously towards the garden, wondering how she would tell them the sad news. She rose and the mullah opened the door. She went into the garden where Yusef was sitting on a wooden bench holding Pansy in his arms. Rhamat was standing on the grass watching ants run up a tree. She could tell by their sad faces that they had already been told. Yusef gazed at her, his dark eyes troubled, and she bent and kissed him. 'I'm sorry, my son.' Then she reached down and lifted up Pansy, holding her close. She sat beside her older son and Rhamat came and sat beside her, resting his head on her knee.

Later the mullah came out to join them. 'I will pray for you,' he said. 'I have made arrangements for you to stay in one of the tenements until you decide what you will do. I will send in some food and you can rest there. The children can play in the garden. They will be safe here. I will talk to you again tomorrow. Pray to Allah. He will guide you.'

It was a week before Winifred was able to think clearly. She tried to remain composed in front of the children, but wept to herself when they were asleep. She was terrified of the future, and the knowledge that she would never see her husband again. He had been her whole life. Now he had died, taking her happiness with him. And she was left with three children to feed and clothe, to bring up alone.

She asked the mullah how she could go about claiming her husband's estate. He was quiet for a few moments, staring at her. Then he spoke. 'You are not one of us. You do not know the Islamic code. You have no claim on your husband's estate because there is no record of your marriage.'

Winifred stared at him in disbelief. 'But what about his children ... his two sons?'

'You could send them back to India. Their uncle is their legal guardian now their father is dead. Your daughter ... that is different. A daughter may stay with her mother till puberty. And then she will be found a husband.'

'I will not give up my children.'

'That is your choice,' he replied.

'How will we live?'

'I will find you another husband.'

'I cannot marry again. I loved my husband.' She rose and walked into the garden, unable to control the flood of tears. She could not bear the thought that she would never see Ali's dear face again, never tease him as she ruffled his beard, never lie in his arms again, or feel the warmth of his body against hers in the night. Overcome with grief she flung her arms around a quince tree growing in the garden, sinking to her knees in despair, until the mullah raised her and took her inside.

The crying eased her pain and later she told the mullah, 'I must find work ... where or how, I don't know. I understand camels, I can boil a piece of beef, make damper. I will try and look for a situation in a house where I can take my children.'

The following week she registered with the labour exchange and went to say goodbye to the mullah. 'Bring the children to play in the garden. Come and talk to me. Allah will guide you. *Bismallah*,' and he bowed to her as she led the children out into the street.

Winifred booked into a hostel and the family stayed there for six weeks until she had only four pounds left. There was no widow's pension, no supporting mother's benefit. She had asked the labour exchange to find her a live-in situation doing domestic work. But with three children it had proved impossible. The only work was as a washerwoman where she could earn two shillings and sixpence for half a day's washing.

Her day began at seven-thirty and finished at twelve-thirty. Sometimes she worked for a whole day and earned five shillings. If it was wet, she was unable to work, and by the time she had paid her rent and bought food, there was little left for anything else. A neighbour looked after her children and in return Winifred did her washing on Saturday.

It was a hard life and Winifred was exploited. One employer was always out of soap so that Winifred found herself supplying it. Part of the arrangement was that she be given lunch. Often it was just a meagre slice of bread and jam and a cup of weak tea. She put up with it, needing the work. But when she found she was also expected to chop the wood for the fuel copper she lost her temper and flung the axe across the yard. 'Damn you! What do you think I am? Keep your wretched washing and get some other fool to do it!'

It made her realise that she had to find some way to get back to Oodnadatta. The children missed their free and easy life there and though the boys went to a small local school here in Adelaide they were not happy. She knew that Yusef missed his father. They had been very close. But he kept his feelings to himself. She found herself talking to him as if he were an adult.

'You're the man of the house now,' she told him. I need you to help me bring up the little ones.' He looked at her gravely and it was as if Ali was looking at her. Allah may have taken her husband, she thought, but he had given her a strong son to take his place

Winifred was saved when she met Lumut at the mosque. He was about to start a travelling picture show and offered to teach her to drive a car. In addition to the car he needed a utility truck for the equipment, such as the generator to supply power. The idea of a picture show scandalised many of the Moslems at the mosque. With the embargo on reproducing the human form in artwork they felt Lumut was committing blasphemy.

The mullah was not in favour of Winifred and Lumut travelling together and suggested they get married. Lumut protested that he was married already and managed to convince the mullah that he was a distant relative of Winifred's husband, so in the end he gave them his blessing.

They worked the little towns such as Beltana and Marree, with about forty people in the audience and an entrance fee of one shilling for adults and sixpence for children. The hire of the hall was usually one pound and there was the cost of petrol for the vehicles on top of that. Winifred would drive ahead and hire the hall, then put posters up around the town advertising the show and selling tickets. The children enjoyed it. It was the life they knew. And though they missed their father, there were other camel-men around who talked to the boys and took them to the mosque. Pansy was only three and though she sometimes asked for *Baba*, she was too young to realise that he had gone from her life forever.

They were travelling for three months. Sometimes the car broke down. Other times it was the truck. It was a good experience for Winifred. She became proficient at driving and Yusef learned how to change a tyre and fill the car with petrol and water. He could make a batch of chapattis and boil the billy. And even the five-year-old Rhamat was able to make himself useful gathering firewood. It was a peaceful interlude that had a healing influence on the family. Lumut was like a kind uncle and the boys prayed with him and treated him with respect.

Winifred knew it could not last. It was not the real world. Her children needed a settled home. When the travelling show reached Oodnadatta she told Lumut she would not be going on. He took it in good spirits. It had not been a profitable exercise so he sold the vehicles and his equipment and returned to India.

Winifred moved back into her old home in ghantown and enrolled her sons in the local school. She had no money and their camels seemed to have vanished. At the suggestion of the local storekeeper who was after shirts for his shop, she took up dressmaking. He advanced her the money for the cloth but she had no pattern so that she found it difficult to make the collars sit right. Instead she ordered some cheap shirting in bright colours and made shirts for the natives, without collars. She followed this up with bright red mother-hubbards for the women. To her surprise they didn't sell. It was the colour. The women said, 'Too much thunder, missus. All about him jump up.'

She eventually settled on *shalwars* for the cameleers. These contained about twelve yards of gathered calico, secured around the waist with a strong cord. She cut them out on the floor of her hut and embroidered coloured flowers on the leg cuffs. She also invested in some goats and sold goat's milk. It was not enough to live on, so she also took in washing for single men, mostly travellers passing through the town. This meant a frequent stream of men coming and going to and from her hut and the camel-men did not like it.

She was at the washtub one day when a deputation led by Goolam called on her. 'Sister, we have been thinking that it is not good that your *butcha* have no father. We have thought long on this matter and now say that from any one of us you must pick a man for their father.'

Winifred was incensed. She knew that many of them had left wives behind in India. 'I do not wish to marry again,' she said.

Goolam regarded her gravely, then said, 'It is not right this thing you do … the mother of Moslem children washing dirty clothes for Christians. In the name of Allah we forbid you to do this kind of work.'

She put down her scrubbing board and faced the men. 'Muster all my husband's camels and I will send them out as we did before. I can get good boys I can trust. Then there will be no need for me to take in washing.' She had been told by her Aboriginal workers that the other Indian men had taken her camels into their own strings. They had denied it, and told her to go and pick out her camels. But she had no way of identifying them.

In the end she capitulated and on 26 June 1925 married Karum Bux in a Moslem ceremony in ghantown.

PART FOUR

20

THE ROAD TO MECCA

THE MARRIAGE SUITED BOTH WINIFRED and Karum Bux. Winifred had security for herself and her children. Karum Bux acquired not only a wife but someone to run his shop in ghantown. He had witnessed her competence with figures as she worked out the consignment notes and bills of lading for the camel-men, and he knew she was honest. It meant that he was free to travel and pursue his other business interests in the Moslem community. She was also a very handsome woman.

There were other aspects to the marriage. Under Islam it was considered an act of mercy for a man to marry a widow and raise her children as his own, an act that gave him spiritual credit in the next world. As for Winifred, though she knew in her heart that no one could take the place of Ali, she made up her mind to try to be a good wife. In return her children would have a father, particularly her sons, who were at an age when they needed guidance.

Unlike her marriage to Ali, which they had celebrated privately, there was a wedding feast, with the men spending days preparing the food. Goolam was kept busy killing extra goats which they cooked in the open in huge boilers. The smell of cooking meat simmering for hours with carrots and onions, together with the pungent odour of cloves, cinnamon, turmeric and ginger, filled the air. There was a mountain of chapattis, and to follow the main course dried fruits, oranges and nuts.

Karum Bux had given Winifred a length of grey silk and she made herself a two-piece suit with short sleeves because of the heat. She waited with the women, while Karum Bux went to the mosque with the men to make his vows before Goolam, until she was sent for, a length of white silk covering her hair. She was surprised to find that she had no part in the service, except to receive the wedding gift of a string of gold coins which Karum Bux fastened around her neck.

Later, after the feast, there was dancing, and one of the camel-men played the accordion. Her mind went back to the dances she had gone to on the Darling Downs and to her husband, Charles. She wondered if she had done wrong in concealing the fact that she already had a husband. Then she thought that a Moslem man could have four wives, so why shouldn't a woman do the same? But she didn't think Karum Bux had another wife, like some of the camel-men. She had asked and was told that his wife had died not long after he arrived in Australia.

She put aside thoughts of her first marriage and concentrated on the dancing, watching the men, the fringes of their turbans flying out behind them and their *shalwars* flapping as they twirled around, while every now and then a shower of sparks shot into the sky as a knot of wood exploded in the fire. The sight stirred her and she could feel the music coursing through her body. She yearned to get up and dance, but she knew that Moslem women did not dance with men. They had their own celebrations. But that was in India. Here many of the women were Aborigines or half-castes and had not grown up in the Moslem tradition. They were just as alien to it as she was.

As she sat watching she wondered how much longer the celebration would go on for and whether she would be missed if she left. Pansy and Rhamat had fallen asleep and Yusef's head was nodding. She rose and, carrying Pansy, walked the boys back to the hut where she put them to bed. Then she put on her nightgown and made herself a cup of tea and waited, not sure what was expected of her. She was half asleep when she heard men's voices outside and the sound of laughter. Then the door opened and her husband was standing in the doorway. She raised her face, trying to read his expression. He had taken off his turban and his long white hair seemed to blend in with his beard. Only his eyes were visible.

Winifred rose and felt him gazing at her. She had made a new nightgown for her wedding, with drawn threadwork over the bodice and lace trimming at the throat. Her arms were bare and she had taken down her hair which hung loosely around her face.

'You have waited up like a good wife. Go to bed. It is late. I will sleep in the shop tonight and come to you when you are rested.'

When they finally came together it was all over quickly, almost as if Karum Bux was consummating their marriage from a sense of duty rather than from desire. But she had no way of knowing. He was an old man and she was unable to respond. Without Ali her body felt cold and lifeless.

Karum Bux did not spend much time in Oodnadatta. Winifred ran the shop for him, finding it easy after the hard work of washing and ironing. The boys helped, enjoying the novelty of weighing up dates, sugar, flour, lentils and dried peas. They were allowed to eat the broken biscuits in the bottom of the tin.

Goolam looked after her sons' religious instruction and Winifred was pleased to see they were growing up to be good Moslems, as Ali would have wished. The children seemed happy and Karum Bux was kind to them, but her life had settled into a humdrum pattern. She still met the train and did the bills of lading and calculated the freight for the camel-men. She checked the goods coming into the shop, weighed out the food supplies for the camel-men and measured dress lengths, counted buttons and matched thread for their wives. But she had nothing in common with them. The women seemed content with their lives, while she was filled with a gnawing hunger for something different. What it was she did not know — an indefinable longing for change, which she put down to the fact that Ali was dead. Without him her life was empty. Even though she had her children it was not the same. However, she was careful to keep her feelings from Karum Bux. She married him because she needed the security of a home while her children were growing up. Living with him was easier than doing washing and ironing.

The couple had been married a little over five months when he told her he was going to undertake the hadj. 'Soon the railway will go to Alice Springs. And then what will happen to us? There will be nothing to carry. Our camels will be worthless. We must return to live in India. But before we do I will make the pilgrimage to Mecca, and follow in the footsteps of Mohammed. See the holy places that I have only heard about.' His eyes gleamed. 'It has long been my dream.'

Winifred knew that once in a lifetime every Moslem who could make the trip was obliged to go on the pilgrimage to the city where the Prophet had his first revelation, and her heart quickened. If he was going then she could go with him.

They were in the shop, with Karum Bux standing on a box, counting the stock on a high shelf, while Winifred prepared the order ready for him to sign.

She looked up at him and said, 'Mecca? You're going to Mecca?' The thought of getting away from Oodnadatta and travelling overseas, seeing the things she had heard so much about from returning pilgrims, sent a shiver through her and she could feel her pulse racing. 'Can I go too?' She found it hard to control her voice.

Karum Bux moved the tins of vegetables to a higher shelf. 'We'll need another two cases of vegetables.'

Winifred put her pen down. 'I said, will you take me with you?'

Her husband turned and stared at her. 'It is not possible. I need you to look after the shop. In any case non-believers are not admitted.'

'Do women go to Mecca?' She felt she had to know. If the answer was yes then she would go with him whether he liked it or not. It was not just to see the holy places but for the chance to escape, if only for a few months.

'Yes,' he replied. 'But they are born to the faith.'

She digested his words while they went on with their work, only asking in a small voice, 'How soon are you going?'

'It will take about five months to get the necessary papers and arrange things here.'

She kept silent, sensing that this was not the right time to tackle him head-on. She had to think about it and work out some way to make him change his mind, knowing how hard it would be. She had not been able to persuade Ali to take her to India and he had loved her. It would be harder with Karum Bux because their relationship was different. But she was a good wife to him, and she thought that if she could prove she was a good Moslem he could not deny her the trip.

A few days later she saw Goolam striding along the road, his beard flying, his knife belt bobbing up and down on his thigh, and she ran to the front of the shop. 'Can you spare a moment?' she asked him.

He stopped. 'What is it, sister? I have to get to the abattoir before dusk to kill the goats and say the prayers over their departing souls. Otherwise there will be no meat tomorrow.'

She poured him a mug of water from the canvas bag hanging in the doorway of the shop and handed it to him.

He stood there drinking and looking down at her with his piercing black eyes.

'I need some information,' she said and wiped her hands on her apron. 'How many women go to Mecca?'

'Many thousands.'

'My husband is going to Mecca.'

'I know,' he said. 'I envy him.'

'He refuses to take me with him.'

'He has his reasons.'

'What reasons? You say women go to Mecca. Then I should be able to go as his wife.'

'Women must also obey their husbands.'

'You promised me that if I married again I would be given three hundred pounds a year and my sons would be educated in India. I have not received the money that was promised me.'

'Be patient, sister.'

'I'm tired of being patient. If my husband goes to Mecca I want to go too. I let one husband go to India without me. He never returned.'

'It was the will of Allah.'

'And what if I say that it is the will of Allah that I go to Mecca? Does He not speak to women also?' She wondered at her own temerity and whether she would be punished by some unseen force. But then she thought she had already been punished, through no fault of her own, because Ali had been taken from her.

'But are you a true believer?'

'I became a Moslem when I married my first husband. I have kept the faith and raised my sons to be good Moslems.

I can recite the Five Pillars of Islam.' She stood very straight and looked him in the eye. 'The First Pillar is the profession of faith. The other four are the prayers, which may be taken privately or publicly and must be preceded by ablutions; the need to fast during the month of Ramadan; the official giving of alms, which my husband does on my behalf when he goes to the mosque; and the pilgrimage to Mecca. I have lived my life accordingly. I know that once in every lifetime a Moslem must make the pilgrimage to Mecca. If my husband does not take me, then how am I to get there?' The words had come tumbling out and she was conscious that Goolam was staring at her with a puzzled frown.

She refilled his tin mug and handed it to him, then poured herself a drink of water. Her cheeks were flushed and she wondered if she had been too outspoken. She softened her voice. 'I have no money. My husband does not pay me for the work I do in his shop. And I work for the camel-men for nothing, checking the bills of lading and the freight charges. Do I not deserve some reward?'

He gazed at her for a long time without speaking. Then he said, 'What you ask is difficult. Yet you speak the truth. A husband cannot deny his wife permission to make the hadj. You could go with a woman friend or a relative. But you have a husband. It is better that you go with him. You are a good woman. I will speak to the men at the mosque. If they think it is fitting, then I will tell your husband. *Bismallah.*'

Winifred watched him as he strode off, his *shalwars* ballooning around his legs, his sandalled feet kicking up little eddies of dust as he made his way along the dirt track.

It was a week before Winifred had her answer, a week in which she was careful not to make Karum Bux angry, a week in which she kept her tongue under control, playing at being a good Moslem wife. She made hot scones when she knew he would be in the shop during the day and cooked his favourite curry at night, making sure the children were quiet. She willed her body to relax when he took her in his arms, stroking his forehead, kissing his lips, thinking all the while of Mecca and the chance to travel, meet new people and see new places.

He returned from the mosque one night to tell her that he had changed his mind and that she could accompany him. She gave a squeal of joy and danced around the little hut in her white nightgown before flinging herself into his arms and covering his bearded face with kisses. She had won.

Five months later, their camels sold, the farewells said, the family was on its way to Fremantle to catch a ship to Bombay, and from there a train to Lahore to stay with her husband's people.

The first thing that struck Winifred was the lushness of the vegetation after the barrenness of Oodnadatta. Karum Bux's family home in Lahore was a typical multi-storeyed Indian house with a flat roof where the occupants could cool off at night, and where corn and herbs were set out to dry in the sun. There were fields of sugarcane and melons, the air fragrant with the perfume of roses and jasmine. In the distance were the snow-clad peaks of the Himalayas.

Winifred joined the women of the household, listening to them squabbling, enduring their curiosity about her dress as they pulled at her skirts to glimpse what she wore underneath. Her husband tried to get her to wear a yashmak, as the other women in the family did when they ventured out. But she refused, thinking it was hideous to see them enveloped in black, their faces covered and only slits for their eyes. She wondered how on earth they could endure the heat.

Yusef and Rhamat soon settled in, running through the sugar cane with the older boys in the household, learning to speak the local dialect and going to the mosque with the men, and Pansy had another little girl to play with, however, Winifred felt constrained, conscious that she was an outsider. She found it difficult to become accustomed to the food, finding the curry too hot and the glass of hot water flavoured with cinnamon no substitute for a cup of tea. When she complained to Karum Bux he offered no sympathy. 'No one asked you to come,' he would say. And she had no answer. She did not want to quarrel with him in public, and living as they were in close confines with the other members of his family there was no privacy.

Apart from her husband's objections there were other obstacles that made it difficult for Winifred to go to Mecca. She needed documents from four different governments. The first was a passport to travel from India. And then an entry permit from the French colony in Arabia she would be passing through. The Khalifat, the supreme body of the Moslem church, had to be persuaded, and last of all she needed permission from the government of the Wahabis, whose king, Ibn Saud, ruled over the Holy Land. It was two months before Winifred's papers were in order and they were free to begin their journey, taking Pansy with them and leaving the boys behind with relatives in Karachi, from where they were to catch the ship to Jedda.

The family stayed in a *messafa khana* in Karachi, one of the many rest houses supplied by the government, where people were permitted to stay free of charge for two weeks. There was a fireplace, bathroom and clean water, but they had to supply their own food and firewood. In Karachi they stocked up on food for the journey by ship. The amount they could carry was limited and they bought only a few pounds of flour, some chilies, a few lentils, rice, onions, a few pounds of sugar, a pound of tea, a pound of dates, a tin of condensed milk and, as a luxury for Winifred, a few tins of sardines.

It was an expensive trip from the point of view of the pilgrims but also an austere one. Once they entered the Holy Land no display of wealth was permitted. The men were required to wear two pieces of unsewn calico, one to wind around the waist and the other to drape over the shoulders. The women could please themselves what they wore and went unveiled. Sexual intercourse was forbidden — the pilgrims were expected to travel with a pure heart. If they were ill-treated they were expected to endure it without retaliation.

Though Winifred had resisted wearing the yashmak, she was forced to don Moslem dress by the hierarchy of the Moslem church. It gave her a protection she would not have enjoyed if she had worn Western dress, which could have subjected her to persecution by fanatics among the pilgrims. She was given two pairs of trousers, one white and one black, and two white shirts. She found the *shalwars* cumbersome at first. Made of ten yards of material they were gathered into a narrow cuff at the ankle and into a strong cord at the waist Once the journey wore on she appreciated their comfort, particularly after long hours on a camel.

The morning they were due to embark from the wharf at Karachi was not without difficulties. Winifred was suffering from malaria, with waves of fever followed by shivering fits sweeping through her body. The women were marched outside to a great whitewashed wall in the blazing sun. Here they were lined up for a medical inspection. She found the sun almost unbearably hot and had no hat or umbrella to shade her head. The men, who were also undergoing an inspection, were taken into a nearby shed. The women had been assigned a female doctor with an assistant, whom she began to abuse by striking across the face. She then turned to the women and demanded they undress. The women had been brought up to be modest, covering their face with a veil when they appeared in public. Now they were being asked to disrobe in public, in full view of the other women and the male medical officials who were looking after the men. When the women tried to cover themselves, the doctor banged their heads against the wall.

It came to Winifred's turn to disrobe and she refused. The doctor grabbed at her shirt and tried to tear it off. Incensed at the insensitive way the other women had been treated, and by now feeling the full effects of malaria, Winifred lashed out and punched the doctor in the ear. The blow sent her reeling and Winifred let loose with two more punches which knocked off the doctor's spectacles and sent her false teeth flying. By this time Winifred was wound up and she lashed out again. The woman tumbled backwards onto her assistant.

The red ink the assistant was using to make notes spattered everywhere. The doctor began to pummel her servant. At the sight of this Winifred lost her head completely and leapt on the doctor and began to hit her until someone intervened.

She became conscious of the pilgrim women gaping at her, and a crowd of men who had come running out of the shed when they heard her shouting. Among them was her husband and a group of customs and immigration officials and police assigned to organise the formalities associated with the embarkation of over one thousand pilgrims. They gathered around, demanding to know what had happened. There was a babble of voices as they all spoke at once.

Winifred sat down on the ground and buried her face in her hands. All she wanted was somewhere to lie down. She heard her husband's voice through a daze. 'Now look what you've done. You'll be arrested and I'll miss the hadj.' He was angry, but she was past caring.

He followed when she was led away with Pansy by her side. To his surprise she was treated with respect, given quinine for her malaria and the use of a room at a hotel where she could rest and have a meal. The next day she was issued with a new passport bearing the name Zatoon, after a famous Moslem woman warrior.

A representative from the Khalifat, which looked after the welfare of the Moslem community in India, approached Karum Bux before he went on board 'Your wife is a courageous woman. We have long suspected that all is not right with the way the women passengers are treated. Now we have proof. If you will permit it we would like your wife to be the official guardian of the female passengers and to report back to us if they are mistreated.' Karum Bux could do nothing but agree, even though he was angry at Winifred for the way she had drawn attention to herself. He had an uneasy feeling that he had made a mistake in bringing her with him, but it was too late to change his mind. He had married an unruly woman whom he was unable to control.

Winifred had no idea of his feelings. The malaria had subsided and the rest had refreshed her. She had been told that there was no need to hurry to board the ship and it was late when she made her way to the wharf with Pansy. When she saw the *Istophan,* the ship that was to carry the pilgrims across the sea, she was filled with apprehension. She was to discover that the ship had been in service as a Chinese convict transport but had sunk. Later it was resurrected and put into service on the lucrative pilgrim run.

On the wharf there was a scene of frantic activity, with vendors shouting and waving to attract the attention of pilgrims already on board. Baskets of fruit were hauled up by ropes and the money sent down the same way. She saw one man order a dozen mangoes, but halfway up the side the jute twine broke and the mangoes fell in the water. The man refused to pay for the fruit so the vendor pelted him with stones. The jostling on the wharf became so bad that an old woman of the sweeper class was pushed to the extreme edge of the wharf, and then, with a scream and a flutter of her garments, disappeared under the water.

Watching, Winifred was appalled. She closed her eyes and said a prayer for the old woman's departing soul. But to her amazement, when she opened her eyes she saw the old woman strike out for the jetty. There was a log jammed underneath the wharf and the woman perched there and scooped up the mangoes, which were still bobbing on top of the water, and tied them in the corner of her chador. She then scooped up another two and, seated comfortably on her log, peeled them and slowly ate them.

She looked so contented and happy that Winifred was deeply moved. The thought came to her that Allah had looked after the old woman, a woman of no consequence. She recalled how she had told her husband and Goolam that she was a true daughter of Islam, knowing that she had only become a Moslem because it had been expedient to do so when she married Ali. She had accepted Allah as the supreme being without any real conviction. Now she felt more confident. If Allah had cared for the old woman he would surely care for her and her daughter. With a feeling of peace she took Pansy by the hand and led her up the gangplank to where her husband was waiting.

21

THROUGH THE LAND
OF ABRAHAM

THOUGH THE EPISODE WITH THE OLD woman reinforced Winifred's faith, it was to be sorely tested by the appalling conditions on the ship. There were 1100 people crowded on board, including the crew, the only ones to have cabins. The passengers spread their prayer rugs wherever they could find space. Winifred was late arriving and all Karum Bux had been able to secure was a hatch three decks down. She hung her blankets around the iron stanchions and was happy to have a private place to sleep and dress, until she looked up to see hundreds of eyes peering down at her. Her encounter with the woman doctor had made her notorious and she knew she would remain the centre of attention. She consoled herself with the thought that it was better than being on the open deck, or in an area washed with bilge water.

She had smuggled Pansy's doll on board, hoping that the child could play with it when they were alone. But now she realised she would have to keep it hidden and find some other way to amuse her five-year-old daughter. Her husband had warned her that fanatical Moslems considered it profane to paint the likeness of a human face on any object, because the head was sacred to Allah. Later she was to see dolls in the Arabian markets that were beautifully dressed but with a square wooden head without features.

Added to the other miseries was the fact that there were only twelve small fireplaces to accommodate all those people. For three days Winifred was unable to make a cup of tea and she and Pansy survived by eating dates.

But there were compensations. She found herself being drawn deeper and deeper into the world of Islam because of the devotion of the other pilgrims. Five times a day, facing Mecca, they prostrated themselves on the deck, their voices rising in a mighty chorus as they recited their prayers, while she prayed quietly in her spot below deck. There was a feeling of euphoria that overrode the squalor, the overcrowding, the stench of unwashed human bodies and the groans of those who became ill and died.

The first port of call was Kamerad, a French quarantine station past Aden. It was the first sight of the sacred land and Winifred looked across to where long rolling hills and sand merged into the horizon. In the foreground was a small group of galvanised-iron buildings with one or two whitewashed bungalows. There was not a skerrick of vegetation, not a blade of grass, not a tree for shade. The sun blazed down on the pilgrims as they were taken ashore. At the water's edge was a trolley line to handle the cargo, which was pulled by coolies in loincloths.

Here the pilgrims were required to bathe and have their clothes fumigated. A message had been sent from Karachi. Winifred was singled out for special attention and told to wait until the other women had gone through, so that she could bathe in private. It was a relief to walk on dry land and Winifred took Pansy to the water's edge so that the child could run around and play.

Later, they were escorted into the bathhouse and handed two pieces of clean white calico to wear while their clothes were taken away to be fumigated. The female doctor was kind and courteous, unlike the woman who had examined them when they were about to board the *Istophan*. It was wonderful to stand under a stream of cool water and mother and daughter were enjoying themselves enormously when the doctor came in and asked if Winifred had noticed three women in purdah among the pilgrims. She explained that they had refused to remove their clothes, even though she had promised them a private bath; they said they were of royal birth and bathed every day, not like the common people.

'Would you mind if they came in and saw you bathing?' the doctor asked. 'Then they will know there are no exceptions.'

Winifred had noticed three women who had remained veiled on board ship, even though it was forbidden. Now they came into the bathhouse and stood huddled together in their black yashmaks while the doctor tried to persuade them to undress. When they still refused, she removed the head covering from one woman, who began to scream as if she was being assaulted, her companions joining in. In desperation the doctor turned on all the overhead jets and the women were soaked, looking for all the world like three bedraggled black crows. Only then did they allow the doctor to remove their clothes and accept the squares of clean calico they were offered.

Winifred was rewarded for her cooperation. The family was housed overnight in a lodge, with a bathroom at their disposal. A bed was sent for and a large block of ice arrived with buckets of drinking water. Nearby were several shops where they could buy food, and Winifred was overjoyed when Karum Bux returned with a tin of Australian pineapple.

The next day they were back on board. After the rest on shore the water in their petrol tin tasted hot and brackish, and the smell of bilge water was almost overpowering. Winifred wondered how much longer she could endure the sound of coughing, the constant noise going on, the cooking fires on deck. Those who could not get near a fire during the day had to cook at night, and the sparks blew in the wind, making Winifred fearful and unable to sleep in case the ship caught fire.

The *Istophan* ploughed through the Red Sea, until the day came when the chief officer called the pilgrims together and announced that at two o'clock they would catch their first glimpse of Hejaz. The mood on board changed as each pilgrim began to prepare for the sight of the sacred mountain which would mean the beginning of the hadj. All must be bathed and dressed in new clothing. The men were required to wear two strips of unbleached calico and put aside their head covering. Women had a choice of dress as long as it was new, but they must bind their head so that not one hair showed, otherwise they would have to sacrifice a sheep or goat for every hair. Winifred wore a white *shalwar kameez* with a white chador, with a matching outfit for Pansy.

They were bathed and dressed and ready to go on deck when Winifred heard angry shouts and saw men running with knives and sticks. Karum Bux came hurrying to her side. 'There's danger. The water pipe in the men's bathhouse has broken and there's no water. Unless they can bathe and change they will miss the hadj. Anything can happen. Stay below with Pansy where you will be safe.'

Instead, Winifred handed the child to him and pushed her way to the upper deck and called out to the first officer who was standing on the bridge. 'The ship is in danger,' she said, and hurried up to join him. 'There is no water in the men's bathroom. If they cannot bathe they will miss the hadj. And they will be so angry there will be a riot. People will be killed.'

'Tell them to be calm,' he said. 'We will cut the engines till the water is restored.'

Winifred threw back her chador and looked down at the pilgrims who were still in an agitated state. She called out to them, 'Be calm ... You will have time to bathe.' She watched as the crewmen dragged heavy hoses along the deck to the men's bathroom. Within an hour the ship was moving again and the men were bathed and dressed and waiting. At two o'clock a dim shadow rose on the horizon.

The ship's funnel gave a loud blast and the cry of '*Allah Akbar!*' filled the air.

Later, as Winifred walked on the deck, people came up to thank her, touching her chador in deference.

They dropped anchor in the roadstead at Jedda. The sun was directly overhead. Winifred was dazzled by the luminous blue–green water and the white tower-like buildings set against purple hills that lined the beachfront. She turned to Karum Bux, her eyes shining, 'How beautiful,' she said. She wanted to kiss him but held back, knowing that no show of affection between men and women was permitted. Instead she smiled at him and touched him lightly on the arm.

He returned her smile. 'The name of this city means grandmother. It's something to do with Mother Eve. She's buried here. Her tomb is the most sacred of places.'

'Will we be able to see it?'

'It all depends. There's a new ruler — King Ibn Saud. With the help of the British he has driven the Turks out of the Holy Land after skirmishes lasting twenty years. He has pledged to guard the pilgrims by promising the Bedouins free food during the hadj. They prey on the pilgrims and no one can touch them because they claim to be descendants of the Prophet. We will go where we are told.'

It was almost dusk before they were allowed into the small lateen boats that came racing towards them through a line of white posts marking the channel. The tide was running swiftly and the small boats were being tossed about, making it difficult to jump aboard. Winifred passed Pansy to Karum Bux who had jumped first. When it came to her turn the mast holding the sail swung around and she was knocked sideways and flung into the sea. She was hauled back into the boat and as she stood there, gasping for breath and fighting back tears, she heard someone say, 'Look,' and saw sharks circling in the clear water. She glanced at Karum Bux who was still holding Pansy. He was standing there impassive, almost as if he thought she had jumped overboard on purpose. And then he said, 'It is of no consequence. You are safe. It is the will of Allah. And your clothes will soon dry in the sun.' He held out one arm and she moved closer until she was leaning against him.

As the boats got closer to the grey sandy beach, Winifred could see the houses more closely, with their ornamental balconies, fancy cornices and carved lattice work in richly toned woodwork. But it was hours before she was able to take a closer look. On shore there were formalities to be completed, which meant a long wait. Other pilgrim ships had also dropped anchor and there were thousands of people milling around until it was their turn to be shown into a long shed smelling strongly of carbolic.

Inside was all clamour and noise as pilgrims argued with men in uniform who were demanding a tax of seven rupees, which was being levied by King Ibn Saud to pay for safe crossing of the desert. Once the levy had been paid and their health and travel documents checked, Winifred and her husband were assigned to a *mutawwif* who collected their passports and retained them until their return from Mecca. They were advised to take full details of the name and whereabouts of the agents to ensure the return of their papers. Without them they would not be able to leave the country.

The *mutawwif* also arranged accommodation and camel transport. Because of the huge influx of visitors during the hadj, it was often difficult to find a room. Many of the poorer pilgrims were housed nineteen to a room for a charge of one rupee each. Winifred and her family were more fortunate. They secured a room to themselves, on the top floor of a five-storey house, with a flat roof where they could walk in the evening. Here there was a sea breeze, which drove away the evil smell of rotting garbage and filth that lay about in the alley below.

Because of the dense crowds Winifred gave up any idea of exploring the city. From the barred window in their room she looked down on a mighty river of people. She had never seen so many jammed so tightly together in one place. She could see right down to the middle of the bazaar which was partly shaded with date palms. There were seagulls and cormorants in the skies overhead. Winifred discovered that the houses were built with beams jutting through the roofs so that the birds would have somewhere to roost. She and Pansy watched the baker with his thin rings of bread looped over both arms, and the old woman with the goat which she milked straight into the customer's container. There were stalls selling silks, prayer rugs, earthenware and gleaming copper bowls. Silversmiths sat by the roadside hammering out metal into bracelets and other jewellery. Winifred was thrilled when Karum Bux bought her a bangle in the shape of a serpent, a large silver crescent to wear in her hair, and a phial of attar of roses.

The sight that delighted mother and daughter most was when the judges and court officials rode to the law courts on donkeys, so small that the judges' feet almost scraped the ground. The animals had their heads and hooves painted red and were hung with coloured tassels and tiny bells that chimed merrily as they trotted along. Hearing the bells Pansy would run to the window and clap her hands and laugh.

Once Winifred saw a judge on foot, his robes almost sweeping the ground. He strode across to the local butcher, who had set up business in the middle of the road with the carcass of a goat hanging between three sticks, and began to haggle. The deal closed, the butcher hacked off a shoulder and a swarm of flies rose in the air, then settled back on the carcass, while the judge strode off with the meat, which he held by the shank end. He was followed by a pack of pariah dogs whom he whacked on the nose with the unwrapped meat when they got too close.

Then there was the man with a handcart filled with rows of coloured jellies, which he carried uncovered and swarming with flies. People in the street bought them and ate them as if the flies did not exist. When she mentioned it to Karum Bux he shrugged his shoulders. 'When you can barely afford food, flies are the least of your worries.'

Winifred's day started when she heard the call to prayer floating across the city. She watched as Karum Bux tied his turban and went to his devotions, rising to stand at the window to listen to the shuffle of thousands of sandalled feet and gaze at the shadowy figures shoulder to shoulder as the faithful hurried to the mosque. She stayed there until the sky became streaked with pink as the sun rose, then she knelt at the barred windows to pray to Allah for a safe journey, never ceasing to marvel at the fact that she had come so far without serious mishap.

By the time she looked out the window again the alley would be filled with vendors opening up their stalls, with steam rising from water pots, the smell of hot brewed coffee, millet cakes and meat slowly roasting on a spit, ready for when the pilgrims returned from the mosque. Because of the desert that stretched beyond the town, there was no local agriculture. The harvest lay in the rich pickings from the thriving pilgrim trade, with 50 000 or more souls on their way to Mecca. Ahead lay a fifty-mile trip by camel, the thousands of pilgrims at the beck and call of the camel drivers.

The scene beside the town hall where thousands of camels were waiting, with everyone clamouring to be first away, was chaotic. It reminded Winifred of Oodnadatta when the train came in and the camels were being loaded, except that this was on a gigantic scale, with pilgrims jostling and being jostled, while the camels snorted and bucked and refused to stay still.

It was too much for Winifred. Concerned that Pansy might be trampled, she asked Karum Bux to find them a place to wait while he secured them a camel and a place in a string. He led them to a group of tables without chairs, where the agents were drinking coffee, and lifted them onto a table. 'Don't move or I may never find you again.'

It was good to sit and relax, away from what Winifred saw as a near riot. There were clouds of dust as the camels kicked and threshed around. She drew her chador tight and made sure Pansy's face was covered. Just the same something lodged in Winifred's right eye. Though she rubbed and rubbed she found it impossible to dislodge. Then she noticed that a little fat man wearing a black fez had come to stand beside their table and was smirking at her. He spoke to her in Arabic, in words she did not understand. For a moment she thought he might be offering to remove the mote from her eye. But there was something suggestive about the way he was looking at her that made her feel uneasy. She looked around for Karum Bux and saw him hurrying towards her. He scowled at the man in the fez and spoke to him angrily, which sent him scuttling away.

'What did he say?' Winifred asked.

Karum Bux, still scowling, looked away and grunted.

'Tell me,' she said. 'I want to know.'

'He was asking how much you charge, and offering to take you to a nice quiet place.'

Winifred began to laugh, rubbing her right eye again to dislodge the speck of dust. Suddenly Karum Bux grabbed her arm and yanked it down. She stared at him, wondering why he was being so rough.

'Damn it, woman. You're doing it again.'

'Doing what?'

'Rubbing your right eye. That's the Arabian courtesan's signal for trade.'

She was tempted to ask what happened if you rubbed your left eye, but knew it would only make him angry. He had enough on his mind, trying to find a place in a string where the camels were properly broken in, and with a driver he could trust. Instead she said, 'I'd like a cup of tea.'

He turned to face her, almost snarling. She was smiling at him, a mischievous grin on her face. 'I was only teasing,' she said and squeezed his hand. His face relaxed and he began to laugh and was still laughing as he strode back to the camels.

It was sundown before they finally rode through the city gates. Beyond them lay the desert. Here they halted and everyone dismounted to pray. They had barely finished when the alarm was raised. The camel drivers prodded the beasts to their knees and called on the pilgrims to take shelter. Winifred could feel her pulse racing. She held Pansy close and, sheltering her with her body, drew her chador over them both and crouched beside the camels, a choking sensation in her throat as a great wall of dust came out of the desert and whirled about them It lasted for only a few minutes and was gone.

The incident alarmed Winifred, though once they had risen and shaken the sand from their garments all was well. Pansy seemed unconcerned, as if it had been a kind of game. It had all happened so quickly the child did not have time to sense her mother's fear.

As the pilgrims stood about drinking water to clear the dust from their throats, she said to the *moulvi* who was travelling with them, 'I am concerned for my child. I was able to shelter her with my body, but what will happen if a dust storm blows up when we are sleeping?'

He gave her a gentle smile. 'That was only a small storm thrown up by the desert to test us. Allah be praised. Your daughter is strong. She would know to cover her face.' He went to turn away and then stopped. 'This is not like the other side of Hejaz where there is the *simoon*. I have heard tell of it. The eye is calm but around it swirl violent gusts of poisonous vapours.' He described a circle in the air with his

331

arms. 'It travels slowly. You know when it is near by the awesome violet light.'

His brown eyes glittered as he leaned towards her. 'I have heard tell there is a feeling in the limbs as if molten lead has burned them. And in the chest a feeling of suffocation. The only way to survive is to cover your face and lie prone without breathing until it passes. The camel has been told by his ancestors to bury his nose in the sand. I have not seen these things but I have heard tell of it.' He smoothed his beard and his expression was kindly as he said, 'Rest assured, sister, Allah is with us.'

Winifred was holding Pansy in her arms. He smiled and passed his hand over the child's head, saying, '*Allahu Akbar La Ilaha Illa Allah.*'

Two pilgrims rode, one on either side of a camel, which was fitted with two string beds, with the camel's hump in between. Because of the beds the camels could not be hooshed down properly. This meant that the first passenger had to climb on the beast's head and balance on the hump until the second person arrived. It was like being on a seesaw. Until she mastered the art Winifred had a few falls. Over the beds was a beehive cover of jute, with a centre prop in line with the animal's neck. The red water-crock was lashed to this. Everything else was stowed behind the pillow. The weight had to be evenly balanced with Karum Bux on one side of the camel and Winifred and her daughter on the other. Their camel train had forty beasts to the string, with two drivers who walked alongside holding pointed sticks.

Winifred was in a dreamlike state that first night as they set out with thousands of camels in strings tied nose to tail. It reminded her of a mighty army, with camels on either side of them as far as the eye could see. She slept fitfully, waking to the sound of the camels, feet shuffling, like running water as they swished though the soft sand. It provided a background to the coughs and groans of the sick and elderly.

Later she said to Karum Bux, 'So many are old and ill. They will be dead before they reach Mecca.'

He seemed unconcerned. 'Many of the elderly hope to die on the hadj and be buried in the land the Prophet has blessed,' he said.

When the sun rose the first morning she looked across at the stark, inhospitable landscape with extinct volcanoes and bare mountains dotted with black basalt boulders, and was surprised to see shadows which seemed to emerge out of the landscape. They turned out to be beggars who ran alongside, invoking the name of Allah and calling out, 'Baksheesh!'

'Where do they come from?' she asked Karum Bux as the beggars ran beside their camel to catch a few coins he had thrown.

'They live in the caves that line the mountains. They know it is an act of mercy to give alms. The money they get may have to last them a whole year. That is why they look so thin.'

Winifred thought about her own life. It had been hard but she had never had to beg for food. There was always something, even if it was only a piece of damper and a cup of tea. And though she had slept without a roof over her head in the prickly pear, it had not been for long. She had always had somewhere to live, even if it was only a small hut. These beggars had nothing.

Towards morning it always became bitterly cold. It was a relief when the camel train halted at dawn for a ten-minute break for prayers and she could stretch her legs and walk around. The camels halted again at midday and there was a rush to buy some firewood to cook chapattis and a little bit of curry. Other times they had to exist on a handful of dates and a drink of water.

The days were long and tedious, with waves of heat shimmering around them and swarms of flies that crawled into their eyes and noses, sucking the moisture from the beads of sweat that gathered on their skin.

The pilgrims prayed five times a day, with different prayers chanted aloud in Arabic on each occasion. Winifred was always conscious of being watched, but survived by giving a dry little cough when she did not know the right word.

When they stopped in the middle of the day Winifred was unable to let Pansy run around and play as she'd hoped, because the sand felt as if it was on fire. All the child could do was hop around on the prayer rug Winifred spread beside their camel for a little bit of shade, or jump up and down while her mother clapped her hands and recited a nursery rhyme. But even being on the rug proved dangerous when Pansy pointed to something moving in the sand. It turned out to be a cluster of scorpions, each only the size of Pansy's little finger. A bite could make an adult ill for a long time. Winifred snatched Pansy up, fearful that if she was stung she would die.

She did not complain, however, keeping her feelings to herself. As she lay awake at night she watched Karum Bux as he slept, a serene expression on his face, as if this was the culmination of a lifelong dream. He had warned her of the hardships of the trip, but she had not really believed him. Now she knew what he'd said was true. For his sake she must endure, wondering if it would have been easier if she had been born a Moslem.

Despite the hardships there were aspects that appealed to Winifred. She was fascinated by the wells where the camels drank, particularly after she was told that the Patriarch Abraham had dug them when he travelled with his flocks. They did not look like ordinary wells. There were two circles of water, each with an eight-inch wall. The water was dipped by bucket from one and poured into the other. Both animals and humans drank from the same well. And once someone pointed out a goldmine and told her it was from this mine the gold had come to build King Solomon's temple.

A welcome respite came when they stopped at an oasis and she could sit under the palm trees enjoying their shade and eat the creamy dates straight from the tree. On *Juma* they camped overnight. It was a relief to be off the camels. With their rocking motion it felt like being on board ship again.

The village people who lived around the oases were friendly and sold them fresh vegetables and an edible grass. She saw coffee trees growing in terraces, sheltered from the direct sun by other shrubs, the beans already harvested, the berries drying in the sun. At one oasis there were pomegranates, which Winifred had never seen before. They looked so beautiful with their smooth red skins. She was disappointed to discover that inside was nearly all seeds.

Another time she watched a farmer working his land with a wooden plough without wheels, which barely scratched the earth. There was no winter. They sowed all the year round, irrigating with water drawn from the well. She watched the oxen which were harnessed to ropes and pulleys attached to leather buckets. When the filled buckets touched the crossbeam on top of the well they tipped over into channels that ran downhill to the crops, which were watered twice a day. As she turned away to leave, the farmer picked a ripe melon from a vine and gave it to her.

That night they feasted well, sitting on their prayer rugs eating boiled mutton with millet cakes, followed by the melon. They gorged themselves on the sweet flesh, laughing as the juice ran down their chins. Later, lying under the date palms, Winifred slept soundly for the first time since they had left Jedda, dreaming just before morning that she was with Ali. When she woke she could hear birds singing in the palm trees and saw large beetles with stilt-like legs clustered around the trunks. The thought came to her that the Garden of Eden must have been like this — an oasis in the desert.

There were children at the oasis for Pansy to play with, children of her own age who ran around naked, like the piccaninnies the child had played with when they had travelled with the camels in Australia. It gave Pansy a welcome respite from the long hours beside her mother in the string bed, as the camels plodded along at five miles an hour. At the oases they were also able to bathe and wash their clothes, and when they left they felt clean and refreshed.

Ten days after they left Jedda the camels were hooshed down early and the *moulvi* announced that Mecca lay before them, hidden from view by two mountain ranges that ran north and south and enclosed the city. The news stirred the pilgrims and a mighty shout went up of '*Lub-bay-yak*', a cry of praise, gratitude and submission to the will of Allah. Tomorrow they would enter the Holy City.

Now began a period of intense preparation in which the moulvis prayed and instructed the pilgrims until it was almost morning. They were not to fight among themselves but to enter the city in peace with a pure heart. They were not to use oils or perfumes on pain of having to sacrifice an extra sheep or goat. And they were not to retaliate if someone ill-treated them. Winifred listened for as long as she could, but fell asleep at about midnight. She woke to find Karum Bux still at his devotions on his prayer rug.

Before it was light, without eating, they mounted the camels again and rode down the mountain-ringed valley. As the sun rose Winifred had her first glimpse of the city below with the Great Mosque at its heart. Houses climbed up the mountains on either side. Every now and again she caught a glimpse of the five minarets with their onion domes and the gilded dome over the Zamzam Well, where the Angel of the Lord had appeared to Hagar after she had fled to the wilderness with her baby son, Ishmael. Winifred was filled with a sense of awe, as well as a feeling of great joy. She reached across and took her husband by the hand. When he turned to face her she saw his eyes were filled with tears.

The camels picked their way down the track which was covered with stones, until they were on the floor of a narrow street lined with houses. Here they halted and a number of the tourists were told to dismount and go into a tall white house. Winifred was ushered into a room with her family and she put down her bundles, ready to stretch out and rest. Instead Karum Bux said, 'Hurry up, woman. Get a move on.'

'Surely there's time for a cup of tea. We haven't eaten since yesterday morning.'

'Be quiet,' he said. 'The moulvis are waiting below,' and he hurried out the door while she followed with Pansy in her arms, holding a handful of dates for the child to eat.

Still not happy with the idea of going off without food, Winifred asked the *moulvi* what was happening and discovered that it was a race to simulate Hagar's search for water for her dying baby, after she had been sent into the desert by Abraham, the father of her child, because of his wife Sarah's jealousy. 'Seven times she ran from hill to hill on this very spot, frantic, until the Angel of the Lord took pity and the sacred spring began to gush at the feet of Ishmael.' He pointed to Pansy who was clinging to her mother. 'You have a child, you will understand what it meant to Hagar to find water. Follow in her footsteps in peace.' He touched Pansy lightly on the head. 'May Allah bless you, my child.'

He gave the signal and the great crowd, which had fallen into single file, began to run madly down the street. Winifred had Pansy to carry and the road was stony. She was unable to slow down because the crush of people was too great and she was afraid of being trampled by those running behind her. She felt exhausted and it occurred to her that it would have been easier if Hagar had found water earlier. On the second lap Karum Bux took Pansy from her arms and Winifred allowed herself to slip to one side, only joining in again on the end of the seventh round, certain that everyone was so intent on themselves that for once she would go unnoticed.

338

Her husband was waiting for her at the mosque gates. He grabbed her by the arm and hurried her inside. There, holding Pansy on his shoulders and urging Winifred forward, he jostled his way through the huge crowd until they reached the shrine of the Kaaba, in the centre of the inner courtyard. Here they had to circle seven times, starting at the black stone and kissing it at each lap. The sacred stone was a large black meteorite embedded in a wall in one corner. In the centre of the stone was a circle of gold. Winifred noticed it was worn down by the imprint of so many lips. Each day the black Mameluke attendants wiped the ring with attar of roses. They wore a dagger strapped to their left arm and were fierce guardians of the relic, made sacred after the Prophet Mohammed kissed it.

It was too much for Winifred to take in on the first morning. She tried to remember the prayers for each circumambulation but had to pretend. No one noticed, each intent on his or her own experience, and she too experienced a strange sensation as she continued to circle, as if her soul had left her body. Later she noticed others in the same trance-like state but could not account for it.

After performing the ritual of the black stone, Winifred and her husband made their way to the Zamzam Well and joined the throng waiting to drink the miraculous water and fill small jars with the precious liquid so that it could be sprinkled on their body at the moment of death. Others were dipping clean calico into the water so that it could be used on their shroud.

The family remained in Mecca for a week, visiting the Great Mosque, a vast building with seven tall minarets.

Winifred was awed by the sight of the interior, with carved pillars supporting the roof, the walls and floors covered with mosaics. The hanging glass chandeliers had been lit by electricity during the Turkish regime but Ibn Saud, who led the strict Wahabi sect, had removed all modern improvements. Each day a *moulvi* spoke to the pilgrims, reading from the Koran and exhorting his listeners to keep the faith. Winifred saw how they breathed in every word in complete silence, many wiping tears from their eyes.

Winifred, too, was moved by their devotion, knowing how much the pilgrimage meant to them. There was no music, no singing, only the voice of the *moulvi* and the swelling chorus rising from thousands of throats as they proclaimed their faith and asked forgiveness of their sins. Women were among the worshippers. On the hadj they walked unveiled, enjoying freedom denied them in their own countries.

Praying in the Great Mosque was a liberating experience which affected Winifred deeply. Carried away with fervour she felt as if her body had turned to water and she was part of a great river. As she prayed tears rolled down her cheeks. She heard Pansy, who was sitting beside her, say, 'Don't cry, Mummy. I'll kiss it better,' and she felt her little daughter's lips on her cheeks, her fingers brushing away the tears. She reached out her arms and hugged the child, wishing with all her heart that she had not had to leave her sons behind in Karachi and that they too could have shared this moment.

22

JOURNEY INTO DANGER

THEY HAD FIVE WEEKS TO FILL BEFORE the culminating ceremonies of the hadj. Karum Bux decided not to wait in Mecca but to join one of the camel trains going inland, through and beyond Medina. Here Mohammed had lived after his flight from Mecca and his tomb could be visited. It was not part of the hadj but an added glory for those who undertook the trip.

'Our history did not begin until 24 September 622,' Karum Bux told Winifred. 'It is hard for you to understand.'

Winifred looked at him. There was no scorn in his voice as there sometimes was when he was angry with her because she was not born into the faith. They had finished their simple evening meal and Pansy was asleep, while Winifred reclined, propped up on one of the bolsters provided in their room.

'Why did he have to leave?' she asked.

'He feared for his life. Mecca was the centre of trade, a place where caravans met and people came to worship at the shrine of the Kaaba. People who believed in many gods. When Mohammed began to preach that there was only one god, the merchants became angry. They were frightened of losing money if the pagans stopped visiting the shrine. He took refuge in Yathrib. Now they call it Medina, the City of the Prophet.'

'Is it far?'

'About four hundred miles. It all depends on how fast the camels go.'

She was tempted to ask if she and Pansy could remain behind till he returned, but knew it was not possible.

As if reading her mind he said, 'Medina is not like this barren place. There is water and over one hundred types of date trees. All manner of fruits and vegetables. You will like it better than waiting here.'

A few days later they were on their way to Medina, the second holiest city in Islam, oblivious to the dangers that lay in wait for them. Karum Bux had been overgenerous and had given liberal tips to the camel-men who had brought them from Jedda. Once the word spread, he was rushed by camel-men from other strings and even those who had nothing to do with their camel train. Now he had closed his purse and refused to give any more tips. The camel drivers were determined to be avenged.

It began out of Mecca when they started poking the sharpened sticks they used to goad the camels through their string beds. When Karum Bux woke feeling the sharp jab, he would sit up yelling, 'Hell and damnation! If I catch you I'll skin you alive.' Then it would be Winifred's turn. When she squealed in pain she would hear the sound of muffled laughter and the swift padding of feet across the sand.

Three days out of Mecca their journey became not only uncomfortable but dangerous. Instead of stopping to let the pilgrims rest, the camel drivers had travelled most of the night. It was 2 a.m. when they stopped beneath a sandy pocket surrounded by towering cliffs which ended in jutting peaks. It was desolate, with no vegetation, just a bare rock-face with caves like gaping black holes. Once these caves had been home to a race of cave-dwellers. The pass which ran between the mountains was barely wide enough for two camels.

Exhausted, the pilgrims dismounted and stretched out on the sand to sleep. Winifred lay watching the moon rise over the crest of the mountains. Karum Bux and Pansy lay asleep. Suddenly there was a glint from the side of one of the cliff walls and she sat up, wondering what it could be. She woke her husband and whispered to him. He in turn wakened the sleeper next to him, till the whole group was watching. Then they saw a bent figure creeping along the cliff edge with what looked like a rifle. At the same moment Karum Bux noticed their head driver, Gunga, gliding away. He realised there was not a camel to be seen.

'Bedouins,' he whispered. 'Our drivers have left us to be robbed.'

In an instant, several of the young men were alert and raced after the head driver, catching him as he was about to disappear into one of the lower caves. They dragged him back at knifepoint, threatening to kill him unless he called the camel drivers back with the camels. Gunga let out a series of loud calls and the men returned with the camels, which Karum Bux ordered them to resaddle. As fast as they were saddled, the women were helped on. By this time Winifred could see several figures crouched on the escarpment.

When ten camels bearing the women were loaded and tied head to tail, Karum Bux handed Winifred the leading string. 'Take the camels through the pass. Hurry!'

Trembling, Winifred handed Pansy to a woman on the lead camel and then, terrified of being shot, began to urge the sleepy camels forward. It was only a short distance but it seemed like a hundred miles, every noise sounding like the click of a rifle. She tried to urge the sleepy camels to go faster but they turned their heads, snapping and snarling, irritable at being woken. Pulling on the lead ropes with all her strength, she forced them forward. They crossed the moonlit sand, lurched through the narrow gap, and were out of range of the guns.

Winifred kept walking, the cold biting through her thin *shalwars* and chador, her feet like lead in the heavy sand. Walking on and on, the camels lurching along behind her, until she could go no further. The sky was streaked with pink when she called 'Hoosta!' and the camels knelt so that the women could dismount. They prostrated themselves and gave thanks to Allah for saving them.

Winifred remained where she was, conscious that the sun had risen and was warming the sand. She was roused by the sound of Karum Bux shouting, 'Stupid woman, why did you have to travel so far? You could have waited outside the gap. It's only by the grace of Allah we have found you. If the wind had sprung up, your tracks would have been hidden.'

Winifred stared at him without speaking until his words sunk in. She flung herself face-down on the sand and wept bitterly. She felt him raise her in his arms and heard him say, 'I was terrified I may not find you. In another hour it could have been too late.' He carried her back to their camel, placed her on her string bed and covered her with a blanket.

The caravan continued, but there was still tension between the drivers and the pilgrims. They were in open country now, away from the cliffs, which seemed safer.

It was night and they were sleeping when Karum Bux woke to find the camels had stopped moving. With a shock he realised the camel drivers had disappeared. Instead of a string of thirty beasts they were reduced to seven.

'The nose rope was deliberately cut,' he said. 'Lord knows how far back on the track they abandoned us. The camels may have swerved round completely by this time.'

There were fifteen people in the group that had been stranded. Winifred wondered if they would be missed by the other pilgrims. And even if they were, the drivers might refuse to turn back. They had no way of knowing which way to go, or how far the camels had travelled after their nose lines were cut.

The pilgrims argued long and bitterly about whether to go forward or wait for someone to find them, which might take days. By then they would have all died of thirst. Their red clay pots only held about three pints of water and few had as much as a pint left.

There was no shade and the camels were edgy, until Karum Bux hooshed them down and the pilgrims sat in the shade of the jute howdahs to conserve their energy. What surprised Winifred was how the pilgrims accepted their fate. They believed that if no one came to their aid it was the will of Allah that they die. Winifred was not so accepting. The following night she cried bitterly but soundlessly into her blankets, terrified at the thought of Pansy dying.

Later, as she lay awake, she could hear the faithful praying. It no longer consoled her, knowing there was little chance of rescue. Their one hope was that the camels would move of their own accord, seeking water when they felt thirsty.

They had been stranded for two days and the water jars were almost empty when the pilgrims began to argue among themselves. Some of the men wanted to move on, though none knew the way. Karum Bux listened to the arguments and said, 'It remains for us to be patient and move as little as possible. The camels will lead us to water if we put our trust in Allah.'

He spoke sense and was able to persuade the rest of the party that it was safer to wait than to die of thirst trying to find the way when there were no tracks. On the evening of the third day Karum Bux spoke to the men again, saying, 'Brothers, it is better that we load the camels while we still have the strength. After prayers mount your camel and wait. It is four days since the camels drank. Help me cut the nose lines so they will feel free to move.'

By this time Pansy was listless with a fever and Winifred felt weak and ill, unable to do much to help the child. That night, as if the pilgrims' prayers had been answered, the camels became restless, turning their heads as if expecting their drivers to urge them on. A short time later one moved, and then another. They paused again, as if waiting for their drivers, then slowly they began to move forward. Just before dawn they broke into a long, loping movement until they pulled up with a jerk, their necks bent. By the dim light Winifred could see they were drinking. In a second Karum Bux was off the camel and had lifted Pansy and Winifred down.

It was another of Abraham's wells, an oasis off the pilgrim route. They were the only travellers. About a dozen Arabs lived nearby, and from them they bought dates and goats' milk, plus a few cucumbers. They stayed for two days to regain their strength and then paid a guide to lead them to the rest of their party. It was late afternoon when they caught up. Their misfortune was treated as an accident and they did not press the point, even though they knew it was no accident. Instead, they kept a sharp eye on their drivers, fearing further treachery.

The rest of the trip passed without incident and they arrived safely in Medina. It was a pleasure to be among trees again. Winifred found the people friendlier than those in Mecca. She thought the men were the most handsome she had ever seen, with a creamy complexion, rather long faces and soft brown eyes. But she had no idea what the women looked like. They were covered with the heavy *burqa*, made heavier by the coins sewn on the face-covering. When they went to the markets she was intrigued to see them cut off a coin to pay for their purchases.

Here there were not the crowds they had encountered in Mecca, and Winifred and Pansy moved around freely. There was a good supply of fresh meat, cucumbers, onions, an edible grass and plenty of fresh water, things that had been short in Mecca and Jedda.

Feeling fresh and rested they went at last to the mosque, which Winifred found imbued with a gentle sadness. She had the feeling that the spirit of the Prophet still lingered, watching over the place he had come to love. As she entered the huge carved door to the courtyard she imagined she was walking underneath the sea because of the soft green light that filtered through the green dome. It was so high that date palms grew beneath it.

Under the dome was a four-roomed dwelling, its outer walls of intricate wrought iron, a peephole in the centre of each wall. Inside the first room the floor was patterned with black and white squares. In the centre stood the tomb of the Prophet Mohammed covered in black velvet. The inner walls were of gilded black wrought iron draped with black velvet curtains and the flags Mohammed had carried in battle. When Winifred asked the *moulvi* about the battles he replied, 'Mohammed, peace be on his name, was a wise and just man. The Prophet had been promised that he could return to Mecca on a pilgrimage, but he and his followers were betrayed. The next time he went he led a force of 10 000. Mohammed, by the grace of Allah, was able to enter the city where he destroyed the pagan idols. He was a lenient and forgiving conqueror. Many of his enemies passed to Islam. His flags are here to remind us of his struggles.'

She was surprised to see a mighty candle in the next room through the peephole. The holder was fashioned in gold and was larger than a human body. It bore a porcelain candle with a spreading flame of thin polished gold. Once again Winifred turned to their *moulvi* guide.

'It is a resting place for Hazarut Esau, the prophet the Christians call Jesus Christ, when he should come to earth again. When he walked the Jordan sands he had no resting place. We have given him one.'

Winifred was overwhelmed by the kindness of a people who would build a resting place for a prophet other than their own.

The other two rooms had dirt floors and enclosed the dwelling of Mohammed and his daughter, Fatima. It was a humble dwelling, in stark contrast to the ornate decorations of the other rooms, containing only some cooking pots and two ancient string charpoys on which they had slept.

The room Karum Bux rented in Medina had the most luxurious carpet Winifred had ever seen. Around the walls were long, bolster-like cushions of embroidered red satin. There was no other furniture. Keeping the room spotless became the bane of her life. She had to restrain Pansy who wanted to run around and jump on the cushions. Cooking had to be done in a large saucepan placed on a charcoal brazier which stood on the carpet. She yearned to put down a few sheets of newspaper to protect the carpet as she would have done in Australia. She compromised by using of one of her husband's shirts to roll out the dough for the chapattis.

There was a narrow, barred window through which she and Pansy could see right to the mosque door. Here the pilgrims took off their outdoor shoes, bathed their feet, then donned the slippers with curled-up toes which were provided. At night Karum Bux would take them to the mosque to see the hundreds of chandeliers hanging from the ceiling. Some were like bunches of fruit and flowers, others in the shape of serpents with lights for eyes, or mosques with windows that lit up. It was the most beautiful sight Winifred had ever seen and she never tired of it. And Pansy would reach up her arms and squeal with delight.

The Al Bakia cemetery lay immediately to the west of the city. With its rusty iron gate it was in stark contrast to the opulence of the Great Mosque. Here there were further rituals to be observed, including entering on the right foot while Karum Bux recited the special prayers.

Winifred could see nothing special about the place and asked him why they had to visit it.

'On the Day of Judgement twenty thousand souls will rise up, the first being Mohammed. Allah be praised.'

To Winifred it all looked sad and depressing. There were no flowers or ornaments, and pariah dogs roamed around scratching at the unmarked graves.

At the village of Old Medina they found another cemetery which was well cared for. Here were the graves of Abraham, his wife Sarah, and their relations and servants. In the town there were no books, except the Koran in Arabic, no pictures, no newspapers. History was handed down by word of mouth. All they knew of the outside world was the tales told them by pilgrims.

A few days later the camels were mustered for the journey back to Mecca. As they were preparing to leave, a woman whom Winifred had not met before came to see her, frantic because her husband was ill. Winifred knew nothing of medicine except Epsom salts, castor oil and Aspro tablets. She was reluctant to go with the woman, who became distraught when Winifred demurred. She knelt, touching the hem of Winifred's chador, pleading with her to come and see the sick man. Winifred allowed herself to be led to where he lay, barely conscious, with a harsh rasping breath. All Winifred could offer were two Aspro tablets which the wife forced into his mouth.

Winifred thought that the man might have pneumonia and suggested the woman call a doctor and remain in Medina until her husband had recovered. But the woman was determined to press on, to give her husband a chance to take part in the closing ceremony so that he could become a hadji. And so the camel train set off with the dying man.

Two days later they had stopped at an oasis to water the camels and rest briefly, when the woman came searching for Winifred. Once again Winifred followed to where the husband had been tied in a sitting position to the stick that held up the howdah. He was so close to death that his wife was unable to force the two Aspro tablets Winifred gave her into his mouth.

The order came to remount and Winifred hurried back to where Karum Bux was waiting anxiously. With tears in her eyes she told him the man was dying. He tried to console her, saying, 'It is considered a great blessing after a good life to sleep the last sleep in the Holy Land.'

Winifred was in a black mood that night. The trip had taken its toll. Hundreds of elderly pilgrims had died. She wondered what further trials lay ahead and whether she would have to watch Pansy die, and whether she and Karum Bux would die also. Then what would become of her two sons in Karachi? The thought that she had been selfish to insist on making the pilgrimage filled her with remorse and she felt weighed down with despair.

Later, there was a terrible cry from the front of the camel train. She knew instinctively that the sick man had died. Karum Bux tried to get the camel drivers to stop the train so they could say a prayer for the departing soul, but the drivers refused. Instead of stopping at the next water, they kept the train moving till late the next afternoon. For the first time the pilgrims could not dismount for morning prayers. When they finally stopped, the body of the man had stiffened around the pole.

The men dug a deep rounded mound in the sand, while the *moulvi* washed the body and swathed it in new calico. Because of rigor mortis the body had to be buried in a sitting position.

Not until the burial was over did anyone attempt to prepare a meal. But the drivers were still in a resentful, vengeful mood and the food was hardly on the fire before the pilgrims were ordered to remount. They had entered into a long stretch of desert and as Winifred looked back she saw the people from the oasis lift out the body and remove the new calico, before dumping the naked corpse on the sand.

Winifred spoke to the *moulvi* about it at the next stop, asking why the law didn't prevent such happenings. He replied, 'There is little law here as you know it. At least his bones will be picked clean by the birds, and polished by the sand until they become part of the desert, part of the Holy Land. No one could wish for anything more.'

The hardest part of the trip still lay ahead of them. The average speed of a loaded camel varied between five to fifteen miles an hour because of the sand. The journey back to Mecca became long and tedious. There were no regular days of travel. It depended on the distance between water. On *Juma* the camels rested. Food became scarce. To assuage the pangs of hunger Winifred took up smoking, making sure there was a piece of bread and a handful of dates for Pansy.

Towards the end of the trip Ibn Saud's caravan caught up with them. It brought a change in the attitude of the camel drivers who, under scrutiny from the king, became more careful in the treatment of those in their care.

It cheered the pilgrims to see the green standard proclaiming, 'There is no God but Allah' fluttering on the lead camel. Behind was an escort mounted on camels, each leading a mare by the halter. The king rode behind, his undergarments covered by a white hooded cloak which floated out behind, his white headpiece held in place by a plaited black circle. A white camel without a rider was part of the entourage. Behind were the bodyguards, riding camels, each with a bandoleer slung across his shoulder and a rifle on the saddle.

When they stopped for evening prayers Ibn Saud's servants erected tents made of grey woven cloth. Winifred walked across with Pansy to where attendants were caring for the animals, grooming the mares and feeding small balls of paste to the camels. Mother and daughter stopped beside the white camel. 'I have never seen a white camel before,' said Winifred to one of the attendants.

'This is a special camel,' she was told. 'It is descended from the camel Fatima rode when she went with her father,

Mohammed, into battle. It will be paraded at the final ceremony of the Hadj at Mount Arafat.'

She was about to walk away when a man came out of the tent and bowed to her. 'Bebe Zatoon, the king is giving an audience. He would like to meet you.'

Startled, Winifred could only stare at him. She looked around for Karum Bux, but he had gone to talk to the men in one of the other camel trains. Holding Pansy by the hand she stepped through the flap the attendant was holding for her. Inside, the tent was crowded. Winifred sat on the ground on a rug that was spread for her and Pansy, and red silk bolsters were brought so that they could recline. The attendant pointed to a handsome man wearing a black fez and dressed in a long white shirt and black silk overrobe. 'The king is busy at the moment. He will speak to you later.'

There was a small stove in one part of the tent and a servant was preparing coffee. First he put the water on to boil. Winifred and Pansy watched as he picked up four handfuls of coffee from a container on the floor and put them on the stove to warm without burning them. Then he ground them in a mortar to a coarse, reddish coloured grit. He put the ground coffee in the pot and began to stir the mixture with a stick. The second it began to boil he took it from the fire and added some spices. It had been a long, slow process and Pansy was restless, but there was nothing Winifred could do but wait.

The coffee was served in small brown cups without handles and Winifred took one when the tray was passed, sipping the muddy liquid and giving Pansy a taste. The coffee tray was passed three times and Winifred noticed that it was served in a different order each time. Then the king rose to his feet and everyone else did the same. She and Pansy followed suit. He walked towards them and Winifred saw how tall he was. He stopped in front of her. 'Bebe Zatoon, I have heard of you. Welcome to Arabia. You are enjoying your visit to my country?'

Before she could answer he had turned away and she found herself and Pansy being escorted out of the tent.

Karum Bux was scowling when he saw her. She hurried to his side. 'I have searched for you everywhere. Where have you been?'

'With the king.'

'Why was I not informed?'

'You were not here.'

She tossed some chapattis in a pan and prepared a meal of curried vegetables with lentils. Karum Bux ate it in silence and then wandered off, leaving her and Pansy to settle down for the night alone. She thought he must be angry with her for going into the king's tent without asking his permission. But there was little she could have done. It would have been ungracious to have refused.

Three days later they rode into Mecca behind the king's entourage.

Winifred had imagined that the most important parts of the pilgrimage were behind them. They had visited the mosques at Mecca and Medina, performed the prescribed rites and made long, arduous journeys by camel. But it was not so. Now they were at the Great Mosque for one last visit and she stood listening to a sermon which she could not understand. She was to learn from Karum Bux that the mullah was telling the faithful about the closing ceremonies. 'They always take place on the ninth day of Dhu'l Hijja, the last month of the Moslem year. A pilgrim could atone for missing other parts of the hadj, but to miss the "stand" at Arafat is to miss the pilgrimage.'

There was a slightly fanatical light in his eyes which she had never seen before. 'We will be walking in the footsteps of the Prophet, peace be upon him, when he made his farewell pilgrimage. Though he died soon after, he died knowing that he had obeyed the Messenger of the Lord. Islam had triumphed.'

Winifred gazed back at him, thinking that it was almost as if he would be happy to die once he had completed the pilgrimage. She wondered how long they would have to stand at Arafat, thinking of Pansy as much as herself, but did not like to ask. They would just have to endure it as best they could. Karum Bux took her by the arm. She was standing close and he had lifted Pansy onto his shoulders because of the mass of people jammed together listening to the sermon.

'The mullah has said that on the day of the "standing" God descends to Arafat, which is the part of the heavens closest to earth. He points out the people of the earth to those in heaven to show them how we have come from all corners of the earth, tired and weary, burnt from the sun, to ask for His mercy.'

The journey to Arafat, which lay about twenty-eight miles east of Mecca, was too far for the family to make on foot so Karum Bux set about hiring a camel and driver, planning to travel with several other families. It was not easy, with so many others wanting the same thing. The camel drivers saw it as their last chance to extort money from the pilgrims. The group had bargained hard and paid for their camels in advance, arranging to meet at a certain place to begin their journey. When they arrived the drivers were waiting, but they demanded more money before they would bring the camels.

While the men argued, Winifred walked away with Pansy. It was then that she heard the soft snorting of a camel and found the camels they had hired already saddled. She went back and whispered the news to Karum Bux who, with some of the men, went to bring in the camels. The party started off with the camels being led by the men, while the drivers walked behind, angry at being thwarted but knowing they had no choice but to follow. If they did not they would lose their camels in the great crowd.

They travelled through the night and just before dawn came to the narrow pass that led to the valley of Arafat, an open area which stretched for miles on either side. Above was the granite outcrop known as the Hill of Mercy, where the Prophet had preached nearly fourteen hundred years before. Overshadowing it were the lofty Hodeheyl Mountains.

It was a sight Winifred was to remember all her life — thousands upon thousands of pilgrims clad in white filled the valley like some exotic crop stretching as far as the eye could see, all waiting to be recognised by the Lord. She was to become part of it. And then the thought came to her that once they had descended into the valley they would be sucked into the moving throng and be unable to escape. She looked down at Karum Bux, who had dismounted from the camel and was holding Pansy by the hand. 'I have never seen so many people in one place before,' she said. Her voice trembled, though she tried to hide it.

'It will be like this on the Day of Judgement, when the whole world stands before God.'

'What if we are separated?' she asked. 'How will I find you again?'

'Allah will protect us,' he said and he helped her dismount.

In the valley they handed the camel back to the owner and were allotted a position on the plains among the Indian pilgrims. She began to feel easier when she saw cleared spaces like an enormous camping ground, with water vendors moving between the rows. Karum Bux drove four sticks into the soft sand. 'According to tradition,' he explained, 'because we come before Allah as a family.' He made a roof and a wall of blankets to simulate a home and spread their prayer rugs on the ground.

Inside their shelter Winifred began to relax. They had a tin of water, which Karum had bought, and she lay down beside Pansy and slept. At twelve she was woken by the sound of prayers which swelled up like waves breaking on the shore. The 'standing' had begun. Karum Bux joined in, reciting prayers, waiting for the sound of the cannon at four o'clock that signalled that the pilgrimage was over.

Winifred looked around. To the rear of them was the Persian encampment with flags flying and cannons pointing towards the Hill of Mercy. On the opposite side, facing the Persians, was the Turkish camp which also had guns. Beside them was the entourage of King Ibn Saud. In the middle was the mass of Indian pilgrims.

As the day wore on, the heat increased, and Winifred found herself becoming tense. It was a day of fasting and she was almost faint with hunger. She had given Pansy a piece of bread and a handful of dates, but had eaten nothing herself.

The guns on either side of them made her uneasy. 'Why do they need guns when we have all come before God?'

'Maybe the Turks and Persians feel it necessary,' Karum Bux shrugged. 'They do not trust Ibn Saud. Two years ago he wiped out the town of Taif, just a few miles away. The guns are to protect themselves.'

As the afternoon progressed, Winifred found herself obsessed with food, speculating on what she would cook when she got back to Australia. Her first thought was of strong tea with cow's milk, hot scones with butter, a beefsteak pie with gravy running over and peas and potatoes. In a lull between prayers she asked Karum Bux if he was hungry and he snapped at her, 'Be quiet, woman.'

She wanted to ask him if it made Allah happy to know that his people below were hungry, but thought better of it. Instead, she tried to turn her mind back to the pilgrimage, thinking of the thousands of people who had sacrificed so much to make the hazardous journey. She knew it was their faith that carried them along. Feeling guilty, she prayed to God to forgive her if her observance had not been all that could be desired and to protect her family from danger. She was certain her prayer was heard because of what followed.

It was early afternoon when a cannon sounded. Karum Bux looked at the sun. 'I do not think it is time.' The cannon was answered by one from the other side and the shot landed in the plain. Panic broke out among the pilgrims caught in the crossfire. Trapped in the vast crowd Winifred could only stare in horror. A camel lurched past with its entrails hanging out. Around them lay people wounded and dying. The air was filled with the smell of gunpowder and the screams and groans of the dead and dying. Still the Persians and the Turks kept on firing at each other. The noise woke Pansy who had been asleep. She screamed each time she heard the sound of the cannon, until Winifred cradled her in her arms, blocking her ears, saying, 'Hush, hush. It's only a bad storm. You can hear the thunder.'

Terrified, Winifred and her husband huddled together, sheltering Pansy until nightfall when the firing stopped. Under the cover of darkness Karum Bux folded the blankets and led his wife and daughter across the vast plain where, in the dim light, they could see bodies. Some were dead, others lay wounded. They could do nothing except protect themselves, though their cries haunted Winifred.

There were no camels to be had so they set out on foot, walking until they had left the nightmare scene behind, not sure which way to go. Every now and then a cannon boomed out and another answered. But they were out of range.

Exhausted, not having eaten since the day before, they were lucky to find a loose camel wandering with its saddle on. Karum Bux seized it and helped Winifred and Pansy onto its back, then led the beast until they saw a line of flares ahead. It was a row of stalls set up to feed the pilgrims. Here they stopped and Karum Bux bought chapattis, curry and roasted kebabs.

Winifred fed some to Pansy who ate hungrily, but the horrors of the day, the smell of blood, the screams of the wounded and dying still filled Winifred's mind. Though she had been dreaming of food all day she could not eat.

Later they set off again, until Karum Bux stopped the camel and told Winifred to get off.

360

'Why are we stopping?' she asked. 'It's still dark.'

'We need to gather some stones.'

'But it's the middle of the night. Why do we need stones?'

'To throw at the devil, who tempted Abraham to disobey the Lord when he ordered him to sacrifice his son, Isaac.'

Groping around in the dark they found a handful of pebbles and set off again. At daylight they said their prayers, then went on again until they came to Mina and the ruins of an ancient wall. At its foot was a huge mound of stones. They threw their pebbles against the wall then continued on to the place of sacrifice. They recognised it by the cries of beasts, the smell of blood and burning meat, and the pall of reddish-brown smoke that hung in the air. And always the packs of pariah dogs that roamed around looking for food.

It was here that they heard the truth about what had happened at the 'standing'. An idle youth in Ibn Saud's entourage had tossed a small stick down on a friend below. It had missed and lightly struck a Turk, who tossed it back in the direction it had come. Again, it missed and struck the wrong man. This time it was hurled down forcefully and with indignation. It was followed by a fusillade of sticks and stones, until a young Turkish prince lost his head and gave the order to fire. The Persians thought they were being fired at and fired back.

Still suffering from shock, Winifred listened but did not comment, wondering how they could have defiled the Holy Place and whether Allah would forgive them. So many innocent people had perished.

Because of the crowds who had come to make the final sacrifice, there was no accommodation to be had. The family made do with their makeshift tent of blankets, eating rings of bread, dates and water which they bought from itinerant vendors, while Karum Bux bargained for his quota of animals to sacrifice. Three for his relatives, two for them and three for the children.

On the second day Winifred was trying to sleep when two Arab water carriers began to fight beside her. They carried water in goatskins. The one who had an empty goatskin tried to steal the full one. The two men struggled until one drew his knife and cut the other's throat. He died, his blood soaking into the sand beside Winifred's blanket.

Karum Bux, who had witnessed the fight, came running. He grabbed up their blankets, tucked Pansy under his arm and hurried his wife away. Winifred felt no sense of fulfilment at completing the pilgrimage, only relief that they had survived.

23

MORE TROUBLE FOR BEBE ZATOON

THERE WAS ANOTHER LONG, WEARY camel ride for Winifred, made bearable by the knowledge that they were on their way back to India. Her mind was still full of the horrors she had witnessed, though she was relieved that Pansy was too young to realise how close they had been to death.

They arrived in Jedda to find that the ship they were due to sail on had not arrived. Karum Bux set off to find somewhere to stay, while Winifred took Pansy down to the beach so that her little daughter could paddle. The sight of the waves breaking on the shore soothed Winifred, and she felt cleansed as she breathed in the sea air. She watched the ships beyond the channel, smoke belching from their funnels as they waited for their passengers and the lateen boats darting in and out, and she thought back to her spill in the water. So much had happened that it seemed like another life.

The bay curved inward like a half-moon, and date palms arched over the tall white houses, casting their shade. It was like being in paradise after the rigours of the hadj, and Winifred found herself giving thanks to Allah for bringing them safely back. Looking around, she noticed a ruined mosque on a steep hill facing the sea. The left-hand wall had collapsed and one of the minarets had fallen. On the right side was a set of stone steps that led to the roof. Telling Pansy to stay where she was, Winifred went to investigate and found that part of the roof was quite strong. She called to the child to come up the stairs and they settled down to wait for Karum Bux.

An hour passed, an hour they spent relaxing on the roof, refreshed by the sea breeze. When Winifred saw Karum Bux searching for them she called out, 'Up here. We're up here.'

He looked up and frowned, calling out, 'Come down at once!'

'No,' she said. 'This is our home. I found it.'

'Are you blind? Can't you see it's a mosque?' And he hurried up the steps.

When he had recovered his breath Winifred said, 'This must be the loveliest spot in Jedda, away from the crowds and with the sea breeze to cool us. Allah guided us here and I intend to stay.'

Though her husband argued, she refused to listen, taking the food he had brought and feeding Pansy and herself, until he fell silent and spread their blankets, using some of the rotting rafters to build a shelter.

Lulled by the sea, Winifred slept soundly that night for the first time and felt herself beginning to heal after the trials of the trip. She was awakened by a commotion and found that a deputation had formed below. They were addressing her, accusing her of blasphemy for defiling a sacred place. The group of men advanced up the stairs and were about to step on the roof which had given way in some places, the whole structure in danger of collapsing. Winifred waved them back, pointing to the rotting timbers, and they retreated, keeping up their harangue from the stairs.

'Who owns this place?' she asked.

The men looked at one another, puzzled. They admitted that no one did.

'What harm are we doing, me and my little one, resting here till our ship sails?'

'But it's the house of Allah.'

'Well then I claim sanctuary. If Mohammed was alive he'd offer us shelter.'

She turned her back on them while they continued arguing among themselves, until eventually they quietened down and left.

At noon the *moulvi* arrived with the town lawyer. The priest spoke first. 'Mem-sahib, we request that you come down from this sacred place.'

Karum Bux, standing behind Winifred, hissed, 'Now see what you've done!'

Winifred ignored her husband and turned to address the *moulvi*, 'Tell me who the owner of this ruin is. I'll take it up with him.'

'Of the earthly owner there is not one. This is the place of Allah.'

'I'm glad to hear that. Allah and I are good friends. He has given me permission to stay here.'

'But mem-sahib, this place is too much good.'

'You have allowed it to fall into ruin. That is how good it is. In the name of Allah I accept the hospitality of this place by divine law. Now will you please leave?'

Her tone of authority had the desired affect. After bowing to her and asking if there was anything she needed, the pair left.

Once again she became the centre of attention, as she had been on board ship, with crowds jamming the lane to the mosque to see what she was doing on the roof. But the blankets Karum Bux had put up screened her from prying eyes.

When they had arrived in Jedda they expected to be sailing within a day or two. But when Karum Bux went to find Ibrahim, the agent who had been assigned to them, he seemed to have vanished. With him had gone their documents and those of over three hundred other pilgrims. Without their documents it was impossible for pilgrims to leave the country. It was a serious situation and the pilgrims gathered on the beach, shouting and waving their arms while Winifred watched from her vantage point. The *moulvi* convinced them that it was no good, the whole three hundred running through the town, creating a disturbance. He pleaded with them to appoint a leader to pursue the matter. The responsibility fell on Karum Bux.

Winifred suggested that he ask for an audience with Ibn Saud but he was warned off by guards with rifles each time he tried. He found the French police not much better. All he had been able to find out was that agents often sold the travel documents to the highest bidder. When the policemen who interviewed him said, 'You were warned not to forget the name of the agent you were assigned to,' Karum Bux lost his temper and shouted, 'I have told you his name is Ibrahim. Do you take me for some ignorant peasant?'

It did him no good because it brought other police running and he was ordered to leave on pain of being arrested. The other pilgrims who had followed Karum Bux gathered together and threatened to attack the police station, until the *moulvi* told them to return to the beach and pray.

When Karum Bux returned that night without food, Winifred became alarmed. They had a meagre meal of chapattis and water and as she lay on her rug in the ruined mosque she made up her mind to look for Ibrahim herself. The next morning she put on her grey silk suit, the one she had been married in. It was crushed from being carried in her suitcase and she had no way of getting out the creases. She dabbed her suntanned face with flour because she had no face powder, and put on her pith helmet.

'Why are you dressed like that?' Karum Bux asked.

'I am going to look for our thieving agent. But first I will go to Ibn Saud and ask for his help. I am British. It was the British who helped him become king.' Despite her husband's protests she went marching down the stairs, leaving him to look after Pansy, who had developed a fever and was listless and fretful.

As she made her way to the palace, Winifred was followed by a great crowd of pilgrims. When she arrived at the gates she was stopped by one of the guards, who demanded to know her business.

'I have come to call on His Highness, Ibn Saud. We were together on the hadj. I wish to thank him for his courtesy before I return to my home in Australia.' She was amused to see the guards talking among themselves and pointing at her until the gates opened.

'Mem-sahib,' the one who appeared to be the leader said, 'I will take you to the entrance.' They were met at the door by another guard and after a whispered conversation she found herself in a rather austere foyer with whitewashed walls, where she was asked to wait. It was not for long. A man dressed in a flowing white robe entered and bowed to her, saying, 'Mem-sahib, you wish to see the king. It is not possible I am afraid. He is at prayers.'

'I have come,' Winifred said, 'because there are three hundred pilgrims ready to board the next ship and their papers have been stolen. When we passed through here on the way to Mecca we paid taxes so that we would be protected. And now we are unable to leave. I am a British subject.'

'It is a matter for the police, mem-sahib. If we catch those responsible they will be severely punished. I will send a man with you to the police station. We would not want you to leave with a bad opinion of our country.'

As Winifred went out of the gates, accompanied by one of the guards, the crowd of waiting pilgrims parted for them and then fell in behind, and the procession continued to the police station. At the police station Ibn Saud's guard spoke to the man on duty on the front desk, then, bowing to Winifred, left. She found her- self being escorted to the office of the commandant, who rose to his feet at the sight of her. Despite her crumpled suit, her sunburnt face, now covered in a fine mist of sweat from the sun, she carried herself with dignity, her back straight and a determined look in her eyes. The pith helmet added to the effect. The commandant was more accustomed to the sight of Indian pilgrims than he was to an English lady.

He held out a chair, saying, 'Madame, please be seated.' He rang a bell and a servant came in with coffee and a jug of cold water. He passed Winifred a demitasse of black coffee and poured her a glass of water, then sat back, waiting for her to begin.

'If you look outside the front door you will see hundreds of people. You can hear them. They are angry because nothing is being done to help them recover their travel documents. Without their documents they cannot return to their homes.'

'I have heard of it, madame. It is what happens here. We have been searching for the man.'

'Ah, so you do know,' Winifred replied. 'It seems strange that a clever French officer cannot catch one ignorant Arab. Kindly give me your name and I will inform your superiors. Every year thousands upon thousands of devout pilgrims come here expecting justice. Instead, they are betrayed.' She rose, 'I hold you responsible.'

Her words had the desired effect. The man stood and paced up and down. 'We have searched and searched, madame. But we cannot find him.'

'I think it is because they are only poor pilgrims. If it was the king who had been wronged … '

He held up his hand. 'Madame, you do me an injustice. We are few in number and there are thousands of pilgrims.'

'Soon most of them will be gone, but it will be too late for those whose documents have been stolen. You have admitted that you cannot find the man we seek. Give me four of your men. Impress on them how important it is. Together we will search. If I do not find him, I promise you will be recalled from service in a week. I have been given the task of looking after the women pilgrims. I intend to do just that.'

She was amazed at her own audacity and was glad that her husband was not there to listen, knowing he would not approve. However, her arguments won and four uniformed policemen were summoned to accompany her on her search.

They spent the day combing alleyways and shops, asking for information on Ibrahim's whereabouts. They visited his relatives and friends. Once they passed the old mosque and saw Karum Bux sitting on the roof. She saw his mouth open in astonishment and he called out something to her but she did not hear. Then, at the end of their lane, they saw their quarry, wiping his mouth as he emerged from an eating house.

One of the policeman called out to him but he took off, with the search party in hot pursuit. Finally they saw him run into a house and there he was cornered and arrested and the documents recovered.

A few days later the last ship for the season dropped anchor in the bay. Winifred said goodbye to the little mosque with a feeling of sadness and, dressed in her *shalwars* and chador, followed Karum Bux to the jetty, where they were told to wait for the immigration officers. Her husband went off to stock up on provisions for the trip. Tired of standing in the hot sun, Winifred sat down on her blanket roll, keeping an eye on Pansy who had gone down to the water's edge.

She was in a relaxed frame of mind, thinking of being back in Australia and eating hot scones and butter, when she felt the stinging cut of a riding whip across her shoulders. She sprang to her feet in anger and, turning, snatched the whip from her aggressor and slashed him across the face. He staggered, and she followed up with other blows. His cries attracted attention. She discovered she had been thrashing a French policeman and was arrested. She was taken before the commandant and listened angrily as the police gabbled out their side of the story. Then it was Winifred's turn and she showed the officer the wound on her back and shoulders.

Turning to the policeman who had struck her, the commandant said, 'What is the meaning of this?'

'Sir, you know these pilgrim women. They are as simple as cattle. One has to keep them moving. This one was sitting down when all the rest were standing. I only gave her a little tap and the next thing she flies at me.'

'What crime did I commit by sitting down on my own blanket?'

The commandant shrugged. 'He seemed to think you did not show enough respect, seeing you were waiting for an official to check your papers before going on board.'

At that moment Karum Bux came running in. He had been told that his wife had been arrested for murdering a policeman. Winifred managed to calm him down, even though her back was in agony. Her skin was broken and she could feel the dried blood sticking to her shirt. 'I was assaulted by one of your men. I will be reporting this to the authorities.'

'But, madame, it was a mistake. If you had been wearing English clothes …'

'So you admit that you and your men are guilty of cruelty to pilgrims, when your duty is to protect them.'

He stammered his regrets and sent for coffee, and a doctor to dress her wounds and give her a sedative. But she carried the welt mark for months.

On the way back to the ship Karum Bux turned on her, his temper out of control. 'Wherever you go there's trouble. I should have left you in Oodnadatta where you belong.'

'And I should never have married you,' she replied.

When they got to the jetty she looked around anxiously for Pansy. In her frenzy she had forgotten the child and was relieved to see that she was still on the beach. She ran to her, gathered her up in her arms and cried bitterly, all her pent-up emotions spilling out.

Later the sedative began to take effect and the pain in her back started to subside. She became more composed and prepared to go on board, hoping that her husband had gone ahead to find them a place to put their things. There were still passengers milling around waiting for a place on the small boats that transported them to the ship. Rather than join the long queue standing in the hot sun, Winifred waited with Pansy in the shade and noticed two young women also standing apart. They looked so sad and forlorn that Winifred walked over to them.

'Why are you waiting here alone? If you don't go on board you will have difficulty finding a place to sleep.'

'We can't go on board. They won't let us. The agent stole our papers and now he has disappeared.' The older of the two girls spoke, while the younger one clung to her arm.

'Have you told the police?'

'Yes, but the agent has disappeared and no one can find him. The shipping agents refuse to let us leave without papers. They say we must wait here until someone from India arranges our return. But there is no one. Our brother died at Mount Arafat. He was wounded when they fired the guns, and there was no one to tend to his wounds and …' She began to cry, clutching her sister who had also begun to cry.

Winifred looked at them — they were little more than teenage girls. If they were left behind, heaven knows what would happen to them. There was no work to be had. The shops were only tiny openings in a wall run by the owner. Restaurants were nothing more than a piece of meat skewered on a stick and sold by the road. In private households there was no need to hire domestics, the women of the house did the work. If the girls were forced to stay, without money or friends, they would be abused and end up as prostitutes, unless they walked into the sea. Winifred thought of going to the police, but the last of the boats was preparing to leave. If she missed it she might be left behind. Karum Bux had all their money. She and Pansy would be destitute.

'Go down to the water,' she told the girls. 'Stand in the centre of the crowd, facing the boats. I will follow with my daughter. I will divert the officer's attention. As soon as you see him turn to talk to me, get into the boat. Don't be afraid. Nothing will happen to you. When he sees you already in the boat later, he will think your papers have been checked.'

Winifred waited until the young women had merged into the crowd and then she walked behind, holding Pansy by the hand, pushing her way through the waiting line until she was behind the official. She raised her hand and hit him between the shoulder blades. He turned, his eyes blazing, and then recognised her.

'What right have you to keep me waiting, after the way I have been treated!'

'But, madame, we left you quietly on the beach. We were letting you wait until the last. We plan to send a special boat for you. These boats are too crowded.'

As Winifred watched, the little boat pulled away and she saw the two young women were on board, standing among the passengers because there was nowhere to sit.

'Very well,' she said, and sat on the edge of the jetty to wait until a police launch pulled up. She handed Pansy to one of the police on board and then took his outstretched hand and stepped into the boat.

There was no examination of papers on board the ship and she was relieved. She could not see the girls and she imagined that they must have hidden themselves. Karum Bux had found a spot beneath an overhanging boat. It was not a pleasant trip, though it was cooler on deck. Below decks the heat was almost unbearable.

The journey through the Red Sea was an ordeal. Winifred began to notice the long bundles that were tossed overboard by the crew. It did not take her long to realise that they were the bodies of people who had died. She discovered that cholera was rife.

'They gorged themselves on bad meat at the sacrifice,'

Karum Bux said. 'Many died at Jedda before we left. I did not want to worry you. We ate little meat. We should be all right.'

The ship became a death ship. Winifred watched women struggling to the latrines, dragging their *shalwars* in the filth because they were too weak to hold them up. A vile stench permeated everything, though the crew hosed down the latrines daily.

This time there had been no stop at Kamaran to break the monotony of the voyage and have a cool bath while their clothes were fumigated. If there had been, Winifred thought, there would not have been so many deaths. But the quarantine station was only to prevent disease entering the country. What happened to the pilgrims when they left was of no account.

For the most part Winifred and Pansy kept themselves isolated. Even though the weather cooled as they neared Karachi, they remained on deck and swathed themselves in blankets. Her husband mixed with the other men, talking and smoking, but he kept his distance from her. She wondered if it was out of consideration in case he was carrying the disease, or whether he was still angry with her. She thought about what she had said about their marriage. She was not sure whether she regretted marrying him or not. She knew he had never loved her. She had been useful to him and he to her. But he had spent a lot of time away from her in Oodnadatta. Now they had been living in each other's pockets for weeks. He had looked after her and Pansy, seeing to their comfort, but she noticed that he had become increasingly irritated at her actions. She thought that perhaps he would divorce her when they arrived back in Australia.

She had no claim on him, and for a Moslem man divorce was just saying the words, 'I divorce thee. I divorce thee. I divorce thee.' But she kept her thoughts to herself, sensing that the time was not right for ironing out their differences. When they got home would be time enough.

Their ship eased quietly into the Karachi dock. There was no frenzied crowd bearing garlands of flowers as there had been when they left for the pilgrimage. Before they were allowed to leave the ship, immigration officers came on board. They counted the passengers, and after deducting the seventy who had died on board, discovered that there were two over. A search revealed the two girls. The rest of the passengers were allowed to leave the ship, but they were forced to remain.

When she saw their plight Winifred refused to leave the ship. Reluctantly Karum Bux stayed with her while the girls were interrogated by the immigration officials. Also present were three members of the Khalifat, who were there to see to the interests of the returning pilgrims. Winifred recognised them. They had been there when she thrashed the woman doctor before they embarked on their voyage. After an hour of questioning they decided that the girls must return to Jedda and threatened to punish Winifred for aiding and abetting them to board the ship.

Once again Karum Bux was very angry. 'Why did you not ask me first? I would have warned you of the dangers of your action!'

'And what if they had been your sisters? Would you have left them stranded, to be ill-used by some man? I thought that being a Moslem meant being kind … I can see I made a mistake.' She gathered Pansy in her arms. The child felt hot

376

and was starting to cry. 'Hush, little one,' she said. Then she turned to one of the men. 'My daughter is tired and thirsty. Is there no water?'

Hastily, a servant poured some water into a glass and handed it to Winifred, who held it to Pansy's lips so that she could drink. She could see that they were concerned. The leader of the Khalifat group said, 'Could you bring some tea?'

With a cup of tea on the table by her side and Pansy in her arms Winifred saw that the mood had changed and she pressed home her advantage. 'Sirs, when you saw me before we sailed on the *Istophan* you charged me with the care of the women. You trusted me and I was proud of that trust. Now you tell me I did wrong in helping these girls to return to their own country. It was not their fault that their papers were stolen. Do you not know what happens when so many thousands of pilgrims are treated as prey? Do not take it on my word alone. Ask others. Ask my husband.' She looked across to where Karum Bux was sitting with head bowed.

'Is it as your wife says?' one asked.

He raised his head. 'Yes, she speaks the truth. We were set upon and only saved by the grace of Allah. Others were not so lucky.'

'Why have we not heard of these things before?'

Winifred said, 'Because we were told that on the hadj we must endure all things without complaint. If someone does us an injury we must not retaliate.'

'But mem-sahib, these men you speak of are also Moslems.'

'Perhaps their perception of Allah differs from ours.' Her voice trailed away. She was too tired to argue. Pansy had fallen asleep and was a dead weight in her arms. 'Do what you will,' she said, 'I can go on no longer.' She lay back feeling faint, the faces staring at her swimming in front of her eyes. She was never sure what happened next except that she found herself lying down in a room with an overhead fan. Pansy was asleep on the bed beside her, and Karum Bux was sitting in a chair.

'Where are we?' she asked.

'You fainted. We are in the British India Hotel. There is a bathroom, and when you are ready they will send in dinner. We are the guests of the Khalifat.'

Winifred looked at him. His face was set in stern lines and there was no warmth in his eyes.

'Are you angry with me?'

'Not angry, but ashamed. You know the rules of the hadj. You should have kept what happened to yourself. You wanted to go. I told you it would be hard but you would not listen. These trials are sent by Allah to strengthen our faith. But you are a woman … and British. You are not one of us. How could you understand?'

Winifred looked at him without speaking. Then she rose and carried Pansy into the bathroom where they splashed in the water and came out refreshed. Later two of the men from the Khalifat called to see her. She was alone. Karum Bux had gone out as soon as they had dined.

'We have been thinking, mem-sahib. We feel we owe you an apology. We asked you to look after the women and you fulfilled your side of the bargain, even though it was at danger to yourself. Now we want to thank you.'

'What happened to the two girls?'

'They are on the train, on their way back to their families, with their tickets paid and a few rupees over.'

Winifred smiled. She had been vindicated.

Before she could speak, one of the men said, 'We have an invitation for you, mem-sahib. You and your family are invited to spend a few days at the palace of the Khalifat in Bombay. Our leader, Maulana Shaukat Ali, wishes to meet you. Tomorrow a car will call for you and take you to the station.' Without waiting for her reply they bowed and left.

24

IN THE PALACE
OF THE KHALIFAT

A CAR MET THEM AT BOMBAY RAILWAY station and drove them to the palace. There they swept up the drive and into a large pavilion which led up a flight of steps. At the top were two huge mahogany doors studded with brass nails in an Arabic design. They were wide enough for two cars to pass abreast. Beyond lay a great hall, the walls hung with ornate tapestries embellished with exotic birds and flowers, and lit by domes of coloured glass set into the ceiling. The floor was tiled in pink and black and in the centre was a sunken pond in the shape of a star, full of clear water for the ceremonial washing of the feet of guests who might happen to be there at prayer time.

The atmosphere was one of peace and reverence and the family stood quietly until they were ushered into another room in a hexagonal shape, lit by windows of red and green leadlight glass. Huge carved marble pillars ran from ceiling to floor.

Here they were welcomed by Maulana Shaukat Ali, head of the Khalifat. 'First you must rest, *hadjana*, and then we will talk. I am interested in what is happening in the Moslem community in Australia. Many of our countrymen have gone there … many have not returned home as we had expected.'

He looked at her two sons and smiled. 'You are wondering about this place? It is not really a palace but an office where we print two newspapers for our people in their own tongue. The people who work on the presses, the journalists and the editors all live here with their families. Then there are private quarters for guests who come through Bombay. And my wife and her family. This place is like a beehive. It is quiet now because the presses have finished for the day. If you hear a rumbling, as if a river is rushing underneath, you will know that it is the machinery turning over.'

He laughed and turned to Winifred. 'I will arrange for someone to show your sons over the office. I am sure it will be of interest to them.'

They were shown to their quarters, with the boys placed in the care of one of the servants, while Pansy remained with her parents. Winifred was reluctant to part with her boys. They had had an emotional reunion the evening before. She was assured she would see them again after prayers. Later an ayah came and took Pansy into the garden where her brothers were playing with some other children.

When the time came for prayers Karum Bux went to join the men, while Winifred was taken to meet the begum,

Maulana Shaukat Ali's wife, a slight elderly woman with a perfect command of English. She took Winifred's right hand and kissed it, placed it on her forehead and then on her heart. 'I salute you, *hadjana*, you have made the hadj ... perhaps some day I too may make the journey.'

The buttercup-yellow silk headscarf, which matched her long flowing gown dropped to her shoulders.

Winifred saw the flash of diamonds as she lifted her hands to smooth her dress, which was embroidered with silver thread in a pattern of waterlilies. She led Winifred out into the garden where they bathed their hands and feet and joined the other women of the household for afternoon prayers.

Later, she showed Winifred over the women's quarters. The first room was in the shape of a heart and had walls of carved pink marble under a ceiling of green glass. Two shallow steps led to another part of the room with high stained-glass windows to the roof. Low divans with embroidered cushions were scattered about and there was a miniature reading desk of gold, bearing an open copy of the Koran. By the doorway stood a huge brass jar full of drinking water and a blue vase decorated with a white stork and large enough to hold a man. Winifred was surprised to see a gramophone, which seemed out of place here. She was to discover the begum had travelled the world and had met Queen Mary in England, even going to the races with the royal family and winning fifty pounds.

She laughed at Winifred's look of astonishment. 'Moslem women are not always what they seem. We are not in purdah here. But we prefer to spend some time in our women's quarters where we can relax. I do not come to Bombay often.

I have residences in Bangalore, Mysore, Delhi and Baroda. But my husband wanted to meet you.'

There were seven women in the apartments, two were sisters of the begum and the others daughters of the house. Winifred met them over tea, which was served with sweet cakes as they sat in a circle on the floor. She found it uncomfortable and her legs developed cramps, but she did not like to complain for fear of offending her hostess, who was intent on hearing about the hadj. She felt flattered by her interest. Just the same she was relieved when they moved into the garden where the children were playing and they could walk about. Below she could see the ocean, and the smell of burning sandalwood drifted across from a nearby mosque to mingle with the perfume of roses and oleanders. To Winifred it seemed like some fantastic dream.

Mixing with high caste Indians was a new experience for Winifred. They had been educated in English schools and spoke English beautifully and yet they had retained their customs, which varied according to their religion and place in society. Now she was to learn that the country was in turmoil as it struggled to rid itself of the British. From her earliest days at school in England she had taken it for granted that India was a British possession. Her father had pointed out the words 'Empress of India' on the coins bearing the likeness of Queen Victoria, and the red parts on a map of the world that showed how far the British Empire stretched. She had thought it rather grand and was proud to be part of it.

Foremost among the Indian leaders was Mahatma Gandhi, who had come to the palace for a meeting with Maulana in an effort to unite Hindus and Moslems in the fight for Home

Rule. Winifred was walking in the garden when she saw Maulana Shaukat Ali approaching with an emaciated looking man in a dhoti, a length of white cloth draped over his shoulders, and yellow sandals. They stopped in front of her and Maulana said, 'Gandhi, this is *Hadjana* Karum Bux. She has just returned from Mecca and is resting here before returning to Australia. I am sure you will find plenty to talk about.' He excused himself to mingle with the other guests.

Gandhi smiled and, putting his palms together, bowed to Winifred, then they sat down on a garden seat near the sea wall.

'You are new to India?' Gandhi asked.

'This is my first visit,' said Winifred as she began to fan herself with a sandalwood fan which she had dipped in the fountain. The breeze had dropped and there was still heat in the sun. Above, a sea eagle hovered and pigeons were pecking on the lawn. There was a sense of peace. Winifred sat back feeling relaxed.

Gandhi touched her arm and she turned to face him. 'Did you enjoy the pilgrimage? he asked.

'It was hard. Often we did not have enough food.'

He did not reply and she gazed at him. He was so thin. She had heard of his hunger strikes. She was sorry she had spoken about food.

'Have you seen the beggars who sleep in the doorways like pariah dogs because they have no home?' He was watching her. His face was gentle.

Winifred was silent, thinking back to the car trip from the station to the palace. The children had been excited but she had been too tired to take much notice, remembering only the sound of someone tapping on the window when they stopped to avoid a bullock cart. She had opened her eyes to see a woman holding a child with no arms. The woman had stretched out one hand begging for money and then the car had moved off. She had turned away from the woman, putting her from her mind. But now that she had been reminded she felt guilty. 'I have seen them,' she said.

'Then you understand. They call them the untouchables. In my religion, which is Hindu, they are regarded as the lowest of the low. And yet they are children of God.'

Before they could finish their conversation, the call to prayer came. Winifred rose and held out her hand and Ghandi took it and placed it on his heart. Then, with his palms pressed together, he bowed. As she made her way to the women's quarters she looked back. He was sitting on the lawn with his legs crossed. His head was bowed as if he was deep in prayer.

She thought about his words later. She had known poverty in England but people had somewhere to sleep, even if it was only the workhouse. Her own life had been one of deprivation and suffering but she had accepted it because it was all she knew. She wondered if the people in India were the same.

The day before she and her family were due to leave for Australia, Winifred had another meeting with Maulana Shaukat Ali. It took place in a small private chamber with a desk and a few easy chairs covered in brown leather. Arched windows led into a secluded garden with a magnificent view over the ocean, where there were several ships at anchor. Soon all this would be forgotten, Winifred thought. She would return to Oodnadatta, tending the shop, looking after their small hut and the children. She had had her great adventure; soon it would be only a memory.

She looked at Karum Bux, who was sitting opposite her. She had fancied he was avoiding her, but couldn't be sure because men and women occupied separate quarters for much of the time. And though they shared a room at night, she was often half asleep when he came in, and he was always gone in the morning when she woke.

She turned her attention back to her host, who was addressing her. 'I have spoken to your husband, *Hadjana*. I have told him I have an important task for you. I worry about our people in your country. We need them to carry the faith down through the generations ... it is too easy to be led astray ... If you would undertake the task of guiding them I will give you written authority so that you may act on my behalf.'

He stopped speaking as a servant padded in with a tea tray, waiting until she and her husband had been served. 'Your husband does not object.'

Winifred looked across at Karum Bux. He did not meet her gaze and she wondered whether he was angry but unwilling to protest for fear of offending their host, who obviously did not think it improper that a woman should exercise authority. His wife was an independent woman, a woman who had been educated and was used to giving orders, a woman who had been brought up not to be subservient to men. Winifred thought it might have something to do with money and the power that comes with it. In Lahore, where she had stayed with her husband's people, the wives had to cover their faces when they left the house. The begum was different. She was one of the ruling class.

Now Winifred was being offered a position of power that would elevate her above the Moslem men in the small community in ghantown. When Maulana handed her a document bearing his signature and the great seal of the Khalifat she took it gladly.

Before they said farewell he held her right hand in his and kissed it, then placed it on his head and heart and said warmly, 'Write to me. I will be eager for news. When you return to India you must come and visit. You will always be welcome.'

The family arrived back in Australia at the end of July 1927 and Winifred found that the news of her exploits had travelled ahead of her. When the ship docked, two women from the Theosophical Society in Adelaide came aboard. They introduced themselves as Mrs Yates and Miss Radcliffe who worked as volunteers for the Society. They brought Winifred an invitation to speak at their next Sunday evening meeting.

'I have never heard of the Theosophical Society,' Winifred said.

'But you have come from India.'

'In Lahore I stayed with my husband's people and did not go anywhere until it was time to leave for Mecca. And when I returned I stayed at the Khalifat headquarters, but only for a few days before we caught the ship home.'

'It is India that interests our members,' Mrs Yates said. 'The Theosophical Society is based on the universal brotherhood of man. It began in New York, but now the world president, Annie Besant, lives in India. She has become active in the fight for Home Rule and was sent to gaol by the British. Like Gandhi she has become a figurehead in the fight.'

'I have met Gandhi,' Winifred said.

'Then you will have much to tell us,' Miss Radcliffe said and held out a bunch of daffodils. 'From my garden.'

As Winifred took the flowers their bittersweet perfume rose up to meet her and memories came flooding back. She saw her mother standing on the wharf clutching a bunch of daffodils, saw them scattered on the gangplank as her mother ran from the ship. It seemed so long ago. She remembered how her mother had always put her down as if she was of no account. Now she marvelled at how her life had expanded; she had met King Ibn Saud, talked with Gandhi and now she was being invited to speak and her opinion was being sought.

'May we expect you on Sunday?' Winifred nodded, and Mrs Yates rose. 'You have no idea how much your visit will mean to our members.'

Just then Winifred looked up. Karum Bux was standing in the doorway, scowling. The women moved towards the door. 'We must not detain you further. You must be tired. We look forward to your visit.' They bowed to Karum Bux and he moved to one side. Winifred could hear their light footsteps clattering as they walked along the wooden passageway, and then they were gone.

She looked at her husband, who had come into the room. 'I have been asked to speak about India. Will you come to the meeting with me?'

'I do not have time to waste in Adelaide. I have business to attend to in Oodnadatta. You can do as you please.'

His tone was brusque and Winifred was tired. When she replied her voice was sharp. 'Very well then, I'll stay on my own with the children and come up later.'

Karum Bux saw her and the children settled in the tenements alongside the mosque and caught the next train to Oodnadatta, leaving her a little money for food and their train fare.

Left alone, after her first elation wore off, Winifred became apprehensive. She had never spoken in public before and her best dress was still her grey silk suit. It was shabby after the sea voyages to and from India and the weeks of being crushed in her suitcase, and her shoes were down at heel too. The only alternative was to wear the *shalwar kameez* she had worn to Mecca. Remembering how the women who had met her at the wharf had looked in their smartly cut suits, cloche hats and kid gloves, she realised that wearing Indian dress would be out of place. But she did not have enough money to buy new clothes.

She washed her dress and borrowed an iron to press it, then polished her shoes until they shone. She washed and ironed the children's clothes so that they looked neat, and asked one of the men at the mosque to trim their hair. Her one extravagance was a box of face powder, which she bought on the way to the Victoria Markets to buy some fruit and vegetables.

She became increasingly agitated as it got closer to the day when she had to present herself at the hall. She found herself snapping at the children and hitting out at them for the slightest misdemeanour, so that they looked at her askance and escaped into the grounds of the mosque as often as they could. On the Sunday morning Yusef said, 'I don't want to come to the meeting. It'll be boring. The mullah said I can stay at the mosque and play.'

'You'll do as you're told or I'll give you a good thrashing.' He was almost as tall as she was and she hadn't beaten him for a long while but she was beside herself, wishing she had gone straight home to Oodnadatta, thinking that it would have been different if Ali had been alive. He would have been proud of her. Not like Karum Bux, who was always angry.

Then Rhamat complained of a stomach ache. He was cured by the sight and smell of the castor oil bottle which she waved under his nose. 'I'll give you a dose of this. That'll fix you, young man.'

Her threats had the desired effect and the boys were subdued. She sent them to play in the garden of the mosque once they were dressed, and promised to buy them a pie floater and a glass of ginger beer if they behaved themselves at the meeting.

She kept Pansy with her, as she didn't want her clothes to get soiled. The child was wearing a little dress with frills at the hemline and neck, which Winifred had made from scraps of red silk, and her long dark hair was tied back with a matching ribbon. 'You look so pretty,' said her mother, hugging her. 'Like one of the red poppies we saw growing in the sugarcane in India.'

They walked from Gilbert Street along Gillies Street to the hall where they were met by the president, Mrs Parry, who told Winifred she was a scientist. There were over one hundred people present, including children, and Winifred's children were whisked away to join them.

She had expected the meeting to begin with prayers, thinking it was a religious meeting. But there were no prayers, no preacher, no form of worship. Some of the members had brought their music and she was surprised when someone started to sing 'Roses are Flowering in Picardy', followed by a duet, 'Drink to Me Only with Thine Eyes.'

It was so informal and friendly, like a party, that Winifred forgot her nerves, until she was seated beside the president on the platform, with more than one hundred pairs of eyes turned towards her. She listened as the president introduced her, telling of her trip to Mecca, then she had to stand and face the audience. Her hands felt clammy, her pulse was racing and she could think of nothing to say, until she met the eyes of a woman who was looking at her with a sardonic expression on her face.

She hesitated and then, looking straight at the woman, said, 'If you were only half as nervous as I am you would understand. I have never spoken in public before and am only the wife of an Indian camel-man, and yet I have had an extraordinary adventure, an adventure in which I was invited to stay at the palace of the leader of the Moslem religion in India. He has made me the secretary of the Khalifat in Australia, with a task to ensure that the Moslem children adhere to the faith. It is a great honour. You see, the men are often away from home for months on end. It falls to their wives, many of whom are Aboriginal and know nothing of Islam, to teach the children.' And she held up the parchment with the red seal. 'Here is the document signed by the Khalifat leader himself.'

An hour later she was still speaking, feeling perfectly at ease, aware her audience was listening intently, until Mrs Parry leaned over and handed her a note that read, 'It's time to stop.'

The applause was deafening as she sat down and Winifred had a sense of triumph. People crowded around to congratulate her and shower her with questions, until Miss Radcliffe took her by the arm and led her to where supper was laid out. The children were already there with a glass of milk, but they were impatient. Rhamat tugged at her dress, 'What about our pie and peas?'

'I haven't forgotten,' Winifred said. 'But this is important. We can always walk down to the station tomorrow when the pie stall is open.'

'Promise?' Rhamat was gazing into her eyes and she laughed and ruffled his hair.

'Promise. Tomorrow we'll have a floater for lunch and I'll take you to the zoo. Now drink up your milk and if you ask nicely I'm sure you can have another biscuit.'

Winifred sipped her tea and nibbled a biscuit, watching Mrs Parry and Miss Radcliffe whispering together, until Mrs Parry turned to her. 'Mrs Karum Bux, can you come back again next week? We'll put a notice in the paper. You have no idea how much your visit has meant to us. India is a world away and yet so much is happening there. You are like a breath of fresh air. Can you wear something Indian?'

Winifred nodded. She would stay in Adelaide a week longer. There was nothing to return to, except to get the children into school. It occurred to her that Karum Bux might be waiting but she dismissed the thought from her mind. She no longer cared how he felt.

The following Sunday Winifred dressed carefully in her white *shalwar kameez* with her white silk chador over her head. She secured it with the silver crescent Karum Bux had given her, and wore the silver snake bangle on her arm. She could smell the perfume of the attar of roses which had impregnated the silk and she was transported back to Mecca.

The audience was just as enthusiastic after her talk and this time Elizabeth Leigh, a reporter from the *Register*, was in the audience. Later she invited Winifred to her office to talk. When Winifred returned to Oodnadatta she had a commission to write an account of her trip to Mecca.

PART FIVE

25

THE INVITATION

BY THE TIME THE FIRST EPISODE of 'Arabian Days' was published on 27 November 1928, under the pen name of Winifred the Washerwoman, Winifred had been home five months and her marriage to Karum Bux had ended. He had not remained in Oodnadatta to meet her or reopened his shop, but had gone to Alice Springs. It had fallen to Goolam to break the news that the marriage was over. He called to see her one morning, his huge bulk filling her doorway, almost shutting out the light. She invited him into the small kitchen and pulled out a chair at the kitchen table. He sat down and enquired about her health and that of the children, watching as she threw some chips into the fuel stove to bring the kettle to the boil and made the tea.

She took a loaf of bread out of the bread crock, cut off two thick slices, then lifted the tin of melon and lemon jam from the dish of water it stood in to keep the ants out and spooned a generous quantity on the bread, which she placed on an enamel plate in front of him.

'I'm sorry there aren't any scones. If I'd known you were coming they would have been hot from the oven.'

'There's nothing wrong with good bread.' He said and ate noisily, wiped a few crumbs off his beard, gulped down the scalding black tea and accepted a refill. When he had finished he pushed the mug to one side and sat regarding her gravely. 'Karum Bux has told me you have a letter from the Khalifat, giving you authority over the camel-men.'

Winifred rose and went into the small bedroom partitioned off by a hessian curtain, and returned holding the letter which she handed to him. He studied it closely, screwing up his eyes, running his finger over the embossed seal, then put it on the table. '*Hadjana*, this is an honour. And I am sure the Khalifat leader is a great and wise man. But we are simple camel-men. Bombay is far away. This letter has no meaning here. You must forget about it. In our community women do not have authority over men. I am the appointed leader. It is I who say the prayers as I slaughter the meat, and give the blessing on *Juma*.'

He handed the letter back to her and she folded it and put it in her apron pocket, knowing that what he said was true. The letter had no meaning here. She was certain that Maulana would never be called on to slaughter the meat for the Moslem community. He was an educated man. Many of the people she was dealing with here were from villages where the Khalifat was unknown. Ghantown was like an Indian village, except that their huts were made of iron instead of mud. She rose and replenished the teapot, filling Goolam's mug for the third time.

He sipped his tea, looking at her over the rim of the mug. 'But that is not why I have come. I have a message from your husband.'

'He has divorced me. Is that what you have come to tell me?' she asked, cradling the teapot, feeling the heat between her palms.

'No. He has not divorced you, though he finds you difficult because you lack obedience. He said you shamed him on the hadj, but he is willing to forget. He is getting his affairs in order so that he can return to India. He has offered to take you and the children, on one condition — you will remain in Lahore with his family and behave like a good Moslem wife.'

'And my boys? Will they be educated?'

'As far as possible. But in a village most men work to help support their family. Your sons would be expected to do the same, as soon as they are old enough.'

'And my daughter?'

He glanced at Pansy who had come running in the door with a bird's feather in her hand. 'She is fair of face. As soon as she is of marriageable age your husband and his brothers will seek out an eligible young man from a good family. She will be well looked after.'

'And if I do not agree?'

'Your husband will divorce you and return to India alone.'

She could see a look of surprise in his eyes when she said, 'I think that will be for the best. You promised me three hundred pounds a year, and that my boys would be sent to college in India. But none of that has happened. I don't want my sons to work as field labourers for a few rupees a day. And I don't want my daughter given away to the highest bidder like a prize heifer. I married Karum Bux to give my children a father. I allowed myself to be persuaded, even though I still loved Ali. In the few years Karum Bux and I have been married I have never stopped loving Ali. I still dream about him.' Her voice broke, she could feel tears starting. She fought to hold them back. She rose and carried the dirty mugs to the washing-up dish, rinsed them in hot water and dried them and put them on the shelf over the stove.

Then she turned to face him. 'As for money, we will manage.' She pointed to a small portable typewriter on the corner of the kitchen table. She had brought it back from Adelaide. 'I have a contract to write the story of the hadj as a serial for the *Register*. I will be well paid. And when I have finished that story I will think of another. I do not need Karum Bux. He does not love me and I do not love him. He took me to Mecca, for that I am grateful. Will you tell him?'

Her face was flushed and she wondered if she had been too outspoken. But there was no antagonism on Goolam's face. 'I am glad, *Hadjana*, for your sake, that things are working out. I will give your husband your message. He is a good man and was only thinking of your welfare.'

Winifred wiped the table with the dishcloth and put the teapot at the back of the stove. She felt ashamed of her outburst but she had spoken the truth. 'I'm sorry,' she said. 'You did your best. But there is more to life than a husband and a home. If there is no love there can be no happiness.'

Without answering, Goolam rose. His expression was troubled as he looked at her. He placed his right hand on his forehead and bowed. '*Salaam, Hadjana*,' he said, and walked out the door.

Winifred watched him striding down the dirt track, the dust whirling around his sandalled feet, his turbaned head erect. He did not look back and the thought crossed her mind that once the camel-men went there would be no reason to keep the mosque open. Ghantown, with its bore drain, its camel yards, the date palms that shaded the tin huts and the herd of goats that wandered up and down the lane foraging for food would be deserted. She and her children might end up here alone. She thought that she would not stay long. As soon as she could afford it she would buy herself a house somewhere else.

She washed Pansy's hands and feet and put her to bed behind the hessian curtain, then went to bring in the washing, standing by the line until the boys came running down the lane, calling out, 'We're hungry. What's for tea?'

As she sliced an onion before dropping it into the pan to braise, adding carrots and chopped goat's meat which she first rolled in flour, and a cup of water and a generous teaspoon of salt, she thought about what Goolam had said, wondering if she had been too hasty. She had lied about her financial position. Once she had used up the little cash Karum Bux had given her in Adelaide, she had become dependent on the owner of Wallis & Fogarty, who had allowed her to run up an account for groceries, and Westmacott, the butcher who let her have meat on credit. It was on the understanding that her husband would pay. Now she had no husband and was not sure whether there would be any money from the *Register* until she had sent them the complete story.

She was finding it difficult, trying to reconstruct the Mecca experience from memory and the few pencil scribbles she had made in an exercise book. It was taking a lot longer than she had expected. It was not like the light-hearted articles she had sold to *Life* magazine when she was a girl. She knew she would have to find some work until she could support herself with her writing.

She called on Lycurgus Underwood who ran the Transcontinental Hotel, to see if he wanted someone to make the beds and do up the rooms. Instead she was offered the job of washerwoman.

It was exhausting work. The boys would call at the hotel and bring the bundles of washing home after school, calling themselves *dhobiwallas*. She was pleased they did not object, though she reminded them that if they really were *dhobiwallas* they would take the clothes down to Hookey's Hole and wash them and lay them out to dry on bushes, as they had seen the men who ran the laundry in Bombay do.

Instead, Winifred would separate the whites from the coloureds and put the whites to soak overnight in the copper, first soaping the dirty collars and cuffs on the shirts and rubbing them on the washing board. The next morning she rose as soon as it was light and put a match to the copper to bring the clothes to the boil, so that she could have them washed and hung on the line while it was still cool, washing the socks and stockings and delicate garments, like women's underwear, by hand in a tin tub.

Once the clothes were dry she would damp them and roll them ready to iron in the late afternoon when the sun had dipped down in the west, and the temperature, which was always over one hundred degrees fahrenheit in the tin hut in the middle of the day, had started to drop. She made starch for the shirts and pillowslips from cornflour when she boiled the kettle for a cup of tea, while the flatirons heated on top of the stove until they were hot enough to begin the ironing.

It had not rained for a long while and water was scarce. She could only do two rinses, the final rinse with the addition of a twist of blue-bag to whiten the sheets and towels and the white shirts of businessmen who stayed at the hotel.

Later, the children would bathe in the tin tub, using the water from the copper, which was still warm in the evening. When they were washed and dried and in their pyjamas ready to go to sleep, she would sit beside them telling them a story. Sometimes it was an incident she remembered from her life in England, or a story of something that had happened on the hadj. She read them the story of Abraham and how God tested his obedience by ordering him to kill his son, Isaac. The children would gaze at her, their eyes anxious until they heard that Isaac was spared when his father found a ram in the burning bush, which he sacrificed instead. 'I have seen those places,' their mother told them.

She listened to their prayers, making sure they said, 'God bless *Baba*,' remembering their father. And after she had blown out the candle and the stars twinkled through the pinholes in the iron roof she would say, 'If you listen the stars will speak to you. Pick a star, and if ever you feel lonely or unhappy you can tell it your troubles. Then you'll feel better.'

Later she would undress and sit in the dark in the tin tub in the lean-to, with its iron roof held up by saplings and open to the elements on three sides. She would soak herself, sitting there until the water was quite cold. In the morning the boys would carry the water to the vegetable garden and the few flowers Winifred was trying to cultivate.

As she sat in the tub her mind would travel back to India as she thought of what she would write. Feeling refreshed, once she had dried herself and sprinkled her body with talcum powder and put on her nightgown, she would light the kerosene lamp. With a pot of tea on the table beside her, she would begin to tap away at her typewriter with two fingers, sometimes pausing to listen to the night noises. There was the tinkle of camel bells in the yards, the whimper of her goat tethered near the front door, the howl of a dingo in the distance, or bush rats scurrying across the roof as an owl hooped softly in the date palms at the back door. One palm was male, and the other female. She called them Sidon and Ruth. The seeds had come from dates the camel-men had brought from India and planted wherever they settled. The men pollinated the flowers by hand, brushing a spray of blossom from the male tree over the female tree.

Thinking of the date palms always brought her back to Mecca. In her mind's eyes she could see the oases where they had rested, and relive the feeling of religious fervour, the excitement, the horrors, and marvel at how she had managed to survive and bring Pansy safely home none the worse for the experience.

Her new life was a lonely one, with only the companionship

of her children. Living in ghantown meant that she lived apart from the white settlement which was the town. Once there had been great festivities, such as the feast at the end of Ramadan, and weddings and the birth of children. But now the camel-men were leaving, the heart seemed to have gone out of ghantown. Once the whole town had turned up to enjoy the curries the men cooked in great round boilers, the huge mound of chapattis, the dried fruits, the nuts and oranges. Yet the hospitality was never returned. There were tennis parties in town and dances on Saturday nights. When the wind blew in the right direction Winifred could hear the music. Without an invitation she could not bring herself to go. She had married an Indian man and her children were half-castes. She had cut herself off from her own people.

Sometimes she called on the sisters at the mission; they always made her feel welcome with a cup of tea, but they were even busier than she was, looking after the health of the local people and answering calls to go to the assistance of some lonely settler miles from anywhere.

Trapped in a culture that seemed no longer relevant, Winifred's Moslem faith started to waver. Once she had been sustained by people with a common belief and had taken comfort in the sound of men's voices as they prayed together at the mosque. Goolam had left and now the mosque was silent. The scene was changing rapidly in ghantown with the imminent opening of the railway to Alice Springs. Those who could afford it had already left. Some returned to India to be reunited with their wives and families, others moved south to the ghantowns at Beltana and Marree, and a few to Alice Springs in the north.

Rather than pay the agistment fee of ninepence per head to the government for grazing their camels on common land, the camel-men turned them loose. Soon there were great herds roaming the outback, until the government declared them vermin and put a bounty on their heads. When that happened, the day of the camel-men was well and truly over.

The Aborigines who once worked for the camel-men were still living to the north where the sand dunes began. At night Winifred could see the smoke from their fires. She walked to their camp to see if any of their old helpers were around. Even though her story of her trip to Mecca had started to appear in the *Register* and she was being paid, she was reluctant to give up her job at the hotel. She was living on the money she earned from washing and saving what she received for her writing. She would not have to pay the Aborigines wages. They worked for tea, sugar and flour, plus tobacco, supplementing the rations by hunting and foraging.

Winifred hired Joe and his wife Mary, who had travelled with them on their camel train. She had taught Mary how to make bread and she knew how to light a fuel stove. She could turn the mangle to wring the clothes and peg out washing, but was no good at ironing. On her first attempt she scorched a shirt and burned her hand, dropping the iron because it was too hot. Winifred had to pay for the shirt and Mary refused to return until she had been bribed with extra tobacco and given a new dress.

Winifred was particular about the ironing, taking pride in the shirts with their starched collars and the women's crepe de chine blouses with white lace trim. She would fold them carefully, first doing up the buttons then tucking in the sleeves and wrapping them in brown paper so that they were returned to their owners smelling clean and fresh.

Joe was strong so she used him for carrying water and collecting firewood, which meant going a long way from home. In the desert country that stretched for hundreds of miles around Oodnadatta the only trees were stunted acacia or mulga, and these were few and far between.

Once, when the hotel was quiet and there was little laundry to wash, she left the children with the mission sisters, and travelled through desert country almost to the Western Australian border on a wood-gathering expedition. She took twenty camels and Joe and Mary to help her. After the weeks spent at her typewriter and over the washtub, it was a relief to get away, and she revelled in the freedom.

Eventually they came to luxuriant country with mighty gum trees, where parrots clustered on the branches as they sipped honey from the fragrant blossoms. The trees fringed a waterhole almost a mile long where ducks were swimming. Winifred's Aboriginal companions divested themselves of their clothing and jumped in. She envied them but was too modest to do the same. Instead, she removed her dress and underwear and hung it on a tree. Clad in her petticoat she luxuriated in the cool water, floating on her back, her hair streaming out behind.

Later, dressed, her petticoat hanging on a tree branch to dry, she rested while Mary lit the fire. 'Who owns this place?' she asked when Joe returned with a duck he had shot and threw it at his wife's feet so that she could pluck and clean it before putting it in the camp oven to roast.

Joe replied, 'No that white fella man no bin see him longa this fella place.'

407

She was pleased to hear it and christened the spot Winifred's Joy Waterhole.

While the duck was cooking they each took an axe and stacks of ropes and began to hack away at the sandalwood. It was hard work, but Winifred found it exhilarating and won the admiration of Joe, who said, 'My word, missus too much good one fella longa axe.' Mary was not so inclined to the axe and Winifred, who put it down to laziness, sent her off to find some wild yams to go with the duck. She was hoping she might bring back some wild honey to eat with the breakfast damper and a few wild peaches or apples.

Mary dropped her axe and scampered away on her skinny legs. She came back later carrying a porcupine, a lizard and five grubs in her dillybag. But there were no yams or wild honey.

In the three days they were away they gathered six months' supply of sandalwood. The trip had done Winifred good. She felt as if she was connected to the Australian bush again, to the place she had come to love. It was the way the horizon stretched into the distance as if the land would never end. There were the soft nights, with whispers in the sand as small nocturnal creatures foraged for food. Before she drifted off to sleep she would gaze at the sky blazing with stars, trying to pick out the constellations she knew. She would wake later to see how the positions of the stars had changed, with the Southern Cross low on the horizon, and lie there thinking about life and how insignificant she was in the mighty scheme of things; how people died but the world went on forever.

Then, soothed by the sound of camel bells, she would snuggle closer into her blankets, feeling the chill wind that came out of the desert towards morning, to be woken just before dawn by a shrill chorus of birds. She would see the faint hint of red in the eastern sky and know that it was time to rise, grab a quick breakfast and be on their way before the full heat of the day overtook them.

As they travelled they would see great herds of kangaroos that went bounding off at the sight of the camels, and emus that hovered anxiously while Mary foraged for eggs, until the birds took fright and went thudding through the timbers.

Added to that was the feeling of freedom, the relief of being away from the constraints of civilisation which were still very evident among the white community in Oodnadatta, despite its distance from Adelaide. She thought it must be the same anywhere else in the world where a small community exists in an alien element — a bit like the British in India, who believed themselves superior to the indigenous people. And even in Indian society there were different layers, with the educated Indians at the top and those who did the hard labour, the untouchables, at the bottom. Thinking about it she could understand what Gandhi was trying to achieve.

Winifred planned to leave Oodnadatta as soon as she had saved enough money. Yusef was almost twelve, and Rhamat seven. They had had little or no formal education and were far behind the other pupils in the one-teacher school. It made Winifred feel guilty because she had neglected their education. She knew that if she been willing to settle in one place they could have started school when they were younger. But she could not bear to be parted from Ali. He had been her whole life and she knew that when he died he had taken part of her with him. He still came to her in dreams and she would wake, feeling her heart beating faster, only to find she had folded her arms around herself as she slept and was alone in her bed. But the interval between these episodes was lengthening and the hunger for his body was diminishing, though the pain of her loss was still strong.

Sometimes she thought of Bombay and the luxury of living in a palace with marble floors and servants to bring the food and do the washing. She would remember the jasmine climbing over the trellis in the garden and smell the sweet perfume. She recalled the water springing from the fountain in the women's quarters. There she had been respected and her opinions sought. Often the inactivity had irked her and she had yearned to go outside into the real world — the world of men. Thinking of it she wished with all her heart she could return and spend her days in idleness, telling her children stories, brushing her hair, spending hours deciding what sari to wear, and watching the flashes of light as the sun glinted off the coloured glass bangles the women wore.

Always her thoughts would return to the present and she would look at the dirt floor in her hut and feel the heat radiating from the iron roof as she listened to her sons' voices when they returned from school. If only she could get a piece of real land where they could raise a few cattle and the boys could learn to become stockmen and perhaps end up like Henry Kidman. She had heard that he controlled land the size of England, Scotland and Wales put together. She thought that a piece of land the size of a small island, like one of the Channel Islands, would do just as well. She had a sudden vision of her father and his excitement when he found he could get some land. It hadn't done him any good. He had worked until he was worn out and his only consolation was in drink. Hard work wasn't the answer. You needed money and luck. She knew she had no way of becoming rich, no matter how hard she worked.

That afternoon, while Pansy was asleep, she sat down at her typewriter and wrote a letter to the Minister for Lands, care of Parliament House, Adelaide.

Dear Sir
My name is Winifred Steger and I have three children, two boys grown up and a little daughter who has not yet started school. Where I live in Oodnadatta there is land as far as the eye can see and I am writing to see if it possible for us to get a piece. Just enough land to raise a few head of cattle, and where I can keep a few hens and grow some vegetables.

We are not asking for the land for nothing. My boys are strong and prepared to work hard. Once we start earning we will pay it back.

Yours sincerely
Winifred Steger
Widow

Months later a reply came in an official-looking envelope and she opened it with trembling hands.

Dear Madam,
The Minister has considered your request, but is unable to grant your wish because it would create a precedent.

She cried when she read it, wiping her eyes with her apron so that the children would not notice her distress. That night as she sat by her door looking across to the horizon and the miles upon miles of empty land she felt angry. It had been such a little thing she had asked for. She wondered if it would have been easier if she had been a man. But then you had to be white. The camel-men hadn't been allowed to own land. All they had were their camels. And now with the new railway their camels were worthless. Life was unfair.

Soon, however, Winifred's luck was to change in the most unexpected way. A letter arrived from India. When Yusef brought it home she opened the envelope, expecting it to be a reply to one she had written months before thanking Maulana Shaukat Ali for his hospitality, and telling him that her husband had divorced her and that the camel-men were leaving Oodnadatta. There had been no reply and she put it down to the fact that he and his wife travelled a lot and may not have received her letter.

The letter turned out to be an invitation for Winifred to become governess to the children of King Amanullah and Queen Souriya of Afghanistan, who had just returned from Europe. Impressed by Western culture the king was instigating reforms and the queen had plans to open schools to educate girls. The royal family had sought advice from the Khalifat in Bombay and Winifred's name came up as the ideal choice. She was a Moslem who had been to Mecca, was a mother and was also articulate and forthright.

When Winifred first read the letter she was astonished. In her own eyes she had no qualifications for the position. She read the letter aloud to her children and saw Yusef and Rhamat exchange a look.

'Does that mean that you'll take Pansy, and Ray and me, we'll be left behind with someone we don't know, like last time?' Yusef asked.

'No, I'd never do that. The only reason I took Pansy to Mecca was that she was safer with me. She's only a little girl. I went to Mecca because I had to. We're Moslems. One day you and Ray will go there too, and then you'll understand.'

She thought about the invitation as she stirred a pot of goat's meat and potatoes for their evening meal, wondering if it was an impossible dream. There was the financial side. She would be paid, of course. And she had been promised money for the fare. But they would need clothes. She wondered if it was hot like India, or whether it was closer to the mountains and it snowed. She had no idea. She knew nothing about Afghanistan. They would have to be well dressed, as befitted the position. It meant withdrawing some of her savings. Her story on the hadj was proving popular with readers. She knew by the letters she received from Elizabeth Leigh of the *Register*. Now she thought she might be able to get a commission to send dispatches from Afghanistan about life in the royal court. Few people would have the opportunity to go to see for themselves.

After they had eaten she put the two younger children to bed and told Yusef to come and sit by her in the cool of the evening outside their hut. She handed him a cup of sweet, milky tea, saying, 'I want to talk to you. I know life has been hard on you without a father. Soon you'll have to leave school, and then what will you do? Everyone is leaving ghantown. Before long we'll be here on our own. I've tried to do the best for you but it's hard.' She paused, thinking about how hard she had to work. Some days her hands were red-raw from the washing soda, and in the afternoon when she heated the flatirons on the fuel stove, with the heat off the tin roof, she felt as if she was in hell. But she didn't want to burden her son with that.

She put her arm around him and he rested his head on her shoulder. 'If we go to Afghanistan we'll live in a palace like we did in Bombay. There'll be plenty to eat and a garden to play in and you and Ray will be educated properly. You might even go to Oxford University, like Gandhi. Then you'll amount to something in the world. In Afghanistan it will be like being with your own people.'

She stopped speaking and gazed at her son. He was fighting to stay awake. She kissed him on the forehead and he opened his eyes. The eyes that gazed back at her were the eyes of Ali. 'While my son lives, Ali will never die,' she thought. Some woman would fall in love with those wonderful brown eyes, just as she had done.

'We'll go to Afghanistan. It's what your father would have wished.' She touched her son lightly on the head. 'Run along to bed, otherwise you'll never be up in time to go to school.'

The boy rose. 'It's all right, Mum,' he said. 'I think I understand ... I'll talk to Ray. We like it here. We've got friends at school and there's lots to do — swimming in Hookey's Hole, going rabbiting. But you're a woman and you need something different, and Pansy, she needs looking after.'

Long after he had gone to sleep Winifred sat under the stars, staring into the blackness, thinking about her life and what the future might hold. Allah had answered her prayers. He had offered her a way out, an escape.

Her dreams carried her to England and Buckingham Palace, where she had once stood at the tradesmen's entrance with her father. She could see herself being presented at court, wearing a velvet dress with a train and feathers in her hair, while Pansy stood by her side in white silk. It was with such dreams that Winifred accepted the invitation, sharing the news of her good fortune with the old Moslem men who were still in ghantown. If they wondered why she had been chosen for such a singular honour they did not question it.

26

BEBE ZATOON EN ROUTE TO AFGHANISTAN

HAD WINIFRED BEEN AWARE OF THE growing conflict in Afghanistan she may not have been so willing to undertake the journey. It was not until she was interviewed by Elizabeth Leigh on her way through Adelaide, and was shown the newspaper reports, that she became aware of the precarious position of the King and Queen of Afghanistan who were in open conflict with the religious leaders in Kabul.

The first of these reports appeared in Melbourne's *Sun-News Pictorial* on 5 December 1928, when the question of the king's reforms was being discussed, particularly the decree that all men must wear European dress.

The article concluded by stating:

The Afghan King with his sweeping changes has set his country definitely on the lines of progress. He has already abolished a few barbaric customs, and others which must go the same way. His people, however, include no less than five distinct races and they are all intensely Mohammedan. They are fanatical where their religious customs are threatened and some of these the King has already abolished. Moreover, the Afghans are the most turbulent people in the world.

Winifred admitted to feeling nervous but was confident that she could manage because she had survived the perilous journey to Mecca. But circumstances were not the same. The pilgrims may have been preyed upon by unscrupulous traders who tried to fleece them, but on the whole Mecca was a peaceful place where they were welcome. In Afghanistan, the home of fanatical Moslems, the king's reforms were in direct conflict with the leaders of the church, whose power was threatened. A revolution was in progress.

Winifred still had no real perception of the growing struggle for Home Rule in India, or that Afghanistan was seen as a danger to British interests in India. She had no idea that King Amanullah and his queen were being wooed by the British, hoping to cement closer ties and ward off intervention from Russia which was keen to get a foothold in India and share in the spoils that flowed to Britain.

At the same time King Amanullah's decree that his subjects should wear Western dress, and the Queen's attempt to liberate the women of her country by appearing in public without a veil, had enraged the Moslem leaders in Afghanistan.

By the time Winifred left Australia, King Amanullah and his family were under siege, with reports in the *Sydney Morning Herald* on 19 December 1929 that the king had 'taken refuge in a fort ... then returned to Kabul. He is now residing at the Palace.' Another report in the same issue stated that the leaders of the tribesmen assured the British minister 'that they had no hostile intentions towards the [British] Legation', also that the Indian Government 'would take all possible steps to protect British nationals'.

It was a rough passage through the Indian Ocean with the children seasick, except for Rhamat, who went backwards and forwards to the upper deck to check on the weather. Winifred stayed below to look after Pansy, who cried each time the ship rolled. All Winifred could do was lie beside her in the bunk, holding her to make sure she didn't fall out. Pansy was dozing when Rhamat came bursting into the cabin, his hair wild, his face wet from sea spray and said, 'I've been up to check the lifeboats in case the ship sinks.' Pansy woke with a start and began crying.

'Now look what you've done,' said Winifred and she reached out and boxed Rhamat's ears with all her strength.

At the same time the ship shuddered as a wave hit it full on. The boy went flying across the cabin and hit his head on the wooden ladder beside the lower bunk, where Yusef was vomiting into a basin. He sat on the floor rubbing his head and snivelling, while his mother ignored him. In the end he climbed into the top bunk and lay there holding onto the side as the ship continued to roll.

When the storm had abated Winifred took stock of their clothes in preparation for their entry into Bombay. She had shopped in Adelaide, buying herself a grey two-piece woollen suit, some cream silk blouses and a grey cloche hat. She was determined to make a good impression on her new employers. The shop assistant had pinned a bunch of artificial violets to her lapel, 'for colour', she had said, adding, 'Madam looks very chic. May I suggest a jar of face cream for Madam's complexion. You have lived in the tropics perhaps?'

Winifred had bought the face cream, knowing she had neglected her appearance and wondering if it was too late to repair the damage. She had tried on a pair of grey kid shoes to match her new outfit but had resisted the temptation, buying instead a pair of sensible black shoes.

The boys were neat in knickerbockers and long-sleeved white shirts, polished brown leather shoes, long socks and black ribbon bow ties. Winifred had made Pansy some pretty little dresses from ends of silk. When they went ashore the child was wearing a white dress with puff sleeves and a Peter Pan collar embroidered with tiny pink roses. On her head was a straw hat with pink ribbons that tied under her chin and she wore black patent leather shoes with a strap and long white socks.

Winifred felt very proud of her children as they stood on deck while the ship moved up the harbour into Bombay. She looked across to the spire of the cathedral, the outline of buildings, the Gateway to India at the Apollo Bunder. A surge of excitement went through her, as if she was coming home.

The children felt it too, running from side to side. Below, the water was crowded with small boats, with vendors trying to attract the attention of the passengers. One man was holding up a handful of paper cobras on sticks. 'Look, Mum. Can I have one?' Rhamat pleaded, almost falling over the side and Winifred grabbed him by the back of his shirt. 'If you fall overboard you can stay there. Just be thankful we've arrived safely.'

She looked down at the sea wall, holding Pansy in her arms, averting the child's head at the sight of the bloated body of a dead goat washing backwards and forwards among the driftwood, flowers and sodden paper. Yusef and Rhamat were holding their noses and saying 'Pooh', as they caught a whiff of the smell of rotting garbage mingled with the smell of spices.

Winifred smelt it too, and thought of Gandhi and his untouchables. Beggars lined the sea wall. There were wizened old men with closed eyes being led by thin-faced young children; women holding diseased babies in their arms; coolies in white dhotis, their skin like leather from the sun as they stood between the shafts of small wooden barrows, hoping to earn a few rupees carting luggage to a waiting vehicle.

They were met by Dr John da Silva, with whose parents they were to stay. The da Silva family lived in a magnificent mansion of three storeys, almost hidden from the road behind a high fence. Winifred's first sight of it was when an attendant in white, wearing a red turban, flung open the heavy wrought-iron gates to allow the limousine to sweep up the short gravelled drive to the front door. Inside was a marble floor patterned in a black and white check design, and pillars that reached to the ceiling, from which ornate brass lamps with red glass panels hung. Winifred took it in with one glance and then smiled at the children, who were standing there gazing around in awe. 'Your eyes will fall out if you keep looking like that,' she said, while John da Silva laughed. 'This house was built by a prince. When he died my grandfather bought it. We live rather simple lives here.'

They were led up a carved wooden staircase to a room on the first floor which was furnished with charpoys with mosquito nets hanging from above. A ceiling fan was turning slowly. The ayah, wearing a red cotton sari, padded after them. She cupped her hand to her forehead and, bowing to Winifred, said softly, 'Mem-sahib, I will look after the children while you rest.'

Winifred was conscious of the children looking at her anxiously but she smiled and waved them away. 'It's all right. These people are our friends.'

It was late afternoon when a servant called to escort Winifred to afternoon tea in the drawing room. Her hosts were there to greet her. Mrs da Silva was wearing a soft pink sari, while her husband wore a dark business suit and on his head a black fez.

'Welcome to our home,' Mrs da Silva said. 'I hope you have everything you need,' and guided her to a comfortable chair.

A servant poured Winifred a cup of *masala*. It was sweet and milky and flavoured with cinnamon and she sipped it slowly to be polite. What she yearned for was a cup of strong black tea and she decided that before she left for Afghanistan she would send to the bazaar for a box of black tea and a spirit stove and teapot.

The servant passed her a plate with a small fork on it and put a tiered stand by her side with a selection of cakes and bread and butter. He hovered for a moment until Mr da Silva said, 'You may go. I'll ring if we need anything,' then he padded out on bare feet.

Winifred helped herself to a slice of bread and butter and then looked up. Her hosts were regarding her gravely.

'You have heard the news, Mrs Steger?' Mr da Silva spoke first.

Winifred stared at him. 'What news?'

'I thought your newspapers … It has all happened so suddenly. King Amanullah has been forced to flee the capital with his family. It's all to do with his reforms. The mullahs have told him to put his queen from him. And of course he has refused.' He rose and began to pace up and down, pausing to look out the window where large black birds were circling. 'I think she has been foolish. She unveiled herself at a public meeting. What will happen to them no one knows.'

As his words sank in Winifred could feel her hands trembling. She put her cup and saucer on a side table, trying not to show her agitation. Mr da Silva moved his chair closer and sat down facing Winifred. He was regarding her kindly and she tried to compose herself. 'They said to tell you how sorry they are. They do not think it possible for you to go to Afghanistan. It is no longer safe. You are to stay in India as long as you wish. Enjoy yourself. Have a holiday.'

Winifred could feel her pulse racing and a feeling of nausea swept over her. She had come to India with such high hopes — an education for her sons, and a life of comfort for herself and Pansy. She had uprooted herself for nothing. She was very close to tears.

Mrs da Silva rang the bell and the servant returned. 'Take our guest to her room. See that she has everything she needs.' She turned to Winifred with a look of concern. 'You are tired. It has been a great shock. Rest now. We will try to make your stay as pleasant as possible.'

It was not until the next day that Winifred felt composed enough to leave her room, excusing herself when the servant came to call her to prayers. She was served a meal of dhal with curried vegetables and chapattis, followed by a dish of sliced mango and a pot of strong black tea. By the time the ayah had brought the children to bed she had gathered herself together, determined not to tell the children, hoping things might still work out.

Pansy was already asleep and Winifred tucked her into bed, stroking the child's soft cheek and kissing her. The boys were bubbling over with excitement, telling her of the peacocks in the garden and the little boy who spent the day waving a stick to shoo away the black birds that tried to eat the fish in the lotus pond. But finally she got them to sleep, wondering how long it would be before the novelty wore off and they got sick of being cooped up in the house.

The da Silvas were of Portuguese descent. Their paternal great-grandfather had come to India to trade in precious stones when Bombay had belonged to the Portuguese. He had married an Indian girl. The present Mr da Silva had inherited the family wealth and still carried on the family business. His son had branched out into medicine and practised as a doctor. He and his wife and children shared the family home.

Mr da Silva was a respected member of the Khalifat. It was he who explained the intricacies of the political situation in Afghanistan after dinner the next evening, when they had dismissed the servants and were sitting in the courtyard drinking tea. Winifred was feeling refreshed. She relaxed in a rattan chair, breathing in the languid air perfumed with sandalwood which smouldered in a brazier to drive away mosquitoes. Behind the high wall the street noises were subdued but she could hear the screeching of peacocks in the garden and the chatter of birds from a giant peepul tree as they settled for the night. She felt at peace with herself. For the moment she was content, feeling that fate had placed her where she was. As to what happened next she would leave that in the hands of God.

Mr da Silva's voice brought her back to the present. Lulled by a good meal and the feeling of peace, she had dozed off. She opened her eyes and sat up straight.

'It's an explosive situation. Afghanistan lies between British-occupied India, Persia and Russia. Last century the Afghans fought the English. Skirmishes went on for years until a treaty was signed. England gave the Afghan rulers guns and money to help them remain independent.' He rose and took a cigar from a box on the table and lit it, then continued speaking, pacing up and down, his back to Winifred. 'Forgive me for what I am about to say, but it is the truth. You are British and may find it hard to understand. All England really wanted was to conquer Afghanistan and use it as she has used my poor country. That is why she has wooed King Amanullah. But now the Afghan people are in revolt and there is no guarantee that Russia will not interfere.'

'But what about the queen?' Winifred asked.

'She is trying to emulate the women she met in England and France. But it is too soon. My wife, like other educated Indian women, admires her.'

'When will we know what is really happening?'

He turned and looked at her. 'It could be tomorrow. It could be weeks. We are concerned for the safety of the king. In the meantime you must regard this as your home. Go out. Meet people. Make the most of it while you are here.'

At first Winifred and her children explored the areas where the wealthy Indians lived, and places where there were great public buildings built by the British, such as Victoria Station with its green dome, which looked like some majestic cathedral from the outside. 'It's just like being in London,' Winifred told them. As they gained confidence they ventured further afield, travelling by *tonga*. Though they were approached by beggars who ran alongside holding out their hands, she did not give them money, remembering what had happened on the hadj when Karum Bux had been too generous. Instead, she averted her eyes and told the children not to stare.

Sometimes they caught the bus that ran from the Afghan church to Crawford Markets. It was one of the boys' favourite outings. In the fruit markets monkeys swung from the rafters, darting down to grab a bunch of bananas then pelting the stallholders and customers alike with the skin, or sometimes the fruit, until everyone joined in and pelted the monkeys back. Despite the smell of decaying fruit and vegetables and the swarms of flies, it was a happy place: a refuge from the congested and noisy streets with bullock waggons rumbling along with huge bales of cotton on their way to the mill, *tonga*s weaving in and out and food vendors pushing their carts. Car horns tooted as the drivers tried to dodge horse-drawn vehicles, pedestrians, *dabbawallahs* pushing handcarts laden with tiffin boxes as they delivered hot meals from homes to offices, and the sacred cows that ambled along holding up the traffic.

A woman with a tin box for offerings sat by the entrance to the markets beside a white cow.

'She's a cow-keeper,' John da Silva had explained when the children first saw her. 'The cow is sacred to the Hindus. The woman is a widow. You can tell because she wears white. Widows cannot marry again. Once they were forced to throw themselves on their husband's funeral pyre and be burnt to death; it's called suttee.'

'Why?' Yusef asked.

'It was something to do with Sita, who offered to throw herself into the fire because her husband doubted her honour. She had been kidnapped by the monkey god and taken to Ceylon.'

'Would our mother have had to burn herself when Baba died, if she had been in India?'

Dr da Silva ruffled the boy's hair and laughed. 'We are Moslems. It is only Hindus who worship cows and burn widows. Though when the British came they made it illegal. But this is how this woman lives, caring for the cow.' He gave Yusef a couple of annas to throw into the old woman's tin.

'The cow is a point of contention,' he told Winifred as they stood around a stall eating hot samosas and drinking unfermented palm juice. 'Moslems eat meat. We have no aversion to killing cows. Hindus are vegetarians and revere the cow as the giver of life. It is something to resolve before we can unite Hindus and Moslems in the fight for Home Rule. The Hindus want us to agree to a cow protection act. Gandhi is trying to strike a compromise with the Khalifat.'

On a hot day they bathed at Chowpatty Beach and played ball on the dark sand. Sometimes in the cool of the evening they walked by the water, watching the *koli*s mending their nets as they prepared to put out to sea. Then one day the family found themselves in a place where there were shanties made from scraps of bags and branches of palm trees. It reminded Winifred of the Aboriginal camp at Oodnadatta. But this was different. There the air was dry and the wind from the desert blew away unpleasant smells. People had enough to eat. Here people were starving and you choked on the stench of raw sewage, rotting garbage, dead bodies and scavenging dogs.

She drew her sari over her face and went to turn back, but it was too late. People seemed to emerge from nowhere, pulling at her clothes, touching the children, holding out their hands for money. For the first time in India she felt afraid.

She scooped Pansy up in her arms and called to the boys, 'Run!' and they hurried back the way they had come, pursued by a screeching mob of children. Winifred hailed the first *tonga* she saw and they jumped in without haggling over the fare.

Winifred was still shaken that evening at dinner when she told Mr da Silva what had happened. He regarded her gravely, saying, 'You must be careful where you walk in the city. It is divided into many parts. Some are safer than others. When a person is starving there is no knowing what they will do.'

Winifred paused as the servant stood by her side with a dish of steaming vegetables, then spooned some onto her plate. She began to eat with her fingers, mopping up the hot chilli sauce with a piece of *hati* still warm from the coals. When she had finished she asked, 'Why doesn't the government help?'

Mr da Silva stopped eating, wiping his hands on a damp cloth the servant passed him. 'It does. It does. These people are immigrants, like the rest of us. Bombay was created by the British from a cluster of islands. As it prospered people came from the hinterland to share in the wealth created by the British. All except the *koli*, who were here first. They live as they have always done by the edge of the sea, and earn their living from fishing. Have some curry sauce. It may be hotter than you like, but try it anyway.' He motioned to the servant, who moved towards Winifred with a sauce boat in his hand.

'These people you saw will not be there long. The City Trust is building *chawls*, you have seen those tall, ugly grey buildings. They have small rooms and a place to cook. There are latrines and washing facilities. I have heard that as many as forty live in one room. At least it is shelter when the monsoon comes.'

'But all those children — naked and so thin ...'

'Ah, the children. That is another thing again. You must ask my son. He is the doctor and works among the poor. Children are seen as a gift from God. If they survive they are put to begging — or worse. The government is reclaiming land from the sea at Back Bay. Once the *harijans* find work they move into *chawls*. Sometimes they open a stall and send their sons to school where they learn to speak English, to read and write. Yet for everyone who leaves the shantytown there are a thousand to take their place. It will never be any different while Bombay is seen as a Mecca by the poor.'

Despite his words Winifred was still disturbed. She thought about it as she lay in bed and drifted off to sleep, to dream she was back in Oodnadatta with the camels. Ali was there and they were happy. There was work and plenty of food and somewhere safe to live. When she woke she made up her mind to wait no longer but to return with the children to Australia and take up their old life. At least there were no people starving and it was safe to walk anywhere in the street.

That afternoon a message came from the Khalifat to say that King Amanullah and Queen Souriya were coming to Bombay with their retinue. Mr da Silva passed it on to her. 'They are hoping that the All India Congress will support their request to the British Government for money to fight. The Khalifat is giving a banquet in their honour. The British are to be invited also. Your name is on the list, of course. You will be presented to the king and queen. The Khalifat has a favour to ask. It is that you arrange the food for the British guests.'

The news that the king and his consort were to be in Bombay heartened Winifred. Even though she had made up her mind to return to Australia as soon as possible, now she was not so sure. She had set her heart on going to Afghanistan for the sake of her children, and she did not want to let it go if it was still possible. She thought if she could speak to the queen they might be able to accompany them when the royal family left Bombay.

She was not so happy about the idea of catering for an English banquet. She had never been to one. At home her meals consisted of meat and vegetables with damper cooked in a camp oven or a fuel stove. And yet she knew that if she refused she would lose face.

The function was to be held in the town hall. Built by the British in 1833 in a neoclassical style, it had become the cultural and civic heart of Bombay and contained massive assembly rooms. The exterior had three porticos with fluted Doric columns and an imposing staircase. Winifred went to inspect it with the major-domo, who was to oversee the preparations, and was startled to see the building had been festooned with great quantities of red twill bunting, giving it the appearance in her mind of a furnace of turkey red.

The main room had a raised trestle table for the royal party, plus two other long tables that stretched to the end of the room. Here the Indian dignitaries would be seated. The British had been assigned a smaller room with one long table covered with red twill over which Winifred draped a length of white sheeting. She was not pleased with the finished effect but there was nothing else available. Also the choice of Western-style food was limited so she decided to serve roast chicken and beef, both of which were readily available. There were no potatoes or pumpkin. Instead she settled for tinned green peas and tinned beetroot.

Winifred knew it was a poor menu for a banquet but the cook made a special oven for the occasion, lined with tin and the roasts were cooked to perfection. She had decided on blancmange for pudding and made this by simmering two gallons of buffalo's milk in a boiler. She thickened it with a whole packet of cornflour, flavoured it with vanilla and divided it into three portions, which she coloured saffron, pink and green.

The Indians were accustomed to eating with their fingers but she knew that she would need to provide cutlery for the British. She sent the *khansama* to the bazaar and was far from happy when he returned with some cheap tin spoons, odd forks with bones handles and an assortment of knives. She felt even more mortified when she saw the room reserved for Indian guests and wondered if it had been done deliberately to slight the British. The tables were covered with cloth of gold, with great epergnes of sparkling crystal overflowing with fruit and sweetmeats. The royal table was decorated with the crescent of Islam picked out in precious stones, which gleamed as they caught the light. Later Winifred was to learn that it was part of the loot rescued on the death of Ghengis Khan.

Winifred had been invited to stand in the receiving line to be presented to the royal couple. She had dressed carefully, wearing a long white silk gown she had bought at Laidlaws. With it she wore her silver-crescent brooch and snake bracelet, and she pinned some white jasmine in her hair. As she waited in the entrance hall with the guests, both British and Indian, she rehearsed a little speech in which she planned to express her thanks to the king and queen for the opportunity to serve them. A band, with men in British military uniforms, stood on the footpath, the sun glinting off their brass instruments, the red coats making a splash of colour matching the red carpet covering the steps.

A buzz of excitement ran through the guests as the fleet of black limousines drew up in front of the town hall and the king and queen alighted. They paused briefly as the band struck up the British national anthem, 'God Save the King', and then began to walk slowly up the stairs.

Winifred noticed that the queen had discarded Western dress but was unveiled, with a spray of white jasmine in her hair. She wore a cream satin sari embroidered with pale pink roses with silver leaves. On her right shoulder was a crescent-shaped brooch that gleamed with diamonds and she had a diamond bracelet on her right arm. Despite her magnificent attire she looked sad and withdrawn, her mouth drooping, and Winifred saw she was expecting a child. The king was a disappointment. She had envisaged a dashing warrior, only to find he was nothing more than a tubby little red-faced man, the type she had often seen in London racing to catch a tram, except that the little tubby red-faced man would not have his suit plastered with medals and the tag ends of ribbons.

The royal couple passed along the line as Winifred watched, until it was her turn and they stopped in front of her. Her name was called and she curtseyed, but before she could speak they had passed on.

The banquet had barely begun when the guests were asked to stand while the king and queen left. They were to travel by train to Peshawar, the British end of the Khyber Pass. Later Mr da Silva told Winifred that the banquet had achieved nothing because it was too late. A rumour was circulating that a bandit leader called Baccha Sakao had seized the throne and there was deep concern in both Indian and British circles as to the fate of the royal couple.

Winifred listened in silence, resigned to the fact that now she had no option but to return to Australia as soon as she could get a berth on a steamer. She was bitterly disappointed. She had allowed her hopes to be raised and now she felt cheated.

As the weeks went by the situation in Afghanistan worsened. The story of the beleaguered king and queen captured the attention of the Australian press. The beautiful young queen had fired the public's imagination and photographs of her wearing the latest Parisian fashions were published.

When reports circulated that King Amanullah and Queen Souriya had been declared infidels and that rebel groups in Afghanistan were determined to kill them, the Moslem community in Bombay became concerned. Placed as she was in the da Silva household, Winifred became a party to the events as they unfolded. First there was the news that King Amanullah had abdicated and his place had been taken by the bandit Baccha Sakao, and that Kabul, the capital of Afghanistan, was in ferment. There was no cable or telephone connection with the country and it was impossible to know the true situation or what had happened to the former king and queen. Nadir Khan, concerned for his cousin Amanullah, cabled that he was arriving from France to see if he could assist. Winifred was asked to help look after Nadir Khan and wrote an account in her diary which was later published in the *Register* in South Australia, with Winifred described as 'a special correspondent'.

21 February 1929. Wireless just received from Nadir Khan. Says that the vessel will arrive in Bombay Roads tonight. He is returning from France to see what aid he can give to his cousin. Nadir Khan used to be in command of the Afghan King's forces. Maulana Shaukat Ali has telephoned me to wear Indian saris and come to town and act as hostess for the visiting entourage. Maulana intends that Nadir Khan and party should be guests of Khalifat House.

Later: Am already dressed and waiting for the car. Here it comes.

22 February 1929. Nadir Khan is a very sick man. I believe from the look of him that he has consumption, and that he is very far gone with it, too. He is almost too weak to walk. At seven o'clock last night we went in state to the wharf. Our official car was in the lead, with a great blazing crescent on the radiator. Five other cars followed behind.

Madame Shaukat Ali, Ziad Ali and myself occupied the front car, and lesser dignitaries the hinder one. Arrived at the wharf, our car held the position of honour, with our volunteer corps drawn up in formation on either side. They looked very smart in the Khalifat uniform of light brown, with crescent metal buttons, and caps to match. We had to wait nearly an hour. The city police arrived in files to keep back the great crowds that had gathered around us. It was rather fascinating to watch the gaily coloured, shifting throng beneath the great arc light of the wharf's entrance.

At last they came, and for a while all was confusion as the throng pressed to see our Afghan guests, and the police in vain tried to hold the crowds back.

It seemed that they had wirelessed for accommodation at the Taj Mahal Hotel, and Nadir decided that it was better for the ladies to go there, and the gentlemen of the party to the

Khalifat office. Finally, I got the women away in several car loads. For they had many relations, dependants, and ayahs. After they had been got away I had time to take further stock of Nadir Khan, and it seemed to me that bed was about the best place for him. He was so weak that his voice quivered as he spoke. Maulana and Ziad had the front seat going back to the office, and Nadir Khan and I sat in the rear. As soon as the car started he leaned back against the upholstery and closed his eyes from sheer fatigue. We had borrowed the second chef from the Taj Mahal together with three Indian cooks, to cater for our guests. I stayed during supper, leaving shortly after and travelling home accompanied by four volunteer guards.

23 February. Am just about to leave to take up the day's duties as hostess again. I feel inclined to wipe the floor with Nadir Khan. He considered I have no right to have any ankles. My sari reaches to within two inches of my feet, but that evidently is not enough. He is, of course, polite as far as words are concerned but he does not attempt to disguise his scornful contempt as he lets his eye drop downward. Evidently he has not learned too much toleration. I can see he considers me almost declasse.

Later: They stayed for three days and then entrained for Peshawar. When he arrived there he was so ill that he had to be supported from the train. They rented a little bungalow with a compound and within it Nadir Khan lay in bed for three weeks, while special prayers were offered for his recovery. All his proclamations were made by medium of his brothers, and indeed, are so still, as he is always too weak to raise his voice above a murmur.

435

One paper reports that he has been made king against his will. This is absolutely impossible. He has only to repeat a certain line from the Koran, and not even the boldest would risk the danger of the implied curse. For politic reasons he would not allow himself to be king. I know this definitely. He signed, and also his brothers, a lengthy document at the Peshawar Khalifat office that on condition of the Afghan treasuries being placed at his disposal for the purpose of ousting the bandit usurper, he would fight to place one of the direct line of the blood royal on the throne. He will never aspire to more. Indeed, he would have no benefit or pleasure from such a course. His only desire is for quiet and peace, and the consolation of the church for his last days. For too well he knows the toll runs short.

He was bitterly grieved at Amanullah's abdication and does not hide his thoughts about what he considers has disgraced the family. To mend that disgrace alone is his endeavour ... But people must not run away with the idea that Nadir is a violent reformer. It sounds nice on paper and nice on the tongue, but there is very little reform to be expected from him. He is most conservative for the old ways. One proof is that of his position today. Had he shown the tiniest piece of a reformer, the soldiery would not have stood for him any more than for Amanullah.

27
SECRET MISSION

WHILE WINIFRED WAITED FOR A PASSAGE on a ship back to Australia an invitation came to afternoon tea at the home of Bebe Feroza, wife of the bey, who was very high in Khalifat circles. Her hostess greeted her and led her into a light airy room painted white with high ceilings. There were tapestries hanging on the wall with a design of birds and flowers, and matching rugs on the polished floor. It was much more sparsely furnished than other Indian homes she had visited.

Bebe Feroza followed her gaze, saying 'I like to keep the room simple because of the heat. It allows the air to circulate. There is always a breeze from the sea. The design of the room is French but the furnishings are Indian. The tapestries were stitched locally and the rugs are hand-woven. They are traditional designs. This is a tree of life design, one of the most beautiful. I am not so fond of the traditional Moslem designs with their geometric patterns. I like something that speaks to the heart as these birds and flowers do.' She led Winifred to a large sofa covered in cream brocade and they sat together.

'I am interested in your life in Australia. I know so little of your country. You have children?' she asked.

'Three,' Winifred replied. She did not think to mention the four children of her first marriage. It had been so long ago.

'And your husband was Indian?'

'He died in India. I still miss him.'

Her hostess put out her hand and touched Winifred gently on the arm. 'When you love it is hard to forget,' she said. My husband was chosen for me. I think it is different in your country.'

Winifred thought about her words. She had chosen Charles but then he had not chosen her.

'When I was a girl I was never allowed to leave the house unless someone was with me. My mother never left the house, though she was not in purdah. She entertained visitors, walked in the garden, but that was as far as she went.' She smiled and, leaning across, took Winifred by the hand. 'We have lived different lives. You have been to Mecca. You have travelled to India without your husband. We Indian women need to be more like you.'

She paused and rang a bell, then turned back to Winifred. 'We are worried for Queen Souriya. She is in danger because she tried to help her women. We are afraid for her safety and that of the child she is carrying.'

A servant entered, wheeling a trolley, which he placed beside his mistress.

'I will pour,' Bebe Feroza said, and waved the servant away. 'My husband will be home shortly. He is most anxious to meet you.' She lifted the teapot, and the glass bangles on her arm tinkled. 'How do you like your tea — with milk and sugar?'

'Just black,' Winifred replied, looking at the delicate eggshell china cup decorated with pink roses that her hostess handed her, thinking how different tea tasted from a nice cup than from a tin mug. She had no idea what made the thought come into her head. It was long while since she had used a tin mug.

After they had finished their tea they walked in the garden, where the bey joined them. His wife excused herself and the bey led Winifred to a secluded spot where there was a garden seat and table. It was late afternoon; dappled sunlight fell on a large tree that dominated the corner where they sat. Winifred reached down and picked up a long heart-shaped leaf that had fallen at her feet. She smoothed it with her hand, saying, 'It's so peaceful here.'

'You wouldn't think so if you had been here earlier. The monkeys spend their days playing in the tree,' the bey replied.

'Where are they now?'

'The servants feed them. They say they're sacred because they live in a bo tree, the sacred fig. It was under such a tree that Buddha had his enlightenment.'

'In Medina we saw a shrine to Jesus Christ in the Great Mosque.'

'Just because we are Moslem does not mean we cannot revere the great teachers. There is but one God. We all travel the same path to meet Him.' He raised his hand and a servant came walking along the path and stopped in front of him.

'You wanted something, sahib?'

'Bring the mem-sahib a *nimbu pani*.'

'And for you, sahib?'

'The same.'

The bey turned towards Winifred. 'I want to talk to you. There is fighting in Kabul. There will be wounded. We are sending a small medical team. We would like you to be part of the group.'

Winifred stared at him, wondering if she had heard correctly. His face was serene under a black fez. He returned her gaze, then smiled. 'You are surprised.'

'I know nothing of nursing.'

'It is not your nursing skills we require. You are an Englishwoman. Your presence will assist us.'

The servant returned with two glasses of liquid on a silver tray. He put them on the table and returned to the house.

Winifred picked up the glass and sipped it. 'What is it?'

'Lime juice. We have a lime tree in the back garden.'

'It's very refreshing.' She took another mouthful, tasting the sour-sweet liquid on her tongue. 'I thought the British were not liked.'

'That is true, but they are still respected for their knowledge. Even Gandhi, who is most vocal about the need to get rid of the British, would agree. We have learnt a lot from them.'

'But I know very little. I am only a simple woman.'

'Some of the village people will not bring their women to be treated by a male doctor. If a woman is present, then it will be different.'

She was still doubtful. She had come to India hoping to go to Afghanistan. Now she was being asked to do something completely different. It would mean staying in India.

'There is something more. Did you know that the king has denounced his abdication? He is trying to fight his way back to the throne. There are those who are loyal to him. But those who are not have threatened to kill Amanullah and his queen. We need to find some way to rescue them.' He looked around and whispered, 'Tell no one of what I have said. Even monkeys have ears.'

Winifred's mind was racing. There were so many questions she wanted to ask. Then she thought about her children. How could she leave them again?

As if reading her thoughts the bey said, 'Your children will be cared for. The da Silva family has offered to look after them. Your boys can go to school with their sons.'

'Will we be away that long?'

'It all depends. Refugees will be fleeing from Kabul. We need to make contact. That is the only way we will find out what is happening in the capital and what has happened to Amanullah.'

'When do you plan to leave?'

'Almost immediately. Where we are going the rivers run dry and are easy to cross. Once the monsoon starts they become raging torrents.'

She was still not convinced. 'Will it be dangerous?'

He leaned closer, his eyes fixed on hers. 'Just to be alive is dangerous. Even here we are not safe. At any moment a rogue elephant may come crashing through the wall and crush us to death.'

For a moment she thought he was serious. Then she saw that he was laughing and she laughed in return. It pleased her to know that he had a sense of humour. She thought that with him she would be safe. 'I will have to talk it over with my children.'

The sun was about to set and he rose. 'Come, before the monkeys return,' she said.

It was almost time for prayer. The bey took his leave while Winifred went to join Bebe Feroza, who invited her to join in the prayers and stay for dinner.

Later, with Bebe Feroza present, the bey took out a map and spread it on the table. 'We will travel to Delhi by train, but not together. We will meet there and go by foot through the villages to Lahore, skirting the Punjab to the north. Then we will travel through the foothills of the Himalayas and head for the Khyber Pass. Wear something Indian on the train so as not to draw attention to yourself. Later you will change into Western dress. My wife will help you choose something. The Khalifat will pay for everything.'

As he escorted her to the waiting car he said, 'I think you will enjoy the experience. You will see parts of India that you have never seen before. Life in the country is nothing like life in Bombay.' He was taking it for granted that she would make the trip.

Winifred thought about it as the car sped along, dodging bullock carts, and a herd of donkeys that came charging out of a side street, causing the driver to brake sharply. She was not afraid of danger. Death was everywhere. She could be bitten by a snake, or gored by a bullock. Trying to run away from it didn't work. She had been offered an adventure and would be foolish not to accept.

The next morning Bebe Feroza called for Winifred by car and took her to Laidlaws, where she ordered a white linen suit, a pith helmet and a puggaree to wrap around the helmet as a protection against the sun. 'Dressed in this everyone will bow before you.'

Winifred looked at her reflection in the mirror. The pith helmet gave her a fierce, determined look and she wondered what the villagers would make of her. The few Englishwomen she had met in Bombay wore flowing white muslin or silk garments that hid their figures, and carried a parasol to ward off the sun. The white suit felt tight and she knew she would have to wear corsets, stocking and shoes, instead of the leather sandals she was used to wearing with her saris. She loved these graceful flowing garments that disguised her thickening waistline. Now she looked like a sack tied in the middle, and suddenly she was laughing at herself and how she looked, while her companion stood there, a puzzled expression on her face.

'The white suit is for special occasions when you go into the villages to meet the headman. You will need some cotton skirts for everyday. Divided skirts will be more comfortable than a conventional skirt when you are riding.' She helped Winifred choose some white cotton blouses, a jacket and a pair of riding boots. Then she called the manager, who sent a tailor to take Winifred's measurements, promising to send the garments when they were ready.

Bebe Feroza was not yet finished and ordered a gold-topped walking-stick. 'For your protection, my dear Mrs Steger. I will see that it is packed in my husband's luggage. You would look strange carrying it on the train in a sari.'

It was not until the time came for Winifred to say goodbye to her children that she realised the enormity of what she had promised. If anything happened to her the children would be thrown on the mercy of strangers who might not care for them. They would be brought up in India whether they wanted it or not. She knew she was being selfish and had admitted to herself that she was going not so much because she wanted to help the Afghan king and queen, but because she yearned for change and excitement. It was the reason she had gone to Mecca. That experience had affected her life deeply and her story was still running as a weekly serial in Adelaide. Once she returned to Australia she could tell the story of this latest adventure. And surely when her children were old enough to understand they would be proud of her.

She tried to gloss over the separation. Mrs da Silva had said, 'I will care for your children as if they were my own.' Winifred knew that their lives would go on as usual, except that she would not be there to tuck them into bed at night and tell them a story.

The night before she left, the children stayed up late, sitting in the courtyard with Winifred and their hosts. When the moon rose Winifred pointed to it. 'When you see the moon you will know that I am not far, because the same moon will be shining on me. When you see it think of me, and I will think of you.'

'Your mother is a very brave woman,' Mr da Silva said. 'There is a war in Afghanistan. She is going to help the sick and wounded. It will be a long journey through villages and jungle tracks.'

'Will there man-eating tigers?' Rhamat's eyes shone.

'And elefunts?' Pansy asked, 'I'd like to see an elefunt,' and she climbed onto her mother's lap and snuggled up close.

Mr da Silva laughed. 'There are elephants and tigers in India, of course. But where your mother is going there are no elephants. There may be a tiger or two still around. But I don't expect she'll meet any face to face.'

'All you have to do is to stare it in the eyes and it'll go away,' Rhamat said. 'Our teacher told us.'

'Well, if I see one I won't try it,' Winifred laughed and patted her son on the head.

'There are still tigers roaming in the jungle,' Mr da Silva said. 'The British hunted most of them for sport, other times to save lives. There was one village where a tiger killed over a hundred people. The villagers fled. It was not until an Englishman killed the beast that it was safe for people to return. Most tigers keep away from humans. They live on antelopes and wild pigs. It is only old tigers that can no longer hunt that attack humans.'

He ruffled Rhamat's hair, then walked to where Yusef was standing alone, looking out into the night, and put his arm around the boy's shoulders. 'There is nothing to worry about. My son, the doctor, is going also. Every year before the monsoon he makes this trip through the villages to care for the sick. Your mother will return home safely, I promise. My

445

son will see that she is cared for. While she's away you'll be head of the family.'

After the children had been put to bed Mr da Silva took Winifred into his study and, unlocking his desk, took out a small pearl-handled revolver. 'Have you ever handled a gun?' he asked.

She shook her head. 'I hate the things.'

'Take it,' he said. 'I do not know what dangers you may encounter. I have promised your son that you will return. The bey will show you how to use it. Gandhi would say to face the enemy in peace and without weapons. But sometimes, if the enemy has a gun, it is a matter of who fires first. Use it if you must. Your children are young. They still need you.'

The bey wanted Winifred to be as comfortable as possible and gave her money to buy a first-class ticket to Delhi. Instead she travelled third-class, thinking to pocket the difference, knowing that if she stayed in India much longer all her savings would be gone and she had no way of earning money. Though she lived in luxurious surroundings, at no cost to herself, there were the day-to-day expenses of taking her children on outings and buying new clothes in keeping with the functions she was being invited to attend, where all the people were wealthy.

Once on the train she realised how foolish she had been. Even travelling steerage on the *Istophan* had not been as bad as this. It was not just the hard seats and the lack of ventilation, but the uncouth behaviour of the other passengers, who chewed betel nut and tobacco and spat noisily on the floor. A young boy and his grandfather got in with a goat, which urinated, the urine splashing on those close by. Empty milk cans were tied to the outside of the train and banged against the doors and windows. Passengers were clinging to the outside guard rail and others were sitting on the roof. A group of men passed the hubble-bubble pipe, a woman lit a spirit stove on the floor and cooked a meal with the overpowering smell of ghee and curry until the air was the consistency of a London smog and Winifred felt like fainting.

She had forgotten to bring any drinking water and could not quench her thirst because there was none provided. When she ventured along to the lavatory she found it like a cesspit with brown sludge threatening to spill into the corridor with every movement of the train. It was impossible to use without getting the bottom of her sari and her sandals soiled.

When she returned to her seat she found her neighbour had stretched out and fallen asleep. She managed to wake him and he curled up his legs so that she could squeeze into her seat. Sitting there, cramped, she was feeling savage and wished she had her gold-topped cane to give him a thrashing. The revolver was in her purse and she was tempted to pull it out and order everyone out of the carriage. But she resisted. She didn't want to be arrested. She could imagine the scene and suddenly she was laughing at the thought of the commotion it would cause. It kept her going until the first stop, when she got out and bought a first-class ticket.

The bey and Dr John da Silva met Winifred at Delhi Railway Station. They were both wearing armbands bearing the insignia of the Red Crescent, a Moslem group that performed the same function as the Red Cross. With them was a young woman called Ayesha, who was to be Winifred's companion. The group spent the night in a government rest house. Here Winifred waited while the men organised a cook and bearers to carry the equipment, which consisted of medical supplies, food, tents, bedding and cooking utensils. The next day the small party set off.

The road streamed through the plains like a great river, a river bursting with people and animals. Winifred felt as if she had been sucked into it, that she was no longer an individual but part of something greater than herself. It was as if she was seeing the real India for the first time. Fields stretched into the distance on either side. There were no footpaths. Bullock waggons plodded along laden with sacks of grain, while their drivers walked alongside holding a stick. Women in cotton saris made their way to the village well, holding brass pots on their heads, their bare feet whispering in the dust.

Herds of goats driven by young boys clad only in white dhotis bleated as they threaded their way through men pushing barrow-loads of potatoes, with their wives and children perched on top. Cows ambled along, stopping to browse on thornbush and tufts of coarse grass growing on the verge.

A car with the insignia of Great Britain went flying past with its horn blaring, sending up a whirlwind of dust and scattering everything in its path. As Winifred scrambled up an embankment she saw the bearers spit after the car. The bey put his hand under her arm to steady her. She could see that he was angry. 'The British are so arrogant. This is not their country. We will leave the road and make our way through the villages.'

They stopped for prayers beside a clump of small trees. Dr John spread a waterproof sheet on the ground and they sat there while the cook prepared a meal of millet with curried vegetables and chapattis. A cloud of flies arrived with the smell of food cooking. Winifred brushed them off her face, which was scarlet from the heat and covered in sweat. Her wet sari clung to her body. The *pallus* of her sari, which she had draped over her head, gave her little protection from the sun. She wished she had been able to wear her pith helmet like the bey and Dr John.

The men seemed cooler and more comfortable in riding breeches and long-sleeved white shirts. She thought it was because they were more used to the humidity than she was. It was a different heat from the dry heat of the Australian outback. Either that or she had grown soft since she came to India, living in luxury, with fans to cool the rooms, a sea breeze in the afternoon, no washing to do, no bread to make, nothing more arduous than entertaining her children and socialising.

All she wanted was a cool bath to rinse away the sweat that was pouring down her face, from under her armpits and between her breasts. She looked around, hoping by some miracle to see a lily-covered pond like the ones she had stumbled on in the middle of the Australian desert. The fields were bare, with a few black birds hopping along, and to one side a wooden plough. The bullocks had been freed and were wallowing in a muddy waterhole, while the farmer squatted alongside chewing betel nut. She wondered what he would do if she waded in beside the beasts. The thought made her laugh.

The bey looked at her and smiled. 'What is so amusing, *Hadjana*?'

449

'I was considering jumping in with the bullocks and having a bath.'

'There will be no need for that. I will send one of the men to tell the headman we are here. He will know already, one of the peasants would have told him. It is a courtesy. Ayesha can go with him and bring back water for you to have a bath.'

He spoke to the bearers and they began to unpack the tents, pitching them in the shade of a tall feathery tamarind tree and placing bedding inside with mosquito nets draped from the centre pole. Ayesha returned with two pots of water which she emptied into a tin bath in Winifred's tent, and brought her soap and a towel. She stood there waiting, until Winifred dismissed her. She did not want the girl to see her naked. She felt cooler once she had bathed and put on a clean vest and bloomers, then she lay down to rest. She was tired. It had been a long walk and she had had little sleep the night before. The rest house where they had stayed in Delhi had been infested with fleas. She had been badly bitten.

She woke later to find Ayesha bending over her. The tin tub had disappeared. 'Mem-sahib, the bey has asked me to call you. They are waiting. The bey sahib said to change into Western dress.'

Winifred rose, conscious that she was wearing only her underwear. She took her corsets out of her suitcase and wrapped them around herself, noticing the look of astonishment on Ayesha's face, especially when Winifred asked her to pull the laces tight at the back. The girl watched as she fastened stockings onto the suspenders and pulled a petticoat over her head. Before Winifred could stop her Ayesha knelt and, lifting Winifred's feet one at a time, put on her shoes. Ayesha held out the white linen skirt and Winifred stepped into it. She rubbed some vanishing cream into her face and then powdered her nose, studying her reflection in a small hand mirror before putting on her jacket and pith helmet. As she stood there she wondered what the village headman would make of her. She felt as if she had acquired new strength, as if she was wearing some sort of armour.

She stepped out of the tent and the bey placed his right hand on his forehead and bowed. 'Ah, *Hadjana*, they will think you are the Raj Queen.' He went to his tent and returned with the gold-topped walking stick. 'Your sceptre, Your Majesty.'

With the bey and Dr John, Winifred began to walk across the fields. A pair of bullocks was harnessed to a plough. They were progressing in slow circles around the field. The farmer stopped his team and stared at the visitors. Winifred was conscious of sari-clad women bending over in a field who straightened up and stared. A group of young boys followed as Winifred and the men moved towards the large hut where the headman was waiting. Winifred looked back and saw that the children were imitating her walk. She began to laugh and they laughed back and began to move closer.

The bey explained to the headman that they had come to minister to the sick in his village and would like to stay a few days. The man looked at Winifred and said something which the bey translated as 'He thought you had come to collect taxes.' He began to laugh and Winifred joined in.

They sat outside, with Winifred's chair being placed apart from the men. She watched as a drink was prepared. The headman poured some into his cupped hand and the bey drank. The process was repeated with the headman drinking from the bey's hands.

'It is an opium drink. Now we have been accepted and can begin to work,' Dr John told her.

It was not long before the patients arrived. Groups of men wandered in, talking among themselves, staring with frank curiosity at Winifred, until hundreds were gathered. Among them were old men bent double who could not walk unaided. Some were covered in sores and others were carried in litters or on the backs of their sons.

Winifred wilted in the heat, watching as Dr John moved among the men, trying to separate those who needed medical attention. She was thirsty and the whalebone in her corsets was pinching into her flesh. She wondered how much longer she would have to sit there sweltering, being ignored by the men as if she had become invisible, like the women she had come to help.

She knew the women were somewhere. She had seen them mixing cow dung with straw, patting it into little flat cakes to be dried in the sun. It was the only fuel they had for cooking. In another field young girls had been scrabbling in the dirt with baskets on their hips. At first she thought they must be gathering stones until the bey said, 'They're gleaning grain that has fallen out of the sheaves during the harvest. Once the monsoon brings the spring rain the fields will turn to mud. Often the gleanings are all a poor family has.'

Suddenly Winifred felt angry. She stood and, walking over to the headman, banged her stick on the ground. 'I have come a long way to see the women. Where are they?'

The headman stared at her open-mouthed. She could see

the black stains on his lips and inside his mouth from chewing betel nut. He spoke to one of his men who ran to where the bey was standing with John da Silva. The men turned and stared at her. She was still standing, her hand clenching the gold top of the stick which was planted firmly on the ground, her face set in angry lines.

The bey moved swiftly towards her. 'Are you not well, *Hadjana*?' and put his hand under her elbow. I will ask Ayesha to escort you back to the tent where you can rest.'

'I do not need to rest. I have come to the villages to help the women. This is what you told me.' She waved her hands towards the men, many of whom were sitting in the shade laughing and talking among themselves. 'They are treating this as a holiday.' She thought back to Oodnadatta where the men sat around at night smoking the narghile beside the fire, while the women remained inside their huts. All her pent-up rage burst from her. 'This is not a village fete where the men enjoy themselves while the women work. I came to meet the women. Where are they?'

'They will come presently,' the headman told the bey. 'They cannot come where the men are. Their husbands would not like it.'

Winifred could feel her blood rising to her head. She had to restrain herself from raising her stick and striking the headman. Instead she allowed herself to be led away to a space in front of a cluster of mud huts, where a chair was placed for her under the shade of a large banyan tree. She watched as a small red hen, which had been having a dust bath, called to her chicks and they disappeared into the thicket of the tree.

Ayesha brought her a cup of tea and she drank it. Then she took off her helmet and let down her hair. Her corsets were still pinching her and she asked Ayesha to loosen the strings, conscious of eyes staring at her from between the colonnade of aerial roots that reached to the ground from the ancient tree. She wiped the sweat from her face and forehead, leaving red streaks of dust on her white handkerchief, and undid the top buttons of her jacket, tempted to remove it and sit there in her vest, knowing it was impossible. She had always been modest, as these women were.

She did not have long to wait before the women emerged from behind the tree. They came shyly at first and then, gaining confidence, gathered around her. Winifred looked at the vast crowd of women, barefoot, dressed in cotton saris, many wearing the family wealth in gold and silver necklets and nose studs. She smiled and held out her arms to the children who came and sat at her feet.

In that first day she learned to communicate with gestures and through Ayesha, who could speak Urdu, the language of these people. She separated out the women and children who needed medical attention, and sent Ayesha to fetch Dr John so that he could see to them, helping him bathe wounds, put drops in sore eyes and, hold children while their ears were examined. She forgot her exhaustion, forgot the heat, until the call came for evening prayers and Dr John closed his bag and told them he would continue the next day.

That night Winifred folded her white suit and, together with her corsets, packed it into her suitcase, resolving to wear her skirts and blouses with her helmet during the day, and to change into a sari in the evening. As soon as they had eaten she retired to write up the diary she kept in a large exercise book. She was surprised at how happy she felt — as if she was doing something worthwhile for the first time in her life.

Winifred found that the villagers were friendly once they realised that she had come to help them. Always she was asked the same questions: 'Do you have sons?' She would watch as they smiled and nudged each other when Ayesha told them that she had two.

The other question was, 'How old are you?'

She would answer truthfully, 'Forty-seven,' seeing the look of surprise on their faces.

'They say you are very young and very strong,' Dr John told her. 'Most women are dead before they are thirty. Worn out with child-bearing or dying from some disease. It is the women who go without when food is short. Sometimes when the monsoon does not arrive there is famine and hundreds die.'

Wherever they went Dr John set up an open-air clinic with Winifred helping. Some faces bore the scars of smallpox, others of impending blindness because of cataracts, for which they could do nothing. Many had blackened teeth from chewing betel nut.

'Why do they chew it?' Winifred asked.

'To ward off the pangs of hunger,' replied Dr John.

She could understand, remembering how she had taken up smoking on the hadj because there was not enough food.

Most of the villagers had no idea of sanitation. Diarrhoea was rife among the babies. 'There are many reasons why babies die,' Dr John said as he bent over a sick girl who had been vomiting. She was naked. Flies were crawling over her face and mouth and he wiped her clean with a damp cloth.

'The main reason is infected water. Cattle swim in the pond. The women do not realise it is necessary to boil it before drinking.'

He handed the child back to her mother. 'Give her sips of boiled water,' he said. 'Come back again tomorrow.'

He soaped his hands and rinsed them in a basin of water. 'That child is strong. She does not have a fever. I think she will live.' Ayesha handed him a towel and he dried his hands. 'Infant mortality is high in the villages. Often when the mother dies the baby dies too because there is no milk. Sometimes the mother-in-law will give it buffalo's milk mixed with water If there is no milk the baby is given water in which millet has been soaked. Even if the baby could digest it, unless the water is boiled, the baby will die. Sometimes if the infant is a girl, it is allowed to die.'

He looked at Winifred. 'You are shocked?'

'It saddens me,' she said. She thought about her two daughters. She had loved them equally with her sons. But then there had always been food. Perhaps if she had been born in an Indian village she would think differently.

John da Silva touched her on the arm. 'Do not take it to heart. It is the way things are in India. It happens among the poor. Perhaps you could talk to the women about the care of children. You are a mother. They are more likely to listen to you.'

Winifred agreed and though the women listened politely as Ayesha translated, she did not think they believed her. They were doing things the way their grandmothers and mothers had taught them. 'Babies have always died, that is the way things are,' they said. Winifred did not mention the killing of the baby girls. She knew it must be true, otherwise John da Silva would not have mentioned it, but she did not know how to talk about it.

The villages were dirty, with great mounds of rubbish the haunts of dogs, rats and flies. People would go into the field to defecate and walk away leaving their stools uncovered.

'Flies breed in excrement and carry diseases like cholera,' John da Silva told the village elders. He showed them how to dig latrines that could be covered with soil and how to bury rubbish which would enrich the soil once it decayed, but it was hopeless. The next morning the day's work would have been undone by wild pigs.

'The village wealth is in their trades,' the bey said, 'skills handed down from father to son. The man who makes the farm tools, the potter, the silversmith, the blacksmith, the trader who goes to the cities to sell the produce.' Winifred was being shown around the village and had stopped to admire some huge pots. 'They are to hold grain,' she was told. 'They also serve as boats when the gods send too much rain and the rivers burst their banks.'

She watched the women weaving grey cloth on small looms and saw the men colouring the fabric, using red ochre, plants and flowers, thumping down printing blocks carved in intricate designs before spreading the finished cloth to dry. The colours reminded her of the desert around Oodnadatta. She wondered if she would ever see it again. She had been so long on the road that she had lost track of time.

28

MOTHER OF SONS

THEY TRAVELLED A LONG WAY FROM Delhi, heading for the foothills of the Himalayas towards the Khyber Pass, the gateway to Afghanistan. The bey had hired eight bullock waggons and their drivers. Though the wooden carts had no springs, it was easier than walking and they began to advance more rapidly. Winifred had bought a black umbrella at a village bazaar and was glad of the extra shade. She wore a riding skirt and white blouse with a pith helmet during the day, changing into a sari after her bath. Her gold-topped stick had been put away with the white linen suit, although the bey had said, 'Later, when we go forward on foot, you will be glad of your stick to help you climb the hills or kill a snake.'

Winifred was relieved when they left the plains and reached the upper courses of the rivers. The heat, the exposure to sickness and the plight of the villagers had sapped her strength. Life in India was too fragile. Here the country changed. It was more sparsely populated. Mud huts climbed up hills from the river channels. There were great old trees for shade, and mango groves in flower, the air fragrant with their sweet perfume. The land was terraced and every available space bore signs of cultivation, with small plots of potatoes, pumpkin, cucumber, tobacco, lemons, limes and mulberries.

They pitched their tents among the trees. Away from the villages on the river plains the nights were quieter. As Winifred lay awake she would listen to the voices of the bearers speaking in some dialect she did not understand, the air heavy with smoke from the fire that burned all night to keep tigers at bay. Even though tigers fed on antelope and other small game, there was always the chance that one might wander into the camp and attack. Sometimes she woke to hear the howl of a wolf and for a moment imagined herself back in the Australian bush, listening to the call of the dingo. It was then she would reach under her pillow to feel the revolver she kept there, wondering what she would do if she woke one night to smell the breath of a tiger and see its green eyes glowing in the dark.

Once the terrain was no longer suitable for bullock carts they were exchanged for yaks, which they rode. Among the men who looked after the beasts was Harish, who spoke English and whom Winifred discovered had served with the British on the North-West Frontier. There was a child with the men and he looked about the same age as Rhamat, who had turned eight. She was surprised to hear the child was eleven and already earning his own living. His name was

Amir and she watched him build a bamboo cage in which he placed a little bird like a starling that he had snared while they rested at midday.

The sight of the bird in the cage upset her. 'Ask him how he would like to be locked up,' she said to Harish. She saw him speak to the child, who looked at her with surprise and then said something to the older man.

'It is for his sister,' Harish told Winifred. 'She is in purdah now that she is old enough to be married. She lives behind the curtain. She will only leave the house when she is taken to her husband's house. The bird will keep her company until her father can afford a dowry.'

Winifred was silent, wondering if his sister was like a young girl she had seen in one of the villages. A small boy had come up to Winifred and tugged at her sari. She and Ayesha had followed him to a mud hut where his mother was bending over an open fire, stirring a cooking pot. The hut was filled with smoke which made them cough and their eyes water. The mother stood when she saw Winifred and pulled open a ragged hessian curtain. Behind it a young girl was lying on a pile of bags. Winifred stepped forward and shuddered when the woman pulled aside the child's sari to reveal a hideous sore on her neck.

Winifred had sent Ayesha to call Dr John, knowing it would be difficult because the women were in purdah. When the doctor sought permission from the father to examine the child, he refused, saying, 'It is the will of Allah that she should suffer.' No amount of pleading on the part of Winifred could make him change his mind. She found it hard to accept, sure that Allah was merciful and would not

460

have inflicted such pain on an innocent young girl. It worried her to think that men had such power over women.

She had her revenge in a village where she was called on to become judge and jury. The headman had asked the bey to give his opinion on a dispute between a man and his wife. When he heard the nature of the grievance he convened a court and asked Winifred to dress in her white outfit and hear the case.

The wife was led into the court. She was a pitiful sight, barefooted and dressed in rags, so stooped that her head almost touched the ground. A chair was brought and the old woman was seated, her head lolling, her face criss-crossed with lines. Winifred saw that she was almost blind. Her health was broken and her husband had divorced her and taken a younger wife, a girl of sixteen from a poor family. He had turned his first wife out and refused to feed her. The village had disowned her and she had nowhere to go and was living on scraps she found in the rubbish heap.

'Has your wife borne children?' Winifred asked the man.

He glared at her, his eyes fierce under a dark-green turban. Though he had a long grey beard his back was straight and he looked years younger than his wife. The interpreter repeated her question and the old man nodded.

'How many?'

'Thirteen, but some were girls.'

'Has your wife been faithful to you?'

He nodded, then scowled when Winifred said, 'In the name of Allah I command you to take care of your first wife. She had served you well. It is your duty to give her shelter and feed and clothe her for the rest of her days.' She wondered whether he would take notice and added, 'It is written in the Koran.' She called on the headman to see that her judgement was carried out and made the old man swear on the holy book.

Winifred had become tired and disillusioned, wondering what they had achieved. The plight of the women made her angry but there was nothing she could do to change it. She began to think about her children and how soon she could return home, remembering how peaceful it had been as she sat with them watching the night sky and listening to the owl hooping in the date palms.

Her mood lifted as they got closer to the mountains that had loomed on the horizon for days. The closest she had been to a mountain was the MacDonnell Ranges in Alice Springs, which were pygmies compared to this giant mountain range with its covering of snow that dominated the landscape.

She stood at sunset and watched the dark shadows fall over the valleys and crevasses, while the snow on the peaks took on a deep apricot tinge, until that faded to leave pinpoints of light like candles in the sky. Even after the sun went down she was conscious of the mountains like a living presence.

It was cooler in the foothills and greener underfoot. Winifred gave a cry of joy when she saw violets and other spring flowers blooming under the trees. She stooped to gather a bunch, then screamed as one of the yaks leaned over her shoulder and ate the flowers out of her hand.

The bey laughed. 'You have made a friend,' he said as Winifred wiped her hand on her skirt to remove the creature's dribble. 'He will probably adopt you as his mother.'

She regained her composure and laughed with him. Then she threw her arms wide and breathed in deeply. 'This is a beautiful place. I did not expect to find English spring flowers in India.'

'Perhaps it is Indian flowers that have found their way to England,' he said.

She realised he was laughing at her and she laughed back.

'There are things here you will never see in England.' He waved his arm towards a stand of dark pink rhododendrons in flower. 'Is that not something to make your heart beat faster? Like a living flame. When I think of England, I think of grey skies and people scurrying along with red noses, their breath coming out like smoke.'

She did not reply. He had taken her back to London and the smog, the chill in winter and the rats scrabbling over the roof at night, the dying man in the room below. She raised her eyes to the mountains. They were capped with snow and above the sky was a brilliant blue with a drift of white clouds.

'The abode of snow,' the bey said. 'To Hindus the home of the gods. It is easy to believe.'

'Does anything live there?'

'On the peaks? No, I do not think it would be possible. The air is so thin. And yet, see?' He pointed to a bird flying high above the peaks.

'What do they live on?'

'There are goats and sheep. Sometimes one ventures too high and dies. Birds feed on the corpse. And there is the snow leopard. I have never seen one. They are hunted for their skins. There are bears also. We must be careful. They live on berries and fruits. Sometimes they attack animals.'

'You have been here before?'

'Bombay is too hot in summer. Those who can afford it come to the mountains.'

Winifred thought about his words as she followed the men along the path, making slow progress as her yak stopped to lick the lichen off a tree or bend to snuffle up a clump of primroses. There were oak trees and deodars and a tangle of vines with purple flowers where monkeys jumped from tree to tree, pausing to stare as the small party mounted on yaks lumbered past. The bey had wealth and position. He could afford to leave the heat and smells of Bombay whenever he fancied. Yet millions of others were trapped. She had been told it was their karma, a fate ordained because of some wrongdoing in a past life. That is why the rich could live the way they did while all around them the poor died of hunger. And yet the bey was a good man. Otherwise he would not have travelled so far to help the sick. There was much she did not understand. She thought, 'No matter how long I live here, there are things I will never understand.'

They often heard the weird cry of the jackal and knew that an animal had been killed and the jackals were in for their share. The bearers would point to the sky and she would see the vultures circling. The bey would say, 'Keep close. There could be a tiger,' and he would check his rifle to make sure it was loaded. He was a good shot and could bring down an antelope to provide fresh meat when they wanted a change from wild goat, which often tasted rank, particularly if it was a billygoat.

Winifred and the bey were sitting together after their evening meal. Dr John had gone to check his medical supplies and write up his notes. Ayesha was sitting apart with the bearers. The bey threw a log on the fire, sending a shower of sparks into the air, then turned to Winifred. 'Your children will be proud of you,' he said.

Winifred looked at him. 'Why do you say that?'

'Because of the way you have managed on this trip. It has not been easy and you have been shocked by the things you have seen.'

She sat for a while without answering. Then she turned to him. 'It is the children. Why do they have so many?'

'They know no other way. Often it is the only comfort that a man and a woman have, when they come together.'

She thought about his words. She had been bound to Ali by desire. But what if you were married to a man you did not love, as she had been married off to Charles. 'But these are arranged marriages. Young girls are given away,' she said.

'Love comes later ... my own wife was chosen for me.'

'That is different. Those women behind the curtains, how can they live happy lives when they see only their husbands, brothers and sons?'

'It is a matter of education. We are trying to establish village schools where girls can learn to read and write. Then perhaps their husbands will treat them as equals.'

'Dr John has told me of girl children who are left to die.'

'It happens. The mother-in-law takes the child away and feeds it poisonous berries. The mother never sees the child again. There is no joy when a girl child is born. It is a matter of economics. Boys can work in the fields. They can plough, carry heavy loads. It is the son who cares for his parents in their old age. When he brings home his bride it is her job to give the family sons. There is a blessing used at weddings: may you be the mother of a hundred sons.'

'I value my daughters equally with my sons,' Winifred said.

'It is only the poor who cannot afford to keep their girls. Girls need a dowry to be married. Often the poor have nothing but some simple tools, a cooking pot and the clothes they stand up in. A man has his dhoti and, if he is lucky, a shirt. A woman has one sari. Something to wear on their feet would be a luxury beyond their wildest dreams.' He leaned closer to the fire. A chill breeze was blowing from the mountains.

'They do not own the land they till. They work it, and instead of paying rent, work for the headman of the village and give him a share of their crop. Sometimes even he is bound to the prince who is the real owner. If a headman is good he will care for the peasants who are on the estate. If he is not then they will suffer and may even be put off their land.

'They lose not only the land but a mulberry tree or a lemon or pomegranate tree which the wife has planted and nurtured from a seed or cutting. Sometimes they never get to taste their own fruit but have to sell it.'

Winifred had a sudden memory of the plum tree she had nurtured so many years ago. Charles had taken the money. She had put her children to work to drive away the birds and pick the fruit. She had loved her children … her lost children and a feeling of sadness engulfed her. She had put them from her mind and now they had risen up to haunt her.

'It has upset you, *Hadjana*, the poverty, the suffering.'

She shook her head, unable to tell him the truth, that it had stirred bitter memories, memories she had buried deep.

'Have you seen how the children smile when Dr John produces a handful of sweetmeats? How they play games? These people are not unhappy. They have an acceptance of life and do not complain. That is all any of us can do.'

He leaned across, took her right hand in his and kissed it, then placed it on his forehead and heart before releasing it. 'When you return to your own country, think only of the good things you have seen.'

He was gazing at her, a gentle, kindly look in his dark eyes. It was a look she had sometimes seen in Ali's eyes and she felt as if her heart was turning over. She wanted to put out her hand and stroke his beard. Instead she rose to her feet and with a whispered 'Goodnight' began to walk to her tent. She could feel her heart racing. It had been so long since she had felt a man's arms around her. The bey's likeness to Ali had thrown her off guard. And yet she knew she meant nothing to him. He was just being kind.

Ayesha was waiting for her and had laid out her nightgown. 'Is there anything you need, mem-sahib?'

Winifred shook her head. 'Are you happy, Ayesha?' she asked.

The girl stared at her, puzzled.

'Your life? Does it make you happy?'

'I have never thought about it.'

'But what will you do with it?'

'I will get married and have children.'

'May you be the mother of a hundred sons,' Winifred said and Ayesha smiled.

Winifred lay awake for a long time trying to visualise the faces of her children. She could see Yusef, Rhamat and Pansy quite clearly and wondered if they were missing her. She had been so caught up in what she was doing that they had almost gone from her mind. She tried to think back to the children of her first marriage and realised with a shock that they were no longer children but adults and would be out in the world, struggling to make their own way as she had had to do. It had been a struggle, yet nothing like the struggle of the poor in India. She thought she had suffered poverty but it had not been so. She was seeing it for the first time.

'Cow-dust hour, when the world prepares for the coming of night,' the bey said. He was sitting with Winifred and John da Silva, watching the last rays of the setting sun gleaming on the high peaks.

'Cow-dust hour,' Winifred repeated. 'What does it mean?'

'Have you not noticed how the cows come ambling home in a cloud of dust, as the sun begins to set?'

Winifred's mind went back to Evergreen, the Stegers' farm. She could see the cows waiting for the gate to be let down so that they could make their way to the milking shed in the afternoon. 'I have lived on a dairy farm. The cows walked through a paddock with long grass.' No one had ever called it cow-dust hour. That time when the sun dipped low. She had watched it sink into the sea as a child and imagined that the water put out the sun. 'You stupid child. How can the sun go into the water?' her mother had scoffed.

She wondered if there was more poetry in India than in other places she had been. There were the sacred cows. She had never thought of the cows at Evergreen as sacred. And yet without them there would have been no milk, no butter, no cheese. She could see the soft curds in butter-muslin bags, the whey dripping into a pan, and the round cheeses wrapped in cheesecloth and stored in the pantry to ripen. Beside them hung row upon row of sausages. All made by Mutter Barbara. There was poetry there, though she had never thought of it like that before. Then there were the village women she had seen working in the fields here, carrying water, giving birth. They were like Mutter Barbara. Perhaps it was only men like the bey who had time to see the poetry that surrounded them.

The party had slowed down by now, travelling only five miles a day. Winifred found the change of pace easier. She was able to rest more, she had time to write, and time to walk among the deodars and pine trees that flourished higher up, her feet sinking into the layer of pine needles that covered the ground. It was much colder, the temperature dropping almost to freezing at night. She had exchanged her skirts and jacket for a *shalwar kameez*, hand-woven from goats' wool by one of the village women, with a matching blanket to throw around her head and shoulders as they sat by the camp fire. They were heading towards Peshawar, the British end of the Khyber Pass, and hundreds of refugees were streaming from Kabul. Some passed by silently, carrying all their possessions in bundles on their heads. Others stopped at their camp, talking to Harish as they sat with the bearers sharing a meal. Sometimes it was a group of men, other times a family with young children. Winifred would tell Ayesha to bring the women and children to her tent where she would talk to them. If they were ill she would send the girl to fetch Dr John so that he could examine them. Winifred would bring them food, watching with joy the smiles that flickered across the pinched faces of the children when they were given a chapatti, a handful of warm millet and a bone to pick.

Once a woman asked them to help a child she had been carrying in a sling. When Winifred lifted the small boy to the ground she could see he was already dead, though the body was not yet cold. The next day Winifred stood with her arms around the mother, weeping with her while the child's body, wrapped in clean calico, was lowered into a hole the bearers had dug in a soft patch of earth under a larch tree. As the dirt was shovelled in, the mother sank to her knees sobbing. A small branch of a tree, stripped of leaves, was driven into the ground at the head of the grave and Winifred fastened her puggaree to it.

Later, she took the woman to her tent and put her to rest in her own bed while she sat beside her, wrapped in her blanket, weeping silently, thinking of her own children back in Bombay. Later she heard wolves howling and was glad that the men had rolled large stones onto the grave so that wild animals could not despoil it.

The next day the woman and her husband continued their journey. It had been their first child. As the husband led his wife away, the woman looked back over her shoulder to where the white scarf fluttered in the wind. She seemed reluctant to leave, until her husband took her by the arm and they disappeared around a bend in the road.

It was from Harish that they had the first news of conditions in Kabul. 'So far there has been no fighting in the streets. But the mood of the people has changed. First they welcomed Baccha Sakao, the bandit king who seized the throne. It was the mullahs who turned a blind eye and drove

Amanullah from the capital. But things are worse. Baccha Sakao is a barbarian. He has brought terror to the capital … people are fleeing.'

'Where will they go?' Winifred asked.

'To the villages. Until it is safe to return home. Many have relatives on this side. It has been a good season. There is plenty of grain.'

After Harish had returned to his own fire, the bey leaned closer and whispered, 'Harish has found out that Amanullah has retreated to the Khyber Pass with a few loyal troops. How long they can hold out I do not know. Most of Amanullah's troops deserted when Baccha Sakao, who now calls himself King Habibullah, took over.' He gazed into the fire and sighed, 'There will be famine. It is always the poor who suffer. Persia has closed her borders and Russia is waiting like a giant boa constrictor to swallow Afghanistan and parts of India as well.'

Winifred pulled her blanket closer. There was a chill wind from the snow-clad mountains and a dank smell from the damp undergrowth. A koel was calling from somewhere in the dark like a lost soul. It was a black night and as they huddled by the fire, the flames lit up their faces and the black cliff face that towered above. Below lay a sheer drop to the valley floor. Winifred could hear the yaks moving restlessly. The voices of the bearers and the refugees drifted on the night air.

'There are tales of atrocities,' the bey said. 'A young soldier has been brutally executed. It seems that the usurper king had helped in the abduction of the man's wife. He sent the young man to the front line hoping he would be killed. He deserted and fired at Baccha Sakao when he was praying in the mosque.'

'What happened?' Winifred asked.

'It was a futile gesture. The young soldier was arrested.' The bey touched Winifred on the arm to reassure her. 'What I am going to tell you may upset you. But you need to know the type of adversary we are dealing with. It is for your own safety, so that you do not take any risks.'

Winifred could feel a knot tightening in her stomach.

'Baccha Sakao took a terrible revenge.' He looked at John da Silva. 'You are a doctor. You know that these things go on. The young husband was tied to a post, and his nose, his ears and his fingers were amputated. And then ... and then ... It is almost too awful to contemplate. He was thrown into a vat of boiling oil.'

Winifred listened in horror. She had craved adventure. Instead there had been days and weeks of hardship, with sickness and death wherever she looked. Just when she had begun to enjoy the respite in the mountains, she was confronted by the flood of refugees suffering from hunger and disease. She wondered how she could have been so misguided as to think the trip would be easy. It had been hard on the hadj but she had been with Karum Bux. Now, even though she was with friends, she felt alone. The death of the child and the mother's grief had distressed her. The fire was dying and the night was full of shadows. She found herself weeping and drew her blanket over her face to hide her tears. Uttering a muffled 'Goodnight' she made her way to her tent.

She lay there unable to sleep. She heard the bey calling goodnight to John da Silva as they retired. Later a wind sprang up, whipping around the tent. Above the sound she could hear the incessant calling of the koel. The brain-fever bird, the bey had called it. She tried to blot it from her mind, willing herself to go to sleep. But her mind was a crazy jumble of thoughts. She found herself thinking of her first marriage, wondering why her love for Charles had turned to hate. She could feel the bitterness flooding her mind and thought back to her first meeting with Ali, and the joy she had felt when Yusef was born. She would have been content to stay in one place if Ali had been by her side. But he had been taken. His body lay somewhere in India. Where, she had never been able to find out. She knew that if she could sit by his grave it would ease the pain. Then it occurred to her that she could ask the bey. He would know what to do. And, thinking that, she fell asleep.

It was mid-morning before she woke to find the sun shining on her tent. She poked her head out of the opening and Ayesha came hurrying over with a mug of tea.

The bey returned after lunch with a spotted deer he had shot. 'There are so many more people to be fed. Our supplies will run out if I do not supplement them.'

Winifred watched while one of the men skinned the beast, before pegging the pelt out on the ground and covering it with salt. Later the bey came over to where she was sitting in the shade, writing. 'John and Harish have gone towards Peshawar disguised as peasants.'

Winifred put down her pencil and turned her attention to what he was saying. 'They hope to make contact with Amanullah. We want him to return to Bombay where it will be safer. We are not sure of the whereabouts of the queen. She is in grave danger. If she should fall into Baccha Sakao's hands

473

it would be a disaster.' His voice dropped. 'Do not speak of this to the others. We do not know who we can trust. We will let them think that we are staying here to rest, and that John and Harish have gone exploring in the mountains.'

A week later John and Harish returned with the news that the queen was in Amritsar. The bey was jubilant and hurried to tell Winifred, 'We have found the queen.' Winifred thought back to when she had last seen her, pale and downcast, her pregnancy showing, and she realised she must be very close to giving birth.

'How is she?'

'I do not know. She has sought sanctuary in Amritsar with some of her ladies. They are in purdah.'

'What do we do now?'

'We must go to her and try to persuade her to travel to Bombay where Amanullah can join her. Once she is well enough to travel, they must go to Europe. While they are in India they will never be safe.'

It was Winifred who made the first contact with the queen's entourage, wearing a heavy black *burqa* and bearing a letter from the bey. A few days later they caught the train to Bombay with the queen and her ladies, travelling in a private carriage. At first the bey insisted the women remain veiled for safety. The queen had discarded her silk sari and jewels and was wearing the coarse homespun garments of a peasant woman. Covered in the voluminous black *burqa* with only her eyes visible, there was nothing to identify this woman as the beautiful young queen who had been the toast of Europe such a short time ago.

Winifred found the *burqa* unbearably hot. She could not

see properly out of the slits for eyes, and the sweat poured from her body. She was so hot that she could barely tolerate it. She felt angry thinking that men had such power over women that they could order them to hide their faces and imprison their bodies so that they almost suffocated. It was because she had defied the old men and discarded the veil that the queen had been forced to go into hiding. Winifred suffered the heavy black garment as long as she could, until, despite the bey's protests, she flung it from her and helped the queen to do the same.

'She may be recognised,' the bey said.

Winifred produced her gun. 'I will use this if I must.'

The bey put his hand on hers. 'If there is any fighting then it is up to the men. Praise Allah it will not be necessary. Cover yourselves when we stop at a station.'

It was a long journey and Winifred passed the time by listening to the queen talk of her trip to Europe. 'Once everything seemed possible. For the first time in my life I showed my face to the world. I saw women doing things I have never dreamed of —' Queen Souriya stopped abruptly as a labour pain gripped her.

The contractions became more frequent and Winifred remained by the queen's side, watching as the royal ladies sponged her face. Though she was in pain the queen did not groan or cry out. Winifred was not sure whether it was the pain of leaving her country or the pain of childbirth that Souriya found hardest to bear. She had lost her country, her money, her position of privilege.

Winifred could understand. She knew what it was to lose everything.

Stretcher-bearers met the train. With her ladies and Dr John da Silva and the bey in attendance, the queen was taken to St John's Hospital where a baby girl, Indiah, was born.

Bebe Feroza was at the station and she escorted Winifred back to the da Silva residence to be reunited with her children. The first question they asked was, 'When are we going home?' Winifred hugged them. 'Very soon,' she promised.

A few days later Bebe Feroza took Winifred by car to visit the hospital. The matron came out to where they were waiting, holding the newborn child in her arms. 'The queen has refused all visitors,' she said. 'Last night her husband, the king, arrived. When he bent to kiss her I heard her say, "I would rather have stayed where I belonged and been buried in the soil I loved, than be forced to run like a pariah dog." Then she turned her face to the wall. Now she refuses to speak to him. He is heartbroken.'

Winifred held out her arms and took the child, looking down at the tiny face that was so like the queen's. When she handed the baby back her eyes were full of tears. She was crying for the queen, for the girl child, for the weary women whose lives had crossed hers, and for those whose present hope had vanished in that far place beyond the Khyber Pass.

29

RECONCILIATION

WINIFRED HAD NOT YET DONE WITH INDIA. The idea of finding Ali's grave had nagged at her ever since that night when she first thought of it, as she lay in her tent on the mountainside, listening to the call of the koel. Now, with the bey's help, what had seemed an impossible dream had become a reality.

Cow-dust hour had come and gone. The other women in black yashmaks, who had been in the graveyard pulling up weeds and laying fresh flowers on the graves while their children hopped around like sparrows, had left when they heard the call to prayer. The red bantam chickens that pecked among the weeds had roosted on the high stone wall.

The grave-keeper had brought her tea, asking, 'Are you all right, mem-sahib?', recognising her Englishness — even though she had dressed in her *shalwar kameez* with a chador to cover her face.

She thanked him for his kindness and settled down to watch over her husband's grave, which she had covered with field flowers she had gathered on the way.

The grave-keeper stood there, uncertain. 'Mem-sahib, there may be wild dogs.'

'If they come I will drive them away,' she said as she pointed to the stick she had brought with her.

'It will be dark, mem-sahib.'

'I am not afraid of the dark.'

He stayed, not knowing what to do, and then he cupped one hand to his forehead and bowed, and said, '*Bismallah*, mem-sahib.'

She watched as he walked towards his hut where he had tethered his cow. His lantern cast a circle of light on the stony ground.

Earlier she had watched the setting sun bathe the fields of millet in apricot light, until they turned to mauve. And as the sun set lower the fields had deepened into blackness, as if a curtain had been drawn. In the distance a dog howled and another returned the call.

The birds that had been chattering in the peepul tree that leaned over the cemetery finally settled. In the still night air she saw the cooking fires in the villages go out one by one. The smell of spices and curry still hung in the air and was carried on a little breeze that had sprung up when the sun had gone down.

The grave-keeper's cow, which grazed in the cemetery during the day, had stopped its lowing. She could see its outline where it lay tethered beside the grave-keeper's hut. She heard him talking to it when he came outside, and then the steady stream as he relieved himself, grunting and spitting before he returned to his hut and blew out the lantern.

She thought, 'When the world has gone to sleep, Ali will come to me and take me in his arms once more. We will lie together by the embers of the camp fire as we once did while our children slept.'

In the soft darkness she knelt beside his grave, holding the ends of the tattered turban that Ali's brother had placed there so long ago.

As the night deepened the breeze strengthened and she pulled her chador tighter. Her heart was overflowing with sorrow. A koel began to call, the sound filling the air — the lonely, desolate call of the koel which always sounded to her like a lost soul. She felt her heart melting, her eyes overflowing with tears. She laid herself full length on the grave, as if it was the body of her dead husband. 'Oh Ali. Oh Ali. Why did you have to leave me?'

She began to cry, crying until her chador was wet with tears, crying until she had no more tears. And then she fell asleep, the flowers cushioning her body on the hard ground.

She woke towards dawn, stiff with cold. A rooster on the stone wall began to crow. And quite close by another answered until there was a chorus going backwards and forwards across the fields. The birds in the peepul tree stirred, and the grave-keeper's cow moved restlessly.

Winifred rose, looking down at the crushed flowers and the once gold and yellow turban which had begun to disintegrate. One day it would be carried away by the wind.

Perhaps some bird would gather the tiny fragments of cloth in its beak and line a nest to make a soft place for its young.

She could hear the grave-keeper stirring, and she rose and pulled her chador closer to hide her face. She did not look back as she walked out the gate. She did not understand how it had happened. She had come empty but now she was filled.

PART SIX

30

RETURN OF THE WASHERWOMAN

WINIFRED'S DREAM ENDED, AS DREAMS DO, when she returned to Oodnadatta with her family in August 1929. But her life would never be quite the same. India had taken possession of her soul.

The carpet of Aladdin is not always woven tapestry, indeed its forms are myriad. A piece of torn rag, an old garment, a broken crock, sometimes a show, or a gorgeous sunset, even a strange accent is enough to transport one in less than an instant of time to the northernmost end, if there be one ... of this whirling globe. In my case the carpet today was a tiny *rosebud against an open window, through which a snarling mob of camels can be seen. I gave but one glance, one tiny breath of that dainty rose floated to me and hey presto! I was far away. My carpet carried me to India, right away to Lahore in the distant Punjab, and the days when I made the great pilgrimage which all good Mahommedans hope to make before they die* ... Arabian Days, the Adelaide *Register* 27 November 1927*

Winifred called at the *Register* office on her way home from India and left with a contract to write a weekly serial under the title of 'Star Dust and Soap Bubbles'. She was introduced to readers on 24 August 1929 with the words:

Winifred is no ordinary washerwoman. She has talked with kings and been on the Moslem pilgrimage to Mecca. Read her adventures every week, and you will find more stardust than soap bubbles in it.

Her Indian connection; 'Arabian Days', the story of her trip to Mecca; the appointment as secretary to the Khalifat in Australia; and the invitation to become the governess to the royal family of Afghanistan had lifted Winifred above the common herd. She had gained mystique. Now she reinvented herself as a pioneer woman of the Australian outback by creating a folk hero known as Winifred the Washerwoman. She began her series with the words:

My little iron hut stands four square, with a tiny gabled roof. Its windows have no glass, so require no cleaning. Their

484

shutters are of iron, hung with leather hinges. It has two doors, that give entrance front and back. Inside, my castle is divided into small rooms with the aid of hessian partitions. The windows and the walls are snowy white. No boards are there on my floor, just sweet-smelling earth, with a few white goat-skins scattered here and there.

As well as this the turmoil surrounding the abdication of King Amanullah and his queen was still hot news. The *Register* reported on 24 September 1929:

Cable message states that the sister of ex-King Amanullah had headed a revolt in Afghanistan. Winifred the Washerwoman, who was in the Khyber Pass during the recent Afghan revolution, sends the following interesting facts from the washtub.

Zerah, the sister of ex-King Amanullah, is a middle-aged woman of very forceful personality. I have often heard it said that she ought to have been the man of the family. Very small and frail, yet one word from her will carry more weight than a sentence from the others.

Next to the gracious Souriya, I think the abdication hurt her most. She often pleaded it would be better to die in their own land by the hands of the rebels than be buried afar off in what she called, and I know you will forgive me, lands unholy and accursed.

I am not surprised that she is trying to arouse the people for vengeance. Her little hand is so tiny, scarce bigger than a child's, but I know if she would only get near enough to Baccha she would do her utmost to place her little jewelled knife in his heart or die in the attempt.

She has cause enough and to spare for such feelings. Her poor husband was fortunate in that he met death at the usurper's hands, but her son walks blinded and mutilated, a shattered wreck of his manhood barely nine months ago.

Dear to her also was her now mutilated sister, Nadir Khan's wife, whose daughter has been taken as the wife of Baccha. Yes, she had ample reason. If only someone would find me the money I would go myself and lead these women out. I would make Baccha weep tears of blood before he mutilated these innocents.

The saga continued with a further report on 18 October 1929 that Nadir Khan had defeated the usurper, Baccha Sakao. On 22 October he was driven from Kabul, but after his flight there was a gruesome discovery. The decomposed bodies of the princes of Amanullah's family were found in a locked room. Kabul was described as being 'derelict, poverty stricken and threatened with famine'. Baccha Sakao did not escape. He was captured and brought to the city for justice. King Amanullah and his queen made no attempt to regain the throne but went into exile in Italy.

The *Register* folded in February 1931 and the *Chronicle*, which was part of the *Advertiser* group, took over Winifred's 'Star Dust and Soap Bubbles' series, offering her a second series which she called 'The Tales of Sapphire Bill'. It was written in the persona of a 'big-gun drover'. The real identity of the author was not revealed, 'Otherwise I would have been sued, a million times over,' Winifred said. Soon after it was first published 'The Tales of Sapphire Bill' had top billing in the Saturday edition. For the next nine years she contributed two stories a week.

With an assured income from her writing, Winifred rented the Anna Creek shack in Oodnadatta, a house that belonged to Anna Creek Station, built in the days when the staff travelled to town to meet the train. The house still stands in Billy Goat Lane, behind the dusty main road that runs through the town.

When her son Yusef turned seventeen she had him taught to drive and with her children went to Adelaide, where she took out a hawker's licence and bought an old car. She called on Lloyd Dumas, her editor at the *Chronicle,* who gave her a credit reference to enable her to buy a stock of marked-down items such as buttons, which they sewed on cards, needles, thread and trimmings, which she and her son hawked around the outlying stations. She set up her headquarters at Beltana, where many of the Afghans from Oodnadatta had settled, and left her two younger children in the care of friends and the local schoolmaster. She kept up her writing, sitting on the running board of the car with her small typewriter.

Her hawking days and her writing came to a halt with World War II. Because of the shortage of paper, the *Chronicle* confined itself to essential news. With her daughter, Winifred went to Tennant Creek Mines, where Winifred ran a mess for the workers. Pansy began studying singing and went on to become a successful country and western singer. Winifred's sons were independent by this time. Yusef joined the RAAF. Rhamat, who had been trained in wireless operations with the assistance of Lloyd Dumas, found work in that field.

Winifred was welcomed back to the *Chronicle* at the end of war, with a billboard proclaiming the return of 'Adelaide's foremost humorist'. But times had changed. The *Chronicle* became more of a stock and station journal and Winifred's stories were eventually dropped.

She moved to Alice Springs, and in a street that now bears her name, started the Silver Crescent Poultry Farm on land leased from her former employer in Oodnadatta, Lycurgus Underwood. It was here that she received a letter from Winifred, her daughter from her first marriage, and now a married woman herself. Alarmed that the secret of her marriage to Charles would come out, she wrote back, asking her daughter not to contact her again. She was terrified that the children of her relationship with Ali would find out that she had been married before and that she had another family.

But secrets will out. When her first husband, Charles Steger, died on 4 October 1952, her eldest son, Fred, travelled to Alice Springs to break the news to the mother he had not seen for almost forty-three years.

She sold her poultry farm and travelled to Queensland to try to pick up where she had left off. It was not easy, because the children she had left behind, and who had remained young in her memory, were now adults with children of their own. Two of her sons, Peter and Jack, had no interest in meeting her at all.

Peter was four when his mother left home and he remembered little about her. Life was hard for him and his siblings — when Peter was eight his father belted him so badly that he still bore the scars. He ran away and was picked up by an inspector of police who took him home and raised him as his own son. Peter, however, did not bear a grudge against his father. After Charles suffered brain damage as the result of an accident with a horse, he gave him a home until Charles's death and also buried him.

Jack's grand-daughter, Irene Steger, said:

Jack never forgave his mother for leaving home. He had a ghastly childhood. His father drank and was a difficult man to live with. As children they had very little fun. They were expected to work hard and had no pleasures ... He never spoke of his childhood except twice just before he died ... He was unusual, like his mother. He was well-read and gifted — self-educated ...

Winifred was reconciled with her daughter, Winifred, and they met three times. When Fred, her eldest son, died on 7 October 1977, Winifred wrote her daughter a plaintive letter:

Oh, my girl, what can I say to comfort you. Words are such empty things. Fred has left us and gone to his rest, God be with him. His life was hard since he was born, well soon we shall join him and you my dear one will be at rest from your pains and I too will have found peace at last. So dear, I have not had a happy life at any time. I have done my best to keep our names clean and that's why I have never changed names ... The Steger family put some curse on us but we did nothing but be English. Were we not God's children too?

I look back and see the hatred in the old folks' eyes. Especially the day, or rather the three days, in which Fred awaited birth. Oh, Winnie, they watched [me], in agony, and she cursed me lying there and prayed aloud that we would both die.

All their thoughts on their enemies, the English. The sisters too were bad. Fred showed me the dents on his scalp where Kate's dog chain had bit into him. You will never know the suffering and how they messed up all our lives. Well we must forget and I pray we forgive.

Won't your poor legs ever feel better? Yes, these last ten days have been cruel to us. I heard it through Pansy you received a letter from someone up there that Fred was gone. And I thought owing to your long silence that you too were gone. Then a woman who was my friend dropped dead and a letter came to say that Pansy's youngest brother was very ill in Queensland. Everything at once. I still don't know about the last. I myself am now very weak and not allowed outside the door because am all but blind and hope to pass any night now and finish the long saga of Life. But was glad to know that you at least are still with us.

Fred, Peter, John and the rest are no one knows where. Never was a family so split up. But my dear you have one glorious comfort. Your husband is still alive beside you. I live here quite alone and have too much time to think as I sit and brood and hope for something better in the next life. These things I have spoken of, forget them. I suppose the Great One planned all. Goodbye, darling, we shall meet later in a better world

Your tired and lonely old Mother

Of the four children it was Winifred who suffered the most from her mother's defection. She was seven when her grandmother, Barbara Steger, died on 1 August 1913. She was very close to her grandmother; all the children were. She was kind to them and gave them what she could. After that, the boys cleared out one by one until the girl and her father were on their own. When she was twelve, neighbours decided it wasn't proper for her to be living alone with her father and took the case to court. Her father cried when she was taken away. 'I loved him and he loved me. He was kind to me.'

She was made a ward of the court and taken to live in the home of a policeman and his wife. Of this time, she said:

> *I had six years of hell. Mr P… belted me black and blue with a riding whip because I forgot to shut the back gate. I was in bed. It was 9 pm.*
>
> *The man did some awful things. I won't tell you what the worst ones were. It was too horrible. I told his wife but she didn't believe me. When I was eighteen I left.*
>
> Interview with author, January 1996

In 1969 Winifred Steger was living at Watervale in the Clare Valley, South Australia, when *Always Bells: Life with Ali* was published by Angus & Robertson, as an autobiography, under the name of Winifred Stegar. In the book she claimed to have gone to Mecca with a husband called Ali Mahomed Stegar. Henceforth she spelt her surname two ways. When people asked which was correct she would reply, 'It doesn't matter.'

While at Watervale Winifred wrote fourteen novels, bombarding Angus & Robertson with a new manuscript every few months, until the readers begged the editor,

Beatrice Davis, to 'tell this woman to stop writing novels.' The novels were described as 'unpublishable', though the Clare *Northern Argus* had serialised three over a period of four years without payment, telling Winifred that they had trebled the circulation. When Winifred told Beatrice Davis of her years as a regular writer for the Adelaide papers, she was not believed. The comment was that they 'could find no evidence of this.' Their opinion was that she could not write. Beatrice Davis had no idea that *Always Bells* had first appeared as a newspaper serial in 1927 because Winifred had written in the foreword to the book:

> *I would not tell of it before because one was alive who would not have liked it. Now I can do as I please, yet the years have dimmed my recollections. Yet I have written it to the best of my remembrance. If it should seem at all disjointed, just sigh and say, 'Oh, but she was eighty-seven when she wrote it.'*

The publicity surrounding the release of *Always Bells* brought Winifred back into the limelight. Her identity as Winifred the Washerwoman was made public and she was asked to contribute to the *Senior Citizens' News* (South Australia), retelling old stories and writing new ones.

But life was catching up with her. She suffered the fate of many of those who live to a ripe old age. After a fall she was confined to a nursing home. Here she was no longer able to write because they took away her typewriter. It was like cutting off her hands.

Winifred still had one trump card left. Someone spread the word that she was about to turn one hundred. She celebrated her hundredth birthday with much fanfare, including a message from Queen Elizabeth, three years in advance. Perhaps it was just as well because she died on 16 March 1981, nine months short of her centenary.

She lies in the rose garden in Enfield cemetery, South Australia. On her tombstone are the words: *In loving memory [of] Winifred Jane Stegar, authoress and loved mother of Pam, Ray and Deen, passed away on 16th March 1981, aged 101 years. 'A legend in her time.'*

Tombstones can be unreliable witnesses. There is so much left unsaid. There is no mention of her beloved Ali, whom she still spoke of with tears in her eyes long after his body had turned to dust. And there was no mention of India, the country that haunted her dreams and remained in her heart until the day she died.

I liked going to India. I suppose I've been over there in my heart every day. I suppose because I lived it. You don't get a thing like that inside of you and throw it away. You nurse it like a jewel. I saw India in all her beautifulness. I saw her in her loveliest. I saw mothers with their children. I can't describe it. It's beyond me ... beyond me. Now let me go ...

AFTERWORD

THERE WERE OTHER PLAYERS IN THIS SAGA.

One is the unfortunate Louisa Dennis, who left her child motherless, as Winifred was to leave the children of her first marriage. It is likely that Louisa and Wilfred were never married, which would have made it easier for her to leave and would also account for the fact that I could find no record of the marriage when I did a search at St Catherine's House, London. I did, however, find the marriage of Ivanhoe William Oaten to Lydia.

Then there is Winifred's father, Wilfred Isaac Oaten. His is a sad story. He never prospered. Perhaps he was not the stuff of pioneers, or perhaps he loved Louisa Dennis too much to live without her. Winifred did not know what happened to him, except that he began to drink. Perhaps it was this that caused the accident in which he was thrown from his sulky, and subsequently died in Toowoomba Hospital from 'exposure to prickly pear' on 20 November 1917.

Wilfred died intestate. His personal effects consisted of four blankets and an alarm clock. He had no money on him at the time of the accident. And there was no money included in his estate. He had clear title to two blocks of land, one of which was in the county of Aubigny, near Peranga, on the Cooyar line. It was described by the valuer as 'being of practically no value, the majority being hard sandy soil and heavily infested with pear'. The other block was in the parish of Jondaryan, about three miles from Bowenville. It was described as 'a V-shaped piece of land and not in a marketable position. Value 3 pounds — small hut built of scraps of old iron. Value 2 pounds. Fencing of plain wire fence in bad order. Value 1 pound 10 shillings.'

Wilfred's brother, William, claimed the estate as the only surviving relative in a document written in his own handwriting. He testified that Louisa Dennis, Wilfred's sisters and their children in England, and his daughter, Winifred, were all dead. No mention is made of her four children whom William must have known were still living in the district.

Wilfred Isaac Oaten lies buried at Drayton Cemetery, Toowoomba, in an unmarked grave.

It is time now for these characters to leave the stage. Heroes or villains, it is not for us to judge. Some are still alive. May they prosper. Others, like Wilfred Oaten and his daughter Winifred, sleep in the Land of Dreams. May they rest in peace.

GLOSSARY

Allahu akbar la ilaha illa Allah, Mahommed Rasul Allah:
There is no God but Allah and Mahommed is His
Prophet.

Baba: (Indian) father.

Begum: (Indian) princess, or Moslem lady of high rank.

Bey: formerly the governor of a Turkish province, a title of
respect or rank.

Bismallah: In the name of Allah.

Burqa: outer garment to cover body, with ventilation holes
for eyes and mouth.

Chador: voluminous mantle worn as an outer garment.

Charpoy: an Indian bed

Chawl: Bombay (now Mumbai) multistorey tenement.

Das brot: (German) the bread.

Die kind: (German) the child, *die kinder* children.

Dhobiwalla: (Indian) washerman.

Fruhstuck: (German) breakfast.

Gott im Himmel: (German) expletive. God in Heaven.

Guten morgen: (German) Good morning.

Hadjana: title given to a female who has made the pilgrimage.

Hadj: pilgrimage to Mecca.

Hadji: title given to a male who has made the pilgrimage.

Harijans: (Indian) Children of God. An expression used by Ghandhi to replace the term untouchables.

Hati: type of Indian bread.

Hausfrau: (German) housewife.

Istophan: Chinese convict vessel which had sunk and been refloated to serve the lucrative pilgrim trade.

Juma: Moslem holy day of rest.

Khansama: (Indian) person associated with food preparation and presentation.

Knockenbrot: type of German bread.

Kolis: original inhabitants of Bombay who made their living from fishing.

La Ilaha illa Allah Mahommed Rasul Allah: There is no god but Allah and Mahommed is His Prophet.

Labbayyak: Here I am in Thy presence.

Masala: (Indian) a beverage made from milk and spices.

Mein Gott: (German) expletive. My God.

Messafa khana: (Indian) government rest house.

Mon cheri: (French) term of endearment, my beloved. *Mon cher*, my dear.

Moulvi: guide who instructs pilgrims on religious rites and behaviour.

Mullah: a title of respect for one who is learned in, teaches or expounds the Moslem religious law.

Mutawwif: agent assigned to each pilgrim or group, and responsible for accommodation and travel arrangements in the Holy Land.

Mutter: (German) mother.

Nacht: (German) night.

Nimbu pani:(Indian) refreshing drink made from fresh limes.

Pallus: end of sari which can be draped over head or shoulders.

Purdah: screen hiding women from the sight of men or strangers, or the system of such seclusion.

Salaam alaikum: Peace be with you.

Shalwars: baggy trousers drawn into a band at the ankle.

Shalwar kameez: outfit for women with narrow trousers and a long overshirt.

Shiete: (German) insulting epithet intended to degrade.

Tosher: a rat catcher (slang).

Vater: (German) father.

Yashmak: double veil worn by Moslem women in public.

As a general rule foreign words have been italicised in the text if they do not appear in *The Macquarie Dictionary*.

WORKS BY
WINIFRED STEGER

Copies of all manuscripts are held in the Winifred Steger Papers in the Mortlock Library, South Australia, with the exception of 'Just Fish and Chips' and 'The Wilful Wanton'. These manuscripts appear to be missing, though there is a possibility that they may be under a different title. Copies of the three serials published by the *Northern Argus* (Clare) are in that newspaper's archives.

The dating of the manuscripts has been arrived at after reading the correspondence between Winifred Steger and Beatrice Davis, in the Angus & Robertson collection in the Mitchell Library, State Library of New South Wales.

SERIALISED NOVELS

'Jack's Jane: The Story of a Farmer's Wife Who Goes on
    Strike'
'Four Rings on Her Fingers'
'The Door that Loved'
These were published in the *Northern Argus* (Clare), South
    Australia, from 1963–1967.

AUTOBIOGRAPHICAL TRILOGY

Always Bells: Life with Ali. Sydney: Angus & Robertson,
    1969; (reprinted in paperback as *Life with Ali*,
    Adelaide: Rigby, 1973) It was first serialised in the
    Register (South Australia) from 27 November 1928 to
    22 January 1929 under the title of 'Arabian Days: the
    Wanderings of Winifred the Washerwoman'. After
    publication in 1969 it was serialised in the *Australian
    Women's Weekly* in two parts (24 September 1969 and 1
    October 1969) under the title of 'Always Bells'.
'A King There Was', 1974, unpublished.
'Wandering Winnie', or 'After the Bells', 1970,
    unpublished.

UNPUBLISHED NOVELS

'Lady Nama of the Wongas', 1966 (first novel submitted to
    Angus & Robertson)
'Just Fish and Chips', 1968
'The Wilful Wanton', 1968
'Grace Vance, Convict', 1968
'The Devil's Pearl', 1968
'The Shah Valley', 1969

'The Sleepy Mountain', a novel for children, 1969

'The Golden Chariot: A Novel of a Miner's Daughter', or
 'Sally from Randy Creek', n.d.

'Mrs Biddy Malone', or 'Jumbo Valley', 1972, rewritten as
 'The Irish Washerwoman', n.d.

'The Irish Dreamer', 1974

'The Magnolia Queen', 1974, small section published under
 the title 'Different Gods', *Ink* No. 2, Hilarie Lindsay,
 ed. (Sydney, Society of Women Writers, 1977) p.
 161–156

UNPUBLISHED HALF-HOUR TV PLAYS

'The Trial Marriage'

'Remorse Too Late'

'The Expectant Father'

'House for Sale'

'Ten Little Bottles'

SHORT STORIES

'Twice a Hundred Camels Had I',

'Sweet Wee Jimmy Jamesy', published in two episodes,
 Senior Citizens' News (South Australia), October 1972,
 December 1973

'Ere's One you Nebbe 'Ad', *Senior Citizens' News* (South
 Australia), April 1974

'The Panther'

'Those Green Girls'

'The Cleansing Fires'

'Quiet Afternoon for His Reverence'

'The Smell is not of Cinnamon', or 'Chad's Arm')

BIBLIOGRAPHY

Action Graphics. *Travel Action: Matilda Country*. Dalveen:
    Action Graphics, n.d.

Anderson, Ethel. *Tales of Parramatta and India*. Angus &
    Robertson, 1988.

Anderson, R.J. *Solid Town: the History of Port Augusta*, Port
    Augusta: the author, 1988.

Avery, Gillian. *Victorian People in Life and Literature*,
    London, Michael Joseph, 1974.

Bowen, Jill. *Kidman, the Forgotten King: The True Story of the
    Greatest Pastoral Landholder in Modern History*, Sydney:
    Angus & Robertson, 1988.

Burchill, Elizabeth. *Innamincka*, Melbourne: Hodder &
    Stoughton, 1969.

Carroll, Lewis, *Alice's Adventures in Wonderland*, London:
    Macmillan, 1865.

Chaplin, Charles. *My Autobiography*, London: Bodley Head, 1964.

Chatwin, Bruce. *The Songlines*, London: Pan Books in association with Jonathan Cape, 1987.

Chinchilla Centenary Celebrations Committee, 1878–1978, Chinchilla: Centenary Celebrations Committee and its Historical Research Sub-Committee, 1979.

Clark, C.M.H. *A History of Australia V: The People Make Laws, 1888–1915,* 6 vols., Melbourne, Melbourne University Press, 1981.

Clark, Patricia. *The Governesses: Letters from the Colonies 1861–1882*, Melbourne: Hutchinson, 1985.

Coppock, Rose Rawlins. *Cattle Station Woman*, Alice Springs: the author, 1991.

Country Women's Association. *The Alice: the Story of Alice Springs*, Alice Springs: Alice Springs Branch of the Country Women's Association, 1952.

Dallwitz, John and Fazio, Daniel. *White to Black: Oodnadatta School 1892–1992*. Oodnadatta Aboriginal School, 1992.

Dansie, Robert. *Records of a Dynamic Young Toowoomba*, Toowoomba: Darling Downs Institute Press, 1985.

Davidson, Robyn. *Tracks*, London: Paladin, 1989.

Draper, Marie. C. *Lambeth's Open Spaces*, Lambeth: Borough of Lambeth, 1979.

Dwivedi, Sharada and Rahul Mehrotra. *Bombay: The Cities Within,* Bombay: India Book House PVT Ltd, 1995.

Flinders Ranges & Outback of South Australian Regional
Tourist Assoc. *Flinders Ranges and Outback South
Australia,* Inc. Port Augusta: Flinders Ranges and
Outback South Australia Regional Tourist Assoc.
Inc., 1991.

Florence. *90 Years Down Lambeth Way*, Andy Lewis, ed.
Lambeth: Lambeth Adult Education Institute, n.d.

Francis, Raelene and Scates, Bruce. *Women, Work and the
Labour Movement in Australia and Aoteroa/New
Zealand,* Sydney: The Australian Society for the Study
of Labour History, 1991.

Gandhi, M.K. *The Story of My Experiments with Truth: An
Autobiography,* Translated by Mahadev Desai. 1927.
Ahmedabad: Navajivan Publishing House, 1979,
14th ed.

Gibberd, Graham. *On Lambeth Marsh: The South Bank and
Waterloo,* London, Jane Gibbert, 1992.

Gibson, Jeremy, Rodgers, Colin and Webb, Cliff. *Poor Law
Union Records: South East England and East Anglia,*
Birmingham: Federation of Family History Societies,
1993.

Greater London Records Office. 'The Great Dock Strike,
1889'. London: Greater London History Library,
Leaflet Number 2. n. d.

Grant, Arch. *Camel Train & Aeroplane: The Story of Skipper
Partridge,* 1981. Dee Why Frontier Publishing, 1989,
3rd ed.

Gregory, Dr Cedric E. *All Around the World in Eighty Days,*
Toowoomba: the author, 1995.

Gunn, Aeneas. *We of the Never Never*, London: Hutchinson.

Haddon, Frank. *Australia's Outback: Environmental Field Guide to Flora and Fauna*, Sydney: Simon & Schuster, 1992.

Halvey, Eli. *A History of the English People in the Nineteenth Century: Victorian Years* [Incorporating The Age of Peel and Cobden], 1841–1895. Ernest Benn, paperback 1970.

Hardy, Frank. *The Yarns of Billy Borker*, Melbourne: Mandarin, 1992.

Harney, Bill. *A Bushman's Life: An Autobiography*, Eds. Douglas and Ruth Lockwood, Melbourne: Viking O'Neil, 1990.

Harmstorf, Ian and Gigler, Michael. *The Germans in Australia*, Melbourne: A.E. Press, 1985.

Heckenthorn, Charles William. *London Memories: Social Historical and Topographical*, London: Chatto & Windus, 1900.

Hill, Ernestine, *Flying Doctor Calling*, Sydney: Angus & Robertson in conjunction with the Flying Doctor Service of Australia, 1947.

Hill, Ernestine, *The Territory*. HarperCollins, 1951.

Hill, Ernestine, *The Great Australian Loneliness*. Angus & Robertson, 1940.

Idriess, Ion L. *Flynn of the Inland*, Sydney, Angus & Robertson, 1936, 14th ed.

Jondaryan State School Centenary Committee. *Jondaryan 1872–1972*, Jondaryan: Jondaryan State School Centenary Committee, 1972.

Jones, Mary Lucille, ed. *An Australian Pilgrimage: Muslims in Australia from the Seventeenth Century to the Present*, Melbourne: The Law Printer, 1993.

Jung, Agnes, *Unveiling India: A Woman's Journey*, Delhi: Penguin Books, 1987.

Jupp, James. *Immigration*, Sydney: Sydney University Press in association with Oxford University Press, 1991.

Kaidi, Hamza Nadjm Oud-Dine Bammata and Tidjani El Hachemi. *Mecca and Medinah Today*, Paris: les éditions j.a., 1980.

Litchfield, Lois. *Marree and the Tracks Beyond in Black and White: A History of the Birdsville Track*, Marree: the author, 1983.

Lockwood, Douglas. *I, the Aboriginal: The Story of Waipuldanya*, Sydney: Reader's Book Club, 1964.

Manual of Australasian Geography, London: William Collins, c.1892.

Mayer, Henry. *The Press in Australia*, Melbourne: Lansdowne 1964.

McGrath, Ann. 'Spinifex Fairies: Aboriginal Workers in the Northern Territory', *Women, Class and History*, Elizabeth Windschuttle, ed. Melbourne: Fontana Collins, 1980.

Moorhead, Alan. *Cooper's Creek*, London: New English Library, 1971.

Morven Historical Society Inc. *Morven and District*, 100 years: 1887–1987, Morven: Morven Historical Society Inc,1987.

Musakhan, Mohamed Hasan, ed. *Islam in Australia: 1863–1932*, Adelaide: Mahomet Allum, 1932.

Muslim Women Association Annual Report: 1994–1995:
   Moslem Women Assoc. 1995.

Norman, L. *Pioneer Shipping of Tasmania*. Hobart: the
   author, n.d.

O'Brien, Anne. *Poverty's Prison: the Poor in New South Wales
   1880–1918*, Melbourne: Melbourne University Press,
   1988.

Patel, Sugatya and Thorner, Alice. *Bombay: Mosaic of Modern
   Culture,* Bombay: Ozxford Unviersity Press, 1995.

Patel, Sugatya and Thorner, Alice. *Bombay: Metaphor for
   Modern India*, Bombay: Oxford University Press, 1995.

Penton, Brian. *Landtakers*, Sydney: Endeavour Press, 1934.

Petrick, Jose. *The History of Alice Springs through Street
   Names,* Alice Springs: the author, 1989.

Plowman, Bruce. *The Man from Oodnadatta*, Wangaratta:
   Shoestring Press, 1991.

Polishuk, Nancy and Lockwood, Douglas. *Life on the Daly
   River*, Adelaide: Rigby, 1967.

Pritchard, Katharine Susannah. *Coonardoo*, London:
   Jonathan Cape, 1943.

Queensland Tourist & Travel Corporation. *The Nature of
   Queensland*. Brisbane: Queensland Tourist and Travel
   Corporation, n.d.

Radi, Heather. 'Whose Child? Custody of Children in
   NSW 1854–1934', *In Pursuit of Justice, Australian
   Women and the Law 1788–1979*, Judi Mackinolty and
   Heather Radi, eds. Sydney: Hale & Iremonger, 1979.

Rajowski, Pamela. *In the Tracks of the Camelmen: Outback
   Australia's Most Exotic Pioneers,* Sydney: Angus &
   Robertson, 1987.

Reader's Digest Guide to Australian Places, Sydney: Reader's Digest, 1993.

Rees, Henry. *Australasia. The New Certificate Geography Series: Advanced Level*, London: MacDonald & Evans Ltd, 1962.

Roman, Alvin, 'From the Chronicle: July 17 1858 to September 26 1975'. State Library of South Australia: August 1982.

Ross, Floyd H, Hill, Tynette. *The Great Religions by which Men Live,* New York: Fowcett World Library, 1959.

Rudd, Steele. *On Our Selection*, Sydney: Angus & Robertson, 1979.

Seaman, L.C. *Life in Victorian London.* London: B.T. Batsford, 1973.

Sherrington, Geoffrey. *Australia's Immigrants 1788–1978, The Australian Experience No 1*, North Sydney: George Allen & Unwin, 1980.

Simpson, Horrie. *Horrie Simpson's Oodnadatta,*John Dallwitz ed. Oodnadatta: Oodnadatta Progress Association, 1990.

Strachan, Rod and Scott, Joan. I*n Champagne Country: Stories and Photographs of People and Events in and around Roma,* Roma Railway Centenary 1880, Centenary Bungil Shire Council. Roma: Roma State School Parents & Citizens Association, 1980.

Stevens, Christine. *Tin Mosques & Ghantowns: A History of Afghan Cameldrivers in Australia*, South Melbourne: Oxford University Press, 1989.

Stewart, Desmond. *Great Ages of Man: A History of Early Islam*, New York: Times Inc, 1975.

Taylor, Milly. 'Born out Bush'. *Women of the Centre*, Adele Pring, ed. Apollo Bay: Pascoe Publishing, 1980.

Thorvald, Peter Ludwig Weitemeyer. 'For all the gold in Queensland'. *Gold Fever*, Nancy Keesing ed. Sydney: Angus & Robertson, 1967.

Toowoomba and Golden West Regional Tourist Association. *Discover Toowoomba & the Golden West,* Regional Tourist Association, 1993.

Wasp, David and Davis, Alan. *The Great Dock Strike, 1889,* London: Longman, 1974.

Waterson, D.N. *Squatter, Selector and Storekeeper: A History of the Darling Downs, 1859–93,* Sydney: Sydney University Press, 1968.

Webb, Beatrice. *My Apprenticeship, 1926,* London: Penguin Books, 1971.

Westprint. Booringa Shire: *Mitchell, Amby, Mungallala. The Capital of Kenniff Country.* Charleville: Westprint, n.d.

Young, Pam. *Proud to be a Rebel.,* St. Lucia: University of Queensland Press, 1991.

DOCUMENTS

Archives of the Morven Historical Society.

Carter. G., Manager, Railways Historical Centre, Ipswich. Letter to the author, 18 August 1994.

Davis, Beatrice. Letter to Winifred Steger, 27 November, 1969.

Davis, Beatrice. Letter to Winifred Steger, 2 December 1971.

Fanning, Pauline, National Library of Australia. Letter to Winifred Steger, 18 February 1974.

General Report in the Matter of the Goods of Wilfred
    Oaten late of Goombungee, 22 January 1918. In the
    records of the Public Trustee of Queensland. Ref
    LO33.
Johnson, A.R. (Bob). Letter to the author, 1996.
Johnson, Ethel. Letter to the author, 25 February 1996.
Lindsay, Hilarie. Letter to the National Library of Australia,
    4 February 1974.
Lindsay, Hilarie. Letter to Winifred Steger. 23 February
    1974.
McGowan, A.O. Letter to the author, n.d.
Pearce, Geraldine. Letter to the author, 1995.
Report into the need for a new school at Kulpi. Kulpi
    School Records, Queensland State Archives. Educ.
Simpson, Horrie. Letter to Jose Petrick, 9 April 1989.
Steger, Winifred. Letter to Beatrice Davis. 24 May 1966.
    Angus & Robertson Papers, Mitchell Library, State
    Library of New South Wales.
Steger, Winifred, ibid, 11 February 1969.
Steger, Winifred, ibid, 5 November 1969.
Steger, Winifred. Letter to the author, n.d. March 1973.
Steger, Winifred ibid, 3 January 1974.
Steger, Winifred. ibid, c. 1974.
Steger, Winifred, ibid. c. 1974.
Stuckey, Samuel. 'Reminiscences of Samuel Stuckey'.
    Unpublished MS. Mortlock Library, State Library of
    South Australia.
Vogan James, 'Journals of the Origins of Black Police
    Novel', 4 June 1887. Dixson MS111, Mitchell
    Library, State Library of New South Wales.

INTERVIEWS

Barker, Winifred. Personal interview, 9 January 1996.

Barnes, Rose, Oodnadatta Hospital and Health Services Inc. Personal interview, November 1994.

Bullock, Margaret. Personal interview, 9 January 1996.

Coleman Gill. Personal interview, 8 March 1994.

Diggles, Marionne. Personal interview, 8 January 1996.

Doherty, Hilda. Telephone interview, 10 December 1994.

Engler, Marjory. Personal interview, 9 January 1996.

Johnson, Ethel. Telephone interview, 10 October 1996.

Lindsay, Philip. Personal interview, 30 October 1996.

Mullane, Maisie. Telephone interview, 12 April 1993.

Pigram, Joan. Records Department, Presbyterian Church of Queensland. Telephone interview, 1993.

Rawsthorn, John. Personal interview, 8 May 1995.

Simpson, Horrie, Personal interview, 1 July 1994.

Spokesman, Islamic Society of South Australia. Personal inteview, 3 March 1994.

Steger, Belinda. Personal interview, 1 July 1994.

Steger, Irene. Telephone interview, 6 January 1996.

Steger Peter. Personal interview, 29 June 1994.

Steger, Mark. Personal interview, 29 June 1994.

Steger, Pansy. Telephone interview, 4 April 1992.

Steger, Winifred. Taped interviews. Stella Guthrie, n.d.

A CONVERSATION WITH
HILARIE LINDSAY

Q: Why did you choose Winifred Steger as the subject of your book?
A: Because she was an outstanding woman. When I first heard her interviewed on television I was very impressed. I wanted to know more about her. The more I found out, the more I came to admire her. And yet she had been forgotten. I wanted to restore her to her rightful place as a remarkable Australian woman pioneer.

Q: What was so special about her?
A: Her life was filled with adversity, yet she managed to rise above it. Winifred grew up in an era when women had few expectations outside marriage and children. Those who did not marry were referred to as 'old maids', often spending their life working in a lowly job in a factory or office, where they received less pay than their male counterparts. When they retired they had no financial security. If they wanted to borrow money to buy a house they had to be guaranteed by a male.

Q: But Winifred was married. Surely that made a difference?
A: Once a woman married, she became subservient to her husband. Despite her other qualifications, she was referred to in legal documents as 'married woman', and her occupation on the electoral roll as 'domestic duties'. Other women were legally either widows or spinsters.

Q: Was Winifred's conversion to Islam a lifelong one?

A: One of the most extraordinary aspects of Winifred Steger's life was her conversion to Islam; however, with the end of her Moslem marriages she drifted away. But she was still proud of the title *hadjana*. It set her apart as a woman who had made the pilgrimage to Mecca: an unforgettable experience which added so much colour to her life and helped launch her literary career.

The camel men have faded into history, but it was they who made it possible for the spread of the cattle and sheep industry into remote areas of Australia. Because they were different they were shunned by the predominately European settlers in Australia at the time. Many had wives and children in their own countries, who they continued to support. Others married women on the fringes of society, like Winifred. The men were kind husbands, but also kept their wives confined. They were not allowed to leave home unattended. They were expected to uphold the family honour. Most of the wives spent months alone in Ghan towns, while their husbands travelled with their camels.

Although she had adopted the Moslem faith Winifred refused to be confined to the camel camp like the other wives, many of whom were Aboriginal. Years later she said that she had made a mistake 'marrying out of my caste'.

Q: You say she wrote fourteen novels. How could an uneducated woman achieve this?

A: These days we place too much emphasis on formal education. If you look at successful women writers of the past, you will find that many of them had no formal education. Winifred had an observant eye and her father was the son of a schoolmaster of Bath. In the few years' schooling she had in England she learned to read and write. She was able to exploit her natural talents as a storyteller and writer.

Q: Why did she choose that name as her pseudonym?
A: Despite her success she never forgot the time when she was destitute, and went out doing washing for two and sixpence for a half-day's work, so that she could support the three children of her second marriage. Later her children told her it was demeaning to use that as a pseudonym. But she took no notice. It had been honest work and she was not ashamed of it.

Q: Were her novels published?
A: I think the reason they weren't published was that the plots were contrived. They all had a happy ending with the girl marrying some man who loved her, and cared for her child. Not only that, the problems of the young woman supporting her child were always solved by an unknown benefactor leaving her a fortune, or by her winning the lottery.

Q: What about her other writing?
A: She was a great storyteller with a racy style, so that she was dubbed 'Australia's foremost humorist' because of her articles in the *Chronicle* in Adelaide every week for nine years. One was in the persona of a big gun-drover called Sapphire Bill, under the title of *Tales of Sapphire Bill as told by Himself*, and the other *Star Dust and Soap Bubbles* under the pseudonym of Winifred the Washerwoman.

Q: You did a lot of research. Was it difficult?
A: Not difficult, but demanding, although I enjoyed it. I don't research on the internet. I prefer to go to primary sources, which I consider more accurate. I researched in libraries and did personal interviews with people who remembered Winifred. I travelled to many of the places where Winifred had been, both in Australia and overseas. I found the house where she lived as a child, at 98 Tradescant Street, South Lambeth, England. I also found her small house in Oodnadatta, and her later one in Watervale, South Australia. Later I found the property where she lived when she was married, and the cairn of stones at Dalby, on the land where she and her father lived when they first migrated to Australia.

Q: Are there any relatives living?
A: Yes. There are a lot. I discovered that they planned a family reunion because of my book. Once Winifred left home she was lost to them. They were glad to get her back. Earlier I had visited members of the family in Queensland, who told me the story of her unhappy marriage to Charles.

Q: Were there any mysteries left unsolved in Winifred's life?
A: I could find no trace of Louisa Dennis, Winifred's mother. I think what Winifred said in an interview was true: that her mother saw the chance to be free, and took it when she refused to travel to Australia with her husband and daughter. According to Winifred, they were never married. I don't think Winifred ever saw, or heard from, her mother again.

QUESTIONS FOR
READING GROUPS

1. *The Washerwoman's Dream* is based on sound historical research. What do you think of Hilarie Lindsay's method of using some fictional characters to tell Winifred's story?

2. Do you think Winifred was justified in leaving her husband?

3. Do you think the work of the Afghan camel men, who helped develop the outback of Australia, has been fully appreciated? Was the Australian government too harsh in not allowing the men to bring their womenfolk with them?

4. Travelling across the outback with her husband Ali meant that Winifred deprived her children of a proper education. She tried to teach them by reading jam tin labels and similar, as she had done as a child. Do you think this was adequate, or was she being selfish, putting her own needs before those of her children?

5. For a white woman who had not been born a Moslem, to travel to Mecca was a rare occurrence. Would it be possible to repeat Winifred's trip today?

SUGGESTED READING

Jones, Mary Lucille, ed., *An Australian Pilgrimage: Muslims in Australia from the Seventeenth Century to the Present*, Melbourne: The Law Printer, 1993.

Lindsay, Hilarie, 'The Story Behind the Washerwoman's Dream: An Extraordinary Life 1882–1981', winner of the Walter Stone Gold Medal 2002, Fellowship of the Australian Writers NSW Inc., in *Southerly*, special edition published as a tribute to Professor Elizabeth Webby on her retirement from the Chair of Australian Literature, Sydney University, June 2007.

Musakahan, Mohamed, *Islam in Australia: 1863–1932*, Adelaide: Mahomet Allum, ed., 1952.

Rajowski, Pamela, *In the Tracks of the Camel Men: Outback Australia's Most Exotic Pioneers*, Angus & Robertson, Sydney, 1982. The facts concerning Winifred's personal life in this publication are incorrect, as the author relied on stories told by Winifred, which were false.

Stevens, Christine. *Tin Mosques & Ghantowns: A History of Afghan Camel-drivers in Australia*, South Melbourne: Oxford University Press, 1989.

Hilarie Lindsay has been writing professionally since 1964, with more than twenty books to her credit. She has twice won the Grenfell Henry Lawson Statuette for Prose, in 1966 and again in 1967. She was awarded the MBE for Services to Literature in 1974, the Queen's Jubilee Medal in 1977, and the Order of Australia Medal in 2006 as an author and for mentoring aspiring writers.

Hilarie wears two hats. In addition to her writing, she has spent the last sixty years working in the family's toy manufacturing company. In 1969 she became the first woman president of any division of the Chamber of Manufactures. She was inducted into the Australian Toy Association Hall of Fame in 1998. She is a past federal president of the Toy & Games Manufacturers Association of Australia, the Society of Women Writers (Australia) and of the Fellowship of Australian Writers.

Hilarie enjoys travelling, tai chi, swimming, the theatre and being with her family. She has three children, five grandchildren and two great-grandchildren.